Case Studies in Schizophrenia

CASE STUDIES IN

SCHIZOPHRENIA

Clarence G. Schulz and Rose K. Kilgalen

BASIC BOOKS, INC., PUBLISHERS • NEW YORK • LONDON

Library of Congress Catalog Number: 73–94299

© 1969 by Basic Books, Inc.

Manufactured in the United States of America

TO
Bliss Forbush, LL.D.
QUAKER EDUCATOR, AUTHOR, AND HUMANITARIAN

FOREWORD

HAROLD F. SEARLES, M.D.

Over the course of my nearly fifteen years of work at Chestnut Lodge, I listened to many hundreds of case presentations by a total of about seventy-five different psychotherapists. During the more memorable of these presentations, I often thought of how rich a mine of information, for anyone interested in psychotherapeutic technique, lay in the transcripts of these conferences. A careful study of the endlessly diverse therapeutic responses which had proved effective in the experiences of these various different therapists was sure, I felt, to give one a much enlarged and diversified armamentarium of therapist-responses and therapeutic techniques, far beyond what was to be learned from the work of any one therapist alone. These were therapists, oftentimes, who had published little or nothing of their work. I am sure that my former Chestnut Lodge colleagues will welcome now with eagerness and deep appreciation the opportunity to study, as I have studied in this book, the work of Clarence Schulz, a man greatly admired by that most critical of audiences, his own workaday comrades in arms.

In assessing Dr. Schulz's qualities as a therapist, I am most deeply impressed by his ability to relate himself to the patient's striving toward health—his ability to sense this striving in the patient, to foster it, and above all to avoid interfering with it. I found the reading of this book a tremendous experience. At one point it finally came through to me that this book is, quite simply, magnificent. This realization occurred, significantly, in one of those many passages when a patient's passionate struggle toward health was being conveyed to the reader with overwhelming clarity and force.

It must be counted a rare combination of personal qualities in Dr. Schulz, who manifests here a genuine interest in and respect for the distorted aspects of the patient's subjective experience, though always valuing primarily the latter's areas of healthy functioning. He never succumbs to a morbid fascination with the intricacies of schizophrenic psychopathology per se.

I have long thought it would be a worthwhile project to conceptualize, as regards the kind of therapist-personality most needed for work with schizophrenic patients, the contrasting kind of person who is what one might call the foil for schizophrenia—that is, the kind of therapist whom the schizophrenic patient's interpersonal processes seem precisely designed to thwart. Such a therapist would, no doubt, personify the very qualities against which, at an internal level, the patient is being unconsciously defended by his schizophrenia. Such a therapist is notable for his perfectionism, his hyperconventionality, and his guilt-ridden, unresolved omnipotence; in this last regard, he thirsts unquenchably to conquer the patient's illness omnipotently and single-handedly, without the aid of anyone else, including the patient himself.

Dr. Schulz is to an unusual degree free of the unfortunate qualities I have just detailed. He looks for an ally in the patient, and he counts it crucially important that the patient be given, from the very beginning, responsibility for those areas of his living with which he can still cope, and that all staff members foster a steady increase in the extent of those areas as treatment proceeds, so that the patient becomes, step by step, more responsible for his own life, both intrapsychically and interpersonally.

Among his notable qualities is his ability not to interfere with the patient's expressing positive feelings toward him. His ability to see positive connotations in general, in one clinical event after another, is one of the factors which enables him to function as an auxiliary ego for the patient. Whereas many therapists tend to feel more comfortable in dealing with the patient's hostility, he is—while quite capable of meeting the patient's hostility firmly—outstandingly able to deal with the patient's fondness, his loneliness, and his grief. Notable, too, is his tapping of the patient's sense of humor, wherein is hidden so much of any patient's latent capacity to emerge from tragedy.

It is evident that his superego is much more self-accepting, much less harshly self-punitive, than is that of many a therapist who works with chronically schizophrenic individuals, and this makes a crucial difference. As he says, "The patient tends to identify with the staff around him. The personnel who are mistrustful and doubtful about themselves make it difficult for the patient to be other than mistrustful and doubtful about himself." Characteristic is his trust in his own, and the patient's, essential health, and he is quick to appreciate the significance of the patient's early and subtle signs of deepening trust in the therapist. In the case presentation of an initially awesomely violent young man, for example, we can infer, from seeing how relatively soon this young fellow was allowed to be living outside the hospital, dating, and driving a car, how very much trust and confidence were being accorded him by his therapist and the other members of the treatment team.

Typical of Dr. Schulz's grasping the positive connotation of what might seem a dismaying development is his repeated and valuable emphasis upon the schizophrenic patient's becoming *capable of* experiencing depression, after years of a less knowingly tragic but in actuality more deeply ill paranoid-schizoid ego-integration. While many therapists would react largely with guilt and anxiety to the patient's now-emerging suicidal proclivities, he, following in this regard the theoretical concepts of Klein and Fairbairn, is able to see the essentially healthy nature of the change.

In contrast to many therapists' treating the schizophrenic individual as suprahumanly "precious," essentially fragile and needful of being sheltered from the flesh-and-blood realities of human existence, he is able to state bluntly a harsh fact and forthrightly set a limit. The same man who can remind us, simply and unashamedly, that "deeply ill patients require time," can also reply to a confusing patient who seeks reassurance that his therapist understands his outpouring of autistic verbalizations, "No, I don't understand," and can stop his years of tenaciously devoted work with an assaultive patient who has attacked him once too often.

Dr. Schulz evidently works in a spirit of conviction that if the patient can come to feel that he really has a choice between what we would call the secondary gratifications of schizophrenia—the sadomasochistic gratifications, for example—and the gratifications of healthy living, he will choose the latter, and, in the great majority of the patients described here, he has succeeded in helping the patient reach that freedom to choose.

His acceptance of his own and his fellow human beings' human limitations, his freedom from fantasied-omnipotence-based perfectionism, is conveyed in his comment about the patient's move to outpatient status, "The move out is just one more step. It does not mean he has now solved all his problems and should be free of conflict. Such

is, after all, not the goal of treatment in any case since conflicts are
part of the lives of all human beings. The question is how he deals
with such conflicts."

Turning from an appraisal of Dr. Schulz's personal therapeutic
qualities to the seven case presentations which form the heart of this
book, I emphasize at the outset that nowhere else in the literature, to
the best of my knowledge, is there presented a series of such deeply
ill patients treated so successfully with intensive psychotherapy. I
regard the therapeutic progress made by patient after patient as
nothing short of amazing. That progress is attested to and documented
by the periodic psychological tests, conducted I assume by the extremely competent Dr. Margaret J. Rioch who was for ten years the
clinical psychologist at Chestnut Lodge, and these reports add much
strength to the volume. The follow-up notes, so very unusual to find
in the literature, similarly add greatly to its interest and scientific
value, and are expressive of Dr. Schulz' long-sustained interest in col-
lecting follow-up data concerning the effects of psychiatric treatment.
His interest in this vitally important field was earlier attested to in 1963
by his published follow-up report concerning patients who had been
admitted to Chestnut Lodge between 1948 and 1958. The only other
follow-up study concerning Lodge patients had been contained in the
1954 volume, *The Mental Hospital,* by Stanton and Schwartz.

Although to the reader who has not worked intensively with chronically schizophrenic patients the treatment-spans portrayed here may
seem long, they are in my opinion, in most of these instances, remarkably short. I found it most impressive, for example, that it could be
reported of a patient initially so long and deeply disturbed as the
young man in Case 1 that "Two years after beginning treatment he
enrolled in a postgraduate course at a local university."

The diversity of the severe illnesses described here is such as to
give this volume the widest possible relevance for patients of every
description. This variety enhances, also, the absorbing readability of
the book, as the clinical portrayals range from a stormily assaultive
and acutely schizophrenic girl in her early twenties to a chronically
paranoid man in his mid-forties, and include an eighteen-year-old
borderline schizophrenic youth involved in predominantly antisocial
symptomatology. The diversity of these patients, collectively, calls
upon great versatility of therapeutic technique on the part of the
therapist, and on the part of all members of the staff engaged in
providing the necessary therapeutic milieu.

The case presentations show us patients who were initially, for the most part, awesomely ill. The descriptions are always vivid and lucid, frequently memorable, and not infrequently deeply moving indeed. Many passages are so memorably quotable that I have felt tempted to reproduce various of them here in this Foreword; but the reader is better left free, as I was, to encounter their impact fresh. That Dr. Schulz is able to distill from years of work, in each instance, so simply and movingly written a portrayal of the course of the treatment is testimony of both the clarity of his thought and the coherency of his therapeutic orientation.

I remember well, from my years at Chestnut Lodge, most of the patients described here. I remember how ill they initially were and how remarkable was their subsequent progress. Reading this book was for me like a walk—an oftentimes gripping and deeply moving walk—down memory lane. The private practice of psychoanalysis and intensive psychotherapy, in which I have been engaged predominantly since I left the Lodge more than five years ago, has its special stresses, but one tends mercifully to forget how enormously difficult it is to be working the bulk of one's day with such very ill patients as this book describes. Dr. Schulz has remained in this field for, to my knowledge, at least twenty years at, successively, Saint Elizabeths Hospital, Chestnut Lodge, and The Sheppard and Enoch Pratt Hospital, as, variously, a therapist, a ward administrator, a supervisor of other therapists, a Chief of Administration (at the Lodge), and, at Sheppard, a few years ago, Director of Training and Director of Inpatient Services, and, at present, Assistant Medical Director and Director of Inpatient Services there.

One of the many values of the case descriptions, for me, is the innumerable glimpses they provide into patients' subjective experience of themselves and of their worlds. These glimpses, of inestimable value for anyone endeavoring to form a meaningful therapeutic relationship with these highly private and deeply troubled persons, comprise one of the book's major contributions. Much more broadly, these seven case histories cast illumination upon the normal development of infants and children, the crises of adolescents, the neurotic conflicts of children and adults, and the normal adult's dream life. In fact, these detailed and alive clinical presentations provide pervasive insights into human psychological functioning in its entirety.

At innumerable junctures this book as a whole clarifies the psychodynamics of schizophrenia. Repeatedly, I found passages illuminatingly relevant to my own work with two chronically schizophrenic individuals whom I have long been treating. A major portion of the authors' concerns here is with various clinical entities, various typical and recurrent clinical symptoms, as seen in the context of the hospital milieu. They discuss with simplicity and practical clinical relevance the complex psychodynamics involved in, to give but a few examples, patients' running away, patients' mutism, and patients' manifesting feeding problems. Just as any therapist or analyst who works with borderline or psychotic patients will find this book immensely informative, anyone involved in psychiatric administration or nursing will find it indispensable.

The authors write, "Therapists are often reluctant to join meetings that include relatives, social worker, clinical administrator, and patient. The therapist's participation in such group meetings requires that he broaden his concept of the area of responsibility toward the patient's treatment. Individual therapy hours then become only one aspect of the program." This book, strong though its focus on the therapist-patient relationship, essentially concerns itself with the total therapeutic milieu which, as the authors emphasize, "includes an integration of the physical environment, psychotherapy, nursing, interaction with fellow patients, medications, recreational and occupational therapy activities, together with contacts with the patient's family by the social worker." Their emphasis throughout is upon teamwork, and they convey convincingly their assertion that "the milieu program is a powerful force toward ego-reorganization."

An innovative spirit suffuses their use of the milieu as a therapeutic instrument. At innumerable points one finds creative utilization of nursing and aide personnel, of seclusion rooms, of cold wet sheet packs, and so on. Such a milieu-intervention as this one, in the instance of the physically assaultive young man described in their first case presentation, might seem to the psychoanalytic theoretician too homely a thing to be worthy of one's best creative thought, but undoubtedly proved of deep-reaching therapeutic importance for the patient:

"Another device that was important in the autonomy issue was the change in the lock on his seclusion room. The seclusion room door lock had been arranged so that it could not be opened from the inside but could be opened from the outside without a key. In this way the patient could be placed in his room and the door pulled closed quickly. With this one-way locking arrangement, the patient could be locked in and anyone from outside his room could enter. However, when the lock was turned around, the patient could exit at any time he wished but only those with authorized keys could enter. This mechanical arrangement to the seclusion room made a considerable difference in the patient's sense of security and privacy."

In the above instance we see, again, how much trust is being placed in the healthy aspects of the patient's ego which are trying to gain mastery over his own violent proclivities. Everywhere in their description of the therapeutic milieu, the authors are quick to see and utilize the positive aspects of persons and things. Whereas the patients' relatives have in the past been regarded, in so many institutions, primarily as potential obstacles to treatment, they view "the family as a positive contribution to the patient's treatment program." They show commendable appreciation of the importance, for the individual's course of treatment, of his relationships with his fellow patients. Their thoughtful evaluation of the indications and contraindications for the judicious use of tranquilizing drugs is one of the book's strong features.

Their book, co-authored by a psychiatrist and a director of nursing, is itself tangible evidence of the kind of teamwork which it depicts. Further, it implies throughout that the treatment of these patients is something teachable to the large numbers of personnel necessary to cope with the social need, rather than something radiating from the unique, exclusive, and unconveyable therapeutic gifts of a few superhumanly endowed therapists. One finishes this book with a feeling of having found it immensely reassuring, in its having highlighted not one therapist's superhuman brilliance but, rather, the reliable help of a team of human beings, including the thoroughly human therapist, working together. This is reassuring in the most personal of regards: the threat of insanity, in oneself or in one's loved ones, is diminished by the knowledge that there are teams of psychiatric personnel-and-patients working together in the manner which this book conveys.

Dr. Schulz has received much praise from me here, and deservedly. Although my own theoretical concepts and therapeutic techniques differ in certain quite fundamental regards from his, this is not the place to detail those differences. I have published much of my own views, and plan to elaborate them further in future papers.

Mrs. Rose Kilgalen, whom I have known as a superbly competent nurse at Chestnut Lodge and in more recent years as Director of Nursing at The Sheppard and Enoch Pratt Hospital, has surely contributed much to make the portrayal of the nursing, and overall therapeutic milieu, aspects of this book as strong and valuable as they are. I salute both these authors for a volume which I am confident will promptly become and enduringly remain a classic in its field.

PREFACE

Indeed, I have not yet succeeded in solving the problem of how to record for publication the history of a treatment of long duration.

. . . a single case history, even if it were complete and open to no doubt, cannot provide an answer to *all* the questions arising out of the problem of hysteria. It cannot give an insight into all the types of this disorder, into all the forms of internal structure of the neurosis, into all the possible kinds of relation between the mental and the somatic which are to be found in hysteria. It is not fair to expect from a single case more than it can offer.

—FREUD: Case of Dora

The case history is an important teaching tradition in medicine. This book presents seven case histories of hospitalized patients to illustrate clinical problems and their treatment. Having participated in many clinical case conferences and found them to be enjoyable learning experiences, we have chosen the traditional conference format of a case presentation followed by a discussion of topics illustrated by the case material.

In the past twenty years, during which the authors have had experience both in the practice and teaching of the treatment of the hospitalized mentally ill, particularly with schizophrenic patients, there has been an increasing number of publications in the field. Theory and practice have been written about from many points of view, including individual psychotherapy, direct analysis, group psychotherapy, milieu programs, and behavioral conditioning as well as a variety of physical measures, including tranquilizing drugs, lobotomy, insulin, and electroshock. In this book we are attempting to make up for the lack of a written presentation of an organized, integrated program of treatment for the hospitalized schizophrenic patient. Most authors approach treatment of these patients from the standpoint that their particular method is the only one. Indeed, other approaches in combination may be scarcely mentioned or even be considered as being contraindicated. For example, Cumming and Cumming's excellent book on the milieu treatment approach suggests that the psychotherapy of the patient be postponed until the patient becomes an outpatient.[1]

Our approach might be described as eclectic, in that it attempts to delineate a coordinated, multilateral attack on the problem but not in the sense that we have some pragmatic willingness to try one kind of treatment after another until we find something that works on the patient.

We have worked in clinical settings ranging from the large public mental hospital to the small private hospital. While the cases described herein originate from experiences within the small private hospital, we feel that the principles derived from this experience have application in any clinical setting.

The first chapter develops a background conceptualization to assist in the understanding of the case presentations and discussions in the later chapters. In the final chapter we summarize what we feel are the major implications emerging from the case studies. The remaining chapters are devoted to case presentations and their discussions. The first case (Chapter 2) was selected to give an over-all view of treatment from its initiation to its completion. The discussion of this first case draws heavily on Erikson's concepts of ego identity, and the reader should be familiar with the article referred to in the notes.[2] The remaining cases are presented in a less complete manner in order to emphasize varying features of the different problems encountered in treating a schizophrenic patient. Thus, the selection of cases is related to the symptomatology of the patients rather than to diagnosis in the narrow sense. Obviously, many of the discussion topics are applicable to several different cases. In the interest of avoiding repetitious discussion, we have somewhat arbitrarily assigned different topics to the various chapter discussions. Out of necessity the discussion topics have not been exhaustively explored. The reader will undoubtedly find additional conceptualizations from the case material.

The cases are presented from the point of view of the individual psychotherapist (Clarence Schulz), who is a psychiatrist. Dr. Schulz, at the time the treatment of these patients was in progress, was Board-certified and in the midst of his training with a psychoanalytic institute.

A comment must be made about the length of treatment in these cases. By no means does the course of hospitalization generally run as long as those described herein. The longer treatment cases were selected because of the wide range of problems encountered and the opportunity to observe their course longitudinally.

We have placed the reports from the psychological tests in the case presentations at the point in time when the test was performed. In some cases, the tests were performed at the beginning of treatment and then again at a later time. The tests thus reflect any change that may have been going on prior to or during that phase of the treatment. Generally, the prognosis that is stated in the psychological reports would be the prognosis for the patient in relation to the group of patients at this particular hospital rather than the prognosis on the basis of a national patient population. For example, patients given a "fairly good" prognosis would be those among the group of very difficult patients in this hospital setting whose chances of improvement were good. If this particular patient in the test material were compared with patients throughout hospitals in the country, the prognosis would undoubtedly be relatively poor in most of these instances. The severe degree of illness is reflected in the length of time of treatment. Deeply ill patients require time.

The "postscript," which is a brief statement on each of these patients appearing at the end of the chapter, describes the eventual outcome, several years later, as far as we are able to determine from the standpoint of a follow-up survey. Of course, with any person such "postscripts" are cross-sectional in this person's life and the final longitudinal "postscript" cannot be ascertained until the life cycle has been completed.

Baltimore, Md.   C. G. S.

August 1969   R. K. K.

NOTES

1. John Cumming and Elaine Cumming, *Ego and Milieu* (New York: Atherton Press, 1962), p. 163.
2. Erik Erikson, "The Problem of Ego Identity," *The Journal of the American Psychoanalytic Association,* IV (1956), 56–121.

ACKNOWLEDGMENTS

Working together on this book has enabled us to clarify our thinking about our own professional role and that of the various other disciplines involved in the treatment of the mentally ill and to understand how they must collaborate and at the same time function autonomously in a successful treatment program. Our own analysts, our supervisors, teachers, and students have each contributed to our professional development.

We have remembered sometimes with pleasant nostalgia, sometimes with painful frustration, the patients and the co-workers presented in these case studies. Many psychiatrists, nurses, social workers, and occupational therapists were involved in the treatment of the patients. There are examples of their contributions throughout the text. It would not be possible to list them all by name. Without their combined efforts there would have been no treatment program to describe. Many of the ideas presented were synthesized from discussions with our co-workers in interdisciplinary conferences. The ideas belong to the group rather than any individual member.

We want to make specific acknowledgment to Margaret J. Rioch and Marion W. Handlon who did the valuable psychological test reports which we have quoted in their entirety.

We are especially indebted to Dr. Dexter M. Bullard, Sr., for his guidance during the years we were employed at Chestnut Lodge and for his support and encouragement while we worked on the manuscript.

Dr. Harold Searles has been a co-worker, teacher, and friend. We wish to express our appreciation to him for writing the Foreword.

Robert Kurtz, psychiatric resident, Jeanne Smith and Phyllis Pensyl Sing-Song, psychiatric nurses, and Dr. Schulz's wife, Connie C. Schulz, an occupational therapist, read the manuscript critically and made constructive suggestions for changes.

Our secretaries at the Sheppard and Enoch Pratt Hospital, Mrs. Ferne Ruhl and especially Miss Marie McGuigan, spent long hours typing the manuscript and protecting us from interruptions while we were working on it.

To all of these we are grateful.

CONTENTS

Case Studies in Schizophrenia

CHAPTER I

The Problem

Dr. Frieda Fromm-Reichmann frequently cleared the air in supervisory consultations and staff conference discussions by asking what the therapist-presenter and the patient had agreed upon as problems to be worked on. Following her example, we will state the issues to be discussed in this chapter: (1) how an intensive study of a few hospitalized psychotic patients is relevant to a study of human behavior; (2) if relevant, what are some of the specific differences in treating the hospitalized patient as compared with treating people living outside of a hospital; and (3) what basic concepts apply to all disciplines involved in this treatment.

By listening to the severely emotionally disordered, we can obtain information applicable to human behavior beyond the confines of the hospital ward. A study of the psychopathology of this group of patients provides insights into the normal development of infants and children, an understanding of the normal adult's dream life, the perplexity of some aspects of adolescent crises, and the underlying conflicts of some neurotic patients. The open display of conflicts, feelings, and primitive thinking, which most of us have concealed, makes this group of people a rich lode of potential insight into human functioning. Psychotic behavior, thinking, and speech, which are viewed by the layman as "insane" and alien to normal human experience, can on closer scrutiny be seen as a magnification or distortion of remnants of early experience in the human being's development. These derivatives are directly evidenced by normal people in dreams, fantasies, and the honest, observing person's occasional "weird" ideas.

According to Harry Stack Sullivan:

Far the greater part of the performances, the interpersonal processes, of the psychotic patient are exactly of a piece with processes which we manifest some time every twenty-four hours. Some of the psychotic performances seem very peculiar indeed, and, as I surmised in 1924, for the explanation and familiarization of these performances, we have to look to the inter-personal relations of the infant, to the first eighteen months or so of life after birth. In most general terms, we are all much more simply human than otherwise, be we happy and successful, contented and detached, miserable and mentally disordered, or whatever.[1]

One of the beneficial byproducts obtained from working with severely emotionally disturbed people is the application of this experience to one's own living outside the clinical setting. For example, when a staff person grasps the importance of the use of firm limit-setting with patients, she can then utilize this understanding when she applies firm limits with her own children. Conversely, the theories of normal infant and childhood development provide us with our most useful model in working with patients.

These concepts of human personality development and the principles of child rearing have formed the most useful frame of reference in our treatment of the severely ill. By this we do not mean that psychotic patients or the hospitalized mentally ill are like children or that children are psychotic. However, we must consider the concepts of child development to gain some understanding of the phenomena of psychotic illness. As a guide in responding to a clinical situation, the staff can readily use the knowledge that they have gained from experiences in their family living. This means that the staff are more than "symbols" of the patient's parents or so-called "parent surrogates." In the course of treatment, the patient grows up all over again and the staff member actually rears the patient. We will make repeated references to psychoanalytic theory and observations about child development as we describe our formulation of a rational treatment approach.

An attempt to define "schizophrenia" is an obvious logical approach to our topic.[2] However, as we think about the complexity and variety of human behavior that is included under such a rubric, we find ourselves trying to define the indefinable. Various aspects of the entire personality may become involved in the disorder, and as one looks at the jumble of phenomena reflecting the person's failure to cope with anxiety, mixed with his success at fending off complete panic, one sees fragmentations of the ego organization, failures in reality appraisal, lack of impulse control, distortions of thinking, and restitutional attempts via delusional ideas serving as "explanations." We see a wide variety of phenomena ranging all the way from our severest nightmare experience to the other end of the spectrum illustrated by our minor prejudicial beliefs. If we were to continue to elaborate in this direction, we would find ourselves emphasizing defense and pathology, which, in turn, would lead to a very slanted impression of the human organism caught up in the syndrome "schizophrenia." We could just as well begin in the opposite direction, emphasizing the organism's ability to compromise and adapt to a way of life resulting from certain warping experience and constitutional deficiencies that have led to defects in his development. We are also impressed by the capacity of the human mind to observe itself, even in these conditions of extreme disorganization. Our patient in Chapter III, while in the midst of her perplexity, commented that although she knew she was sitting there, she did not feel she was there. Fortunately, there are instances, particularly in a relationship of trust with a psychotherapist, when the patient, caught up in the midst of an emotional battle, can retain enough self-observation to understand, in part, what is taking place. We also note the tendency to master, to integrate and synthesize, and to bring together while simultaneously splitting apart large chunks of experience and feelings. We submit that even in the act of ultimate destruction by suicide a solution is sometimes being attempted.

The patient needs a therapeutic milieu as well as a psychotherapeutic understanding of his conflicts. He needs physical care, opportunities for socialization, and schooling that will lead to an occupational identity. To accomplish this, our program includes integration of the physical environment, psychotherapy, nursing, interaction with fellow patients, medications, recreational and occupational therapy activities, together with contacts with the patient's family by the social worker. Emphasizing only one aspect of such a treatment program to the exclusion of the others would present the same fallacy as the parent who focuses exclusively on his child's physical health, while another parent might emphasize the child's religious upbringing, and still another might stress limit-setting, the development of the child's creative potential, or the best formal education possible. We think the best child rearing would include a balance of all of these.

We have become curious about the difficulty that hospital personnel have in utilizing such a multidimensional approach. Why, for instance, does the psychotherapist feel threatened if he is asked to reschedule his appointment in order to allow the patient to attend a hall meeting at a certain time during the week? We have concluded that the narrowness of interest in the multilateral aspects of the treatment is related to the staff person's insecurity in his professional identity. Such insecurity is related chiefly to the nature of the treatment of these extremely difficult patients. The humorous observation that the staff speak of "our patient" when things are going well and "your patient" when the patient is not doing well epitomizes the problem. Inexperienced personnel are most vulnerable to a threat to their professional identity. New residents spurn advice from experienced nurses, new nurses refuse help from seasoned aides, and no one listens to the patients.

As a prelude to the case material that follows, we will now focus on certain basic concepts encountered by the various disciplines as they are involved in our treatment approach. We begin with the severely ill patient who is distrustful, suspicious, and withdrawn into himself as his way of coping with his fear of other people, his concern over his own potential assaultiveness toward others, and his sensitivity to rejection. He has very little sense of security and almost no sense of autonomy or feeling of personal privacy. He fears regulation and intrusion by others, and is concerned that his mind can be read or his actions influenced and caused to become uncontrolled. His own hostility is immensely frightening. Experiences of depersonalization and a threatened disappearance of a sense of existence bring him very close to panic. It is important that the staff reach out to such a patient and meet him more than halfway. To offset these attitudes of distrust, fear, and conflict, the staff and fellow patients will join the patient in attempting to understand what takes place in their relationship and in determining how these attitudes came about in terms of his life experience.

Dr. Otto Will has used the term "relatedness" to characterize the interpersonal relationships that exist between human beings.

Relatedness is a condition described in many ways. You may think of it as a thermal state (hot or cold), as a medical condition (healthy or otherwise), as a function of time (enduring, transient), as a system of moral values (good, bad), as associated with emotions (friendly, hostile), as reflecting economics (profitable or not), and so on. I think that relatedness is described in so many ways because it is an ingredient of all human experience, and thus does not lend itself to any but a very particular or a very general description. Whatever man does involves his relationship with others; whether he be content, unhappy, angry, fearful, lonely, or what not, he exists as he does with some reference to his fellows. Death itself is a human experience of relatedness, its interpersonal quality often being distorted as greatly by the withdrawal of the living as of the dying. In brief, relatedness is a requirement of human life, the potential for its full development being a part of the biological equipment of man. One does not so much seek for relatedness or somehow develop it in others; it is there already. Relatedness is of man; without some semblance of it he will not survive. It is our concern as humans seeking our own welfare to comprehend those factors leading to the concealment, distortion, denial, and fear of the fact of our responsibility for—that is, our responses to—one another.

The psychotherapist is not required to create that which exists, but to understand more fully the nature of the relationship in which he joins with his patient. As the distortions and deficiencies of experience are revealed, there will be made possible the natural growth of the relationship toward a more effective and satisfying development. When the relationship functions well, it will go unnoticed, which is to say that relatedness is not the preoccupation of the related, any more than love is the major concern of those who love.[3]

It is important to keep in mind that the patient might be extremely regressed and dependent in one area, and, at the same time, quite competent and able in another. Of the many examples seen in the case studies, one of the most striking was the patient, who while being tube-fed would work out physics problems in his head for the aides. Dr. Fromm-Reichmann emphasized the importance of responding to the multiple levels of regression-progression in any particular patient.[4] A young woman we remember who had been overactive in a chronic manic state for two years remained on the periphery of her therapy group. She busily wrote obscene limericks that she handed to the therapist at the end of each session. The members decided to make her the recording secretary for the group. At first she interspersed occasional relevant notes among numerous obscene limericks. As the proportion of her relevant notes to her limericks increased, her behavior improved. Within a few months, she was able to move off the "disturbed" floor. One must simultaneously relate to the competence as well as the dependence of a patient. The patient is encouraged to care for himself and his room, to take part in physical activities, and to receive staff assistance only when he is unable to care for himself. Participation of the staff with the patient facilitates the development of relationships that at this level may be more in the nature of attention to physical needs rather than complex conceptual dialogue. Hall routines, schedules, and rules and regulations create clearly defined limits in which the patient is expected to function. These limits facilitate integration and constitute support to a fractured personality that is comparable to the support and healing function of an appropriately applied splint to a fractured bone. Cumming and Cumming emphasize the importance of the hospital milieu in facilitating ego reintegration.

> . . . the milieu must offer to the patient a clear, organized and unambiguous social structure, problems to solve in protected situations, and a variety of settings in which to solve these problems. It should also offer him a peer group and a helpful staff to encourage and assist him to live more effectively. The program should aim at equipping the patient to act in clearly defined roles powered by a variety of motivating forces and governed by different cultural values. This should ideally result in an ego structure sufficiently differentiated and varied to allow a wide range of competence. No single disequilibrating event should then be able to disorder the patient's whole ego structure. In a sense, the treatment should prevent the patient from being bound to any particular event or any particular moment in time. This protects him from diffusion of ego feeling, loss of confidence, and paralysis of choice.[5]

Cumming and Cumming also point out what is needed in the milieu.

> For the solution of these various types of problems, the milieu must provide information, facilities, support, considerable freedom of action, and protection against too severe consequences of failure. All this requires adequate physical settings, sufficient supplies, and a social structure whose policy is made and executed in the interests of the therapeutic milieu. Most important, many of the problems must be solved in groups in which everyone has full membership. In this way new ego organizations are learned in lifelike situations involving a full range of ego activity.[6]

Patients vary a great deal as to the rapidity with which they reintegrate. As will be evident in the majority of these cases, the time perspective must be quite different from that of most people's experience with somatic medical disorders. The treatment of such severely ill patients is apt to evoke a variety of reactions within the staff. These reactions are in response to the nature of the severe regression in the patient, the absence of or very slight improvement on the part of the patient, and the lack of precision of our knowledge as to what specifically should be done for such a patient. The severe distress and anxiety of near panic proportion can make the physician and the nursing personnel feel quite helpless. With some staff members it may provoke a feeling of wanting to rescue the patient. This, in turn, may perhaps be related to certain rescue fantasies in the staff member's own background. An otherwise modest and unassuming therapist once solemnly announced in a supervisory session that as he looked around among his colleagues he thought that he was the only one who was capable of treating this particular patient. The omnipotence of the healer stands in counterreaction to the helplessness of the patient. We shall point out in the case chapters how rivalries and feuds within the staff can occur as a reflection of splits and conflicts within the patient. We wish only to make the point here that these staff reactions cannot be avoided by a fiat that everyone will act in a "consistent" way. Communications about disagreement through conferences, supervision, and numerous informal exchanges will heal the splits in the staff, and at the same time will foster such healing within the patient. Diametrically opposed attitudes and feelings with much sense of conviction about who is right are not infrequent within the treatment team. On the other hand, avoidance of all feelings, with an aloof, impersonal, pseudoprofessionalism, may be the staff person's retreat from involvement. A useful treatment relationship requires emotional investment on the part of the staff, as well as the ability to keep a sufficient emotional distance to observe one's situation and to permit the patient to move at his own pace. Joyce Travelbee looks at the bugaboo about "involvement" in the following way:

> Without involvement the nurse will not experience concern for patients, much less express sympathy to them. It is not possible to know patients, much less assist them in any consistently constructive manner, without involvement. Nurses who do not become involved maintain nurse-patient distance and behave in a depersonalized mechanical manner. Neither nurse nor patient benefits by non-involvement. The nurse is deprived of satisfying and meaningful contacts with patients; indeed, is deprived of job satisfaction itself. Patients are deprived of the support they may require in order to cope with the stress of illness. Involvement, however, is not nearly as great a problem in nursing situations as is its lack.[7]

While our description thus far has emphasized the need for treating the patient with respect, approaching him with the expectation of maximal performance, and relating to him in his totality as a human being rather than as merely a "case of schizophrenia," it might be well at this point to emphasize some distinct modifications necessary to the treatment approach for inpatients. There is a natural tendency to draw on accustomed frames of reference from one's own background of professional experience and apply these to the patient in the hospital. One cannot simply transpose one's experience with out-patients or with college students or other groups on the outside to the inpatient treatment situation. The outpatient presents himself voluntarily for treatment, whereas it is often necessary to reach out to the inpatient, who although wishing relief, may, because of distrust, resist all attempts on the part of others. Because of the patient's in-ability to assume sufficient responsibility for himself outside the hos-pital, the staff must assume partial responsibility. In any particular case, this is always relative and in no situation should the staff be thought of as assuming absolute responsibility. When the inpatient relinquishes responsibility, he must at the same time surrender some of his freedom. The very fact that the staff assumes partial but not total responsibility for the patient, implies that there are dependency gratifications connected with the hospitalization. We feel that such dependency is inevitable and is not to be either prevented or ignored. Rather, in the course of treatment "infantile dependence" is replaced by "mature dependence" as described by Fairbairn.[8]

If a staff is to be effective, there must be adequate communication among the various members of the treatment team. The psycho-therapist should avoid becoming isolated from other members of the team. Here, again, is an essential difference between the situation of the hospitalized patient and that of the outpatient. Confidentiality is strictly maintained in the outpatient situation because the patient is presumed able to make his own interventions upon clarification of his problems. Such confidentiality is impossible in a hospital setting. Pa-tients will often attempt to extract a promise of secrecy from the psychotherapist or other staff members in the hospital situation but we have always found that such secrecy pacts interfere with the over-all program of treatment. It is necessary for the treatment team to be able to share the patient's confidences when necessary in order to assess the clinical situation of the patient and make prompt, effective interventions.

Faulty communication seems to us the single most important factor creating difficulties in the coordination of the various aspects of the treatment effort. Strange as it may seem, it is more important to know what decision has been reached than it is that the "right" decision has been reached. For example, the doctor on call may give his verbal permission to a patient to extend her time out with her visitors. Of greater consequence than his actual judgment in this situation is the necessity for him to tell the nursing personnel about his decision. Confusion and ambiguity over what has been decided can foster mismanagement of the patient. In a way, the entire hospital organization can be viewed from the standpoint of its effectiveness as a network of communication among the various members of the treatment team. Staff rounds, morning reports, orders, notes, conferences, patient staff councils, supervisory sessions, consultations, social service meetings, and letters to the family are just some of the provisions made to facilitate communication.

Much of the discouragement experienced by those who have made attempts to treat these deeply disturbed patients can be prevented from becoming an obstacle to the continuation of treatment if the opposition and "resistance" can be understood dynamically. In our chapter on negativism, which we view as "warmth by friction," we illustrate how negativism was overcome and eventually understood by both the patient and those working with her. The negativism, with its attempt to maintain an identity, and avoid submersion, but, at the same time, preserve relatedness, has its counterpart in other eras of human development. Opposition by way of adolescent rebellious behavior is dynamically related to the psychotic patient's negativistic position. Similarly, the child's automatic response of "No" is part of the same effort toward autonomy. Our experience demonstrates the usefulness of persisting through such negativistic periods rather than pronouncing the patient "not yet ready for psychotherapy" or "unreachable." Certainly we have had patients who were unresponsive to our approach but the cases will illustrate how a manifestly uncooperative posture is not a barrier to success in treatment with these patients, or, for that matter, to a successful outcome in the normal adolescent's development.

Frequently, we find important changes occurring as the fragmented patient begins to reorganize. The principal sign of ego reintegration is the change that corresponds to Fairbairn's shift from a paranoid-schizoid position to a depressive position.[9] Instead of the patient's reacting to anxiety by regressive fragmentation, disintegration, paranoid projection, and confusion, he is now capable of becoming depressed. In the face of loss or a sense of helplessness, the patient experiences depression. Again this will be seen quite clearly in our negativistic patient, who, when no longer assaultive or reacting impulsively, experienced profound hopelessness, despair, and helplessness, which called forth a corresponding sense of futility and helplessness on the part of the therapist. A greater sense of autonomy, capacity to assume responsibility, development of foresight, and ability to delay impulse gratification in order to think things through, are all signs of increased reorganization.

The staff must be prepared to relinquish their caretaking functions as the patient is ready to assume responsibility for himself. Maintenance of a splint after a fracture has healed will lead to muscular atrophy. The patient continues to need honest feedback about his behavior as his activities increase. In a hall meeting a patient requested a visit home. The hall doctor gave his approval for this visit on the basis of an over-all plan to mobilize the patient toward an early discharge. However, when other patients in the group pointed up specific examples of her confusion, the doctor postponed the visit and the patient understood why. The amount of freedom to come and go that a patient is given can be increased as he demonstrates through his behavior how much responsibility he can assume for himself.

Self-esteem is important for each of us but especially for the severely disordered. Opportunities for accomplishment through necessary work increase the patient's self-esteem. Actual experience of praise and achievement, while important, is not enough. Self-esteem is also a reflection of the extent to which the patient measures himself against his internal ego-ideals. Here we see an example of the importance of the multiple approach to treatment. If one limited one's efforts to buoying up the patient through praise or actual accomplishments alone, it would be like pumping air into a tire with a leaky valve. On the other hand, if one attempted to diminish the patient's ego-ideals through psychotherapy, without providing opportunities for realistic achievements, treatment would be greatly prolonged. Thus, we see how efforts to enhance a patient's self-esteem involve various aspects of the treatment program: creative activities in occupational therapy and a work program, respect for the patient by the staff, understanding the personal historical contributions to his low self-esteem, together with insight into the patient's internal unrealistic ideals.

As patients improve, the scope of their experiences expands in ways that round out their living. One patient, who, prior to his illness, had graduated from college with honors and had earned a letter in a major sport, showed selective residual deficiencies in living. During the course of treatment, the hospital operator taught him to dial a telephone. Also for the first time in his life, he ordered and paid for a meal in a restaurant by himself. When he hailed a taxi and it actually stopped for him, he was a most surprised man. Now he no longer managed to get his mother to do these things for him.

This is the framework of the treatment program at our hospital today. In the case studies that follow, we have elaborated on these concepts as they apply to specific situations with specific patients. Because the cases presented go back in time ten years or more, the handling of some situations does not necessarily conform to those methods that we would use today for a similar type of patient. Experiences gained clinically with these patients have contributed to the conceptualization of the treatment program just as future clinical experiences will contribute to its revision.

NOTES

1. Harry Stack Sullivan, *Conceptions of Modern Psychiatry* (Washington, D.C.: William Alanson White Foundation, 1940), p. 7.
2. Karl A. Menninger, *The Vital Balance* (New York: The Viking Press, 1963), pp. 47–48, and Lawrence S. Kubie, "The Unfortunate Concept of Schizophrenia" in *Genetic Factors in 'Schizophrenia'* (Charles C Thomas, in press). Dr. Menninger and Dr. Kubie have been most vocal in their objections to the nosological term "schizophrenia." While their arguments have much merit, we feel the label itself is not as important as what is done about it.
3. Otto A. Will, Jr., "Human Relatedness and the Schizophrenic Reaction," *Psychiatry*, XXII (1959), 215.
4. Frieda Fromm-Reichmann, "Psychotherapy of Schizophrenia," *The American Journal of Psychiatry*, III (1954), 411.
5. John Cumming and Elaine Cumming, *Ego and Milieu* (New York: Atherton Press, 1963), p. 71.
6. *Ibid.*, p. 76.
7. Joyce Travelbee, *Interpersonal Aspects of Nursing* (Philadelphia: F. A. Davis Company, 1966), p. 151.
8. W. Ronald D. Fairbairn, *Psychoanalytic Studies of the Personality* (London: Tavistock Publications, 1952), p. 34.
9. *Ibid.*, p. 25.

CHAPTER II

The Treatment Course of a Disturbed Patient

CASE PRESENTATION[1]

Our first case is selected as an over-all report of treatment from its beginning to its termination. It is, therefore, the most complete case to be reported.

This patient was a chronically disturbed schizophrenic in his mid-twenties when he was admitted for treatment as a transfer from another hospital. His illness had begun twenty months previously with a sudden catatonic excitement marked by assaultiveness and destructiveness. He was a single man, who lived at home and worked as a chemist for a large firm. About three months prior to the onset of his illness the patient had become engaged. His mother voiced some objection because the girl's religion was different from that of his family. The evening of the day that the patient had become engaged, he wet his bed. He seemed upset, but his parents assured him that the religious difference was of no consequence. Two weeks prior to his initial hospitalization, the engagement was made official and the patient began to voice uncertainties about marriage. He implied that he felt unequal to it. Suddenly, one Sunday morning he became quite disturbed. He wrapped a bookend in newspaper and threw it up against the wall, broke some windowpanes, and became so upset that the police were called.

He was admitted to a state hospital where he received a total of twenty-three electroshock treatments, eighty-five insulin treatments, and twenty-two combined treatments. He also had some group psychotherapy. Any improvement noted was only of brief duration. In the description given of him at the state hospital, "his affect continued hostile, angry and explosive, boisterous and assaultive. His conversation was arrogant, profane, defiant, and obscene, with bizarre nonsensicalities." It was at this point that the state hospital psychiatrist recommended transorbital lobotomy. The family obtained a consultant who recommended transfer to another hospital with a psychotherapy program. At that hospital the patient experienced continued prolonged disturbed periods, and was placed in a seclusion room. Attempts were made at individual therapy, and electroshock treatment was used. It was during this second hospitalization that his fiancée broke their engagement upon the suggestion of the medical staff. The staff believed that she was maintaining her relationship with him only out of a sense of guilt. His disturbance made him unmanageable. It required eight male attendants to move the patient from the seclusion room to the bathroom. After a period of twenty months of assaultiveness, destructiveness, and psychotic disorganization, his continued disturbance finally led to his transfer to the treatment program about to be described. In order to enable the transfer to be carried out, he received shock treatment on the two days prior to his transfer.

BACKGROUND HISTORY

The patient was the only surviving one of three children. His father was a hardworking, quiet man who had very little to do with his son when he was growing up. His mother, however, was very interested in him all through his life. She emerged in the historical account as a much more emotional, guilt-ridden, and terribly involved parent than the patient's father. Prior to the patient's birth, an older sister, aged four, was killed. As she alighted from a bus with her mother, a car struck her, and killed her instantly. This had a lasting effect on the mother, who dealt with the accident by declaring it to be unmentionable within the family. The patient was born two years after this accident. It was his mother's stated intention that he was to be perfect in order to make up for what she thought was her fault in the death of her first-born child. When the patient was two-and-a-half years old, a younger brother was born. The brother, like the patient, was very precocious, but tended to be much more friendly and popular with people. When the patient was in his third year of college, his brother was killed in a skiing accident. Again, his mother was very shaken, but the patient showed little reaction. He felt that since it was so upsetting to his mother, he had to protect her by retaining his own composure. When the patient was small, he fulfilled the mother's expectations in many ways. He developed quite early. Although his mother thought that he was inclined to be a rather placid child, she considered him to be quite independent. To illustrate this, she described an incident that occurred when he was left alone with a baby-sitter. When the parents returned, they found that the sitter was asleep and that the young child was amusing himself. She gave the following description of him: "We never thought that he was emotional. We thought, on the other hand, that he was phlegmatic. He went along pretty much the same from day to day. He had himself under control all the time. I never saw him lose his temper. He was never depressed. He seemed to be the same all the time. I never saw him express anger —never in his life. Never in all his life did he give any evidence of having a bad disposition. He was conciliatory. He greeted me every morning with 'I have the best little mother in the world.'"

The two boys were guided in the direction of nonhazardous play and games because of the mother's feeling of responsibility for the death of the sister. While the patient did play with other children in the neighborhood, he did not develop any close relationship with any particular boy. He did very well scholastically. In high school, when he found that he could not excel in athletics, he turned to chess, at which he became extremely proficient. Even though the patient enjoyed frequent dating, his brother seemed to be more naturally popular with girls. His father felt that he dated mainly to impress other people with his popularity rather than from any genuine interest in the girl herself.

He went away to college and telephoned his mother almost daily at her request. He was at the top of his class in college and was active in fraternity life. The middle of his college period was interrupted by two years of compulsory military service, which was uneventful. He had one passive participation in a homosexual experience while in service and no heterosexual genital experience at all, although opportunities were available. His brother was killed in the patient's third year of college following his return from the service. Because his brother's death left him as the only remaining child, he turned down two postgraduate fellowships that would have taken him away from home. Instead he remained at home, worked at his job during the day, and attended graduate school in the evenings. About eleven months before the onset of his illness, he had his first serious romance. While his parents were away on vacation, he broke off his relationship with his first fiancée without, as far as they knew, any apparent reaction.

At the time of his admission to the hospital, partly because of his psychotic disorganization but also as a result of the shock treatment, he showed considerable confusion and retardation. His responses were quite fragmentary. He was careless about his dress and appearance. Physically, he was tall, thin, and rather gaunt looking.

The treatment program, which lasted for a period of four years, was divided into an acutely disturbed period lasting five months followed by a postpsychotic period. During the latter he reorganized along the lines of obsessive-compulsive defenses. At first these defenses largely excluded feelings, but with subsequent psychotherapy, the feelings became much more accessible to him.

In spite of this patient's degree of disturbance, fragmentation, and threatening assaultiveness, he showed flashes of a sense of humor and seemed to be rather well-liked by the female nursing personnel. From the beginning, when he came to talk with me, he was extremely suspicious. He felt that the hospital was wired for television and that everything was being recorded. He questioned me and I gave information about myself in brief answers. Somewhere toward the end of our first appointment, he said, "I've told you enough. I've told you more than I've told anybody." I felt rather encouraged. In the second interview, when I was trying to set up a treatment arrangement with him, he protested, saying that I was not friendly enough. Then, a few sentences later, he asked what the schedule would be. I wrote one out on a piece of paper and handed it to him.

During the initial phase, we had many battles in which he would slam the door in my face or throw a chair at me. Sometimes he would barricade his door. I approached him from the standpoint that there must be reasons for his behavior, and I thought we could talk it over. At one time during this early period, I had him placed in a wet sheet pack. He fought this procedure. The only thing he said when he was in the pack was to ask, "Is this your king of clubs?" For the next few days, about the best I could do was to sit outside his door while he remained aloof. At other times I would sit at the end of the hall in an area adjacent to where he was sitting. If there were other people around, we both seemed comfortable enough to exchange a few words. He was fairly persistent in offering me cigarettes even though I do not smoke. I answered some of his questions, each time trying to find out why he wanted to have the information. When the questions became too personal as, for example, when he wanted to know the name of my wife, I declined to answer.

In a session three weeks after beginning treatment, I came to his room and found him nude except for a piece of cloth wrapped around his thigh. He was sitting on the bed. He was pushing the edge of a postcard against the base of his penis and smoking vigorously. I asked him what this was about. He said very little but did say something about being a "devil worshiper." I asked if he felt that his penis got him into trouble, and he said it did. A few minutes later, he threw his cigarette on me. I jumped up, stamped it out, and told him how much this annoyed me and that we would have to do something about his violence. I said that I thought that if he couldn't control himself he should ask for a wet sheet pack. His reply was "All right, give me a pack now." Aides were called in and he cooperated with the pack. In my attempt to continue the discussion about his being a devil worshiper, I asked why he wanted to castrate himself and he said "because of bastards like you." Following that it was necessary to pack him on only one occasion for a treatment hour. At that time he requested it himself. Usually, if I saw him and felt somewhat frightened of him, I would ask him if he felt that he should ask for a pack. He would often quiet down after that and cause me very little difficulty. At one of the sessions he initially refused to see me. Then he said, "Give me a half-hour to think it over." I read a newspaper for a half-hour and then reapproached him. As he came out of his room with his food tray, he gestured as if he were going to throw it at me. Instead he handed it over to the aide and met with me for the remaining time.

After the first month of these verbal and sometimes physical attacks on me, he complained that the treatment would never work and that it was impossible. I replied by saying that I thought it was rather early to come to any conclusive opinions about it. He then surprised me by asking me what my opinion was of him. I replied, "Well, you impress me as a person who must be terribly burdened by all this resentment and hostility that you're carrying around; that you're suspicious of anyone if they take an interest in you; but I think you're a pretty bright person and you seem to have a capacity for relating to somebody. This is all pretty general but it is about as much as I can say now. What do you think?" He said, "Well, that's all true. Another thing I found out that if you're ever happy then people can take advantage of you." I felt very good about this interchange. In the subsequent period, he began to tell me how he felt depressed and suicidal. After an instance when he threw some fruit juice on me and I took this up with him, he said, "Well, did you ever think that I might be as frightened of you as you are of me?" Actually, I had not realized this, and with this having been stated, there was much less fear on both sides. The fighting decreased noticeably.

At a period seven weeks after we started, the patient had been complaining quite a bit about having no privacy and about people barging in on him. He would be masturbating and the aides would come in with a tray. There would be fights around this in which he would kick people and complain about living in a goldfish bowl.

At that time, the parents visited. At the end of the visit his father was urging his mother to begin their drive home. She said, "I would like to stay with him forever." She wept and pleaded, "Oh, if he would only get better, if he'd only get better I would take cancer if he would only get well." She had a sheaf of papers that she had removed from his desk. These contained some writings that he had made just prior to the onset of his psychosis. There was something about the way she offered these to me that led me not to accept the papers from her. I felt this would be an intrusion upon some of his private possessions. I declined, saying that if in the future I thought it could be of use I would ask her for them. In the next appointment with him, I told him that I had met his parents. He asked me what I thought of his mother. I replied, "Well, you know, I think she has a tremendous interest in you and that you might have felt that as a lack of privacy. I wonder if that doesn't carry over here at the hospital when you feel that everybody is barging in on you." At the end of that hour, he shook my hand and I felt that we were on the right track.

More and more, we began to hear about his feelings of depression. At the same time his sense of humor began to shine through. On one occasion I arrived and noticed him holding his ear to the wall and making movements with his face. I asked what the voices were saying. He said, "Oh, I'm not listening to voices, I am watching my two flies, 'Amos' and 'Andy.'" We laughed about this. Then, as I pursued the topic, he went ahead to describe his feelings of loneliness and how he felt very suicidal when he was put in seclusion. He then compared his education to mine. He also noticed the kind of car I drove and said that he had a car at home. More and more, he began to relate facts about himself and some of his problems. When I asked him about his brother and sister, he said that he did have a brother who died and quickly added, "I didn't kill him." Some of this information came out in a way that made it difficult to decide whether it was fact or fantasy. He spoke of his mother waking him up every morning and bathing him. According to him, if he started to curse, she would threaten to wash his mouth out with soap. He felt terribly frightened.

He thought that she was going to try to drown him. He would say, "Don't, Mother, do you want to kill me too?" He alleged this would jolt her out of it and she would cease pressuring him.

He seemed most resentful of the male aides and was much more accepting of female personnel. Even while he was quite upset, one of the nurses was able to take him from the ward to the hospital canteen. He showed steady improvement, became quieter, began dressing, and would go out to activities. He seemed particularly drawn to the student nurses. In the early phases, when he was being spoon-fed, he, in turn, would feed the nurse a cracker. He also began helping the student nurse make his bed. When he started going to occupational therapy, he requested instructions in knitting. He would bring his knitting back to the ward and tell the nurse that his mother wanted him to knit. It was also noticed that he would imitate some of the behavior, speech, and accents of other patients. On one occasion, he was playing "Chopsticks" as a piano duet with a student nurse. Quite spontaneously she said that they should be on television. Much to her surprise, he stopped, picked her up, and sat her on top of the television set.

As his behavior began to improve, his psychotic thinking decreased and he began to report dreams. These dreams contained the identical content that was present in the psychotic period. These delusions were now no longer available during his waking life.

An incident from the treatment that occurred five-and-a-half months after its beginning was especially moving. The patient was still being seen in his room. In this session he complained that the head nurse from that ward was leaving. This was the nurse who first took him out to the canteen. I had not heard she was leaving and expressed my surprise. I asked where she was going. He said that she was moving to Kansas. He then began to make all kinds of paranoid accusations about the possibility of her spreading information from the nurses' notes to the people out there. Because of her they would find out about him and so forth. He went on in this manner for a long time and I listened to him. I remembered how important that nurse was to him. Actually she felt quite fond of him and they had had a very good relationship. When his outpouring subsided somewhat there was a pause and I said, "You really will miss her, won't you?" With that, the whole paranoid outpouring stopped and he choked up with tears. He then handed me a *Time* magazine he was holding, with the back cover turned toward me. On this cover was a Coca Cola advertisement and a picture of a nurse carrying some charts with the caption "Always dependable, always reliable." After he stopped crying, he was able to tell me that he wondered whether he had driven her away and how he felt quite responsible for this. He said that once he had playfully rolled up a newspaper and patted her on the head with it as they were going down in the elevator. He wondered whether any of this had caused her to leave to go to Kansas.

The first of three psychological examinations was accomplished when the patient had calmed down sufficiently.

PSYCHOLOGICAL EXAMINATION

The patient was seen in my office about six months following his admission to this hospital. At the time of admission he had been too disturbed to permit testing. His manner during the tests was very quiet. He did everything he was asked to do with no objections and few questions.

Wechsler-Bellevue Intelligence Scale

The patient's earned I.Q. places him in the bright normal group, but this is obviously not a valid estimate of his capacities. His performance on the subtests varies from far below average (Comprehension and Picture Arrangement) to very superior (Digit Span, Arithmetic, and Block Design).

The patient probably has superior or very superior general intelligence but his present functioning is impaired by grossly psychotic ways of thinking. His attention and concentration, however, are good, and his ability to solve problems that do not involve human relationships or verbal concept formation is excellent. But his judgment in these latter areas is grossly impaired, and his ability to synthesize or integrate material involving social situations is at present very poor.

	I.Q.		Weighted Scores
Full Scale	112	Information	13
Verbal Scale	113	Comprehension	5
Performance Scale	109	Digit Span	16
		Arithmetic	16
		Similarities	7
		(Vocabulary)	(13)
		P. Arrangement	7
		P. Completion	14
		Block Design	16
		Object Assembly	10
		Digit Symbol	8

Rorschach Test and Other Projective Techniques
(DRAWING AND FOUR PICTURES)

The tests indicate clearly that the patient is grossly psychotic. The schizophrenic process seems to pervade almost all of his experience.

His thinking is confused and highly autistic. His perceptions are distorted. His ability to respond to complex social situations is limited, and his behavior is rather rigidly set.

He is probably constantly preoccupied with defending himself in one form or another against attacks of all kinds. He must experience authority, particularly masculine authority figures, as unreasonable and tyrannical. He has to react either as a slave or as a violent desperate rebel. A third alternative is withdrawal into a private world in which he can secretly make fun of all the nonsense that goes on in the "real" world.

He probably has suffered a great deal from feeling pushed to be manly when he felt quite helpless.

PROGNOSIS:

Time before patient can engage in normal life: very long.
Active interest in therapy: weak.
Rigidity of defensive structure: strong.

During this postdisturbed period, he scheduled his life completely. He would go to the library and read fifty pages of the encyclopedia every day. He obtained a college mathematics book and began working on the problems from the beginning of the book all the way through to the end. He had a large number of correspondence chess games going simultaneously and he drew cartoons for the hospital newspaper. He felt comfortable during this time and had a considerable amount of freedom in the hospital. During his therapy appointments he would recite his activities in a mechanical fashion without any willingness to explore them. For example, although his cartoons were really quite revealing of his psychopathology, he would say that they were funny—they were just cartoons. I would agree with what he said but felt that we could also use them to understand him. One cartoon depicted a patient about to step out of an eighth-story window. As the patient looked back into the doctor's office, he said, "Thanks very much, you have helped me a lot, doc." In another one, the patient in the doctor's office looks out the window at a policeman approaching the patient's car parked in a no-parking area. The patient in the cartoon comments, "Yes, you're right, doctor, I am worried about something." His dreams were filled with content about gladiators, men hitting each other, and pointing guns at each other. His waking life was largely free of this content except for occasional vague fears of airplanes crashing into the hospital ward or someone shooting him or killing him with an automobile. On the whole, he thought that he had greatly improved and was ready to go back to work. He saw no reason to continue his therapy. There was a strong denial of any need for me, and he resented the cost of treatment. He thought talking into a tape recorder or writing down his thoughts, then tearing up what he had written, would be equally effective. He was glad whenever I took a vacation because then he didn't have to think up things to say to me. His sessions had the quality of being thoroughly prepared and thought out ahead of time. It was more difficult for him when the appointments were bunched together for several days because fewer events occurred between our sessions. He might then be caught with a spontaneous thought that he would have to report. He was surprised that after about two weeks when I was away on a vacation, he felt a little upset and wished that he had his appointments. He indicated that he had thoughts that maybe Al Capone would have benefited from having spent time in therapy. "He wouldn't go out and do a job until he had first talked this over with his psychiatrist."

The following sample hour is representative of this period of treatment. There were recording difficulties during the first part of the transcript.

CGS: I think we got it now. You were saying about these movies.

PT: Well, two of them were in technicolor, three of them were in technicolor, as a matter of fact, double features both times, and (inaudible) was really beautiful, the story wasn't outstanding but the scenery was, and both the scenery and the story.

CGS: (Inaudible), is that a Marilyn Monroe picture?

PT: No.

CGS: That wasn't one made up in Canada?

PT: It was supposed to have taken place in (inaudible). It was a story of a fight between the (inaudible).
(Pause.)

CGS: Testing—maybe that's got it.
Well, what did you want to take up today, in the way of problems?

PT: We can take up the problem of trying to trisect any angle with a compass and a straight edge, only we wouldn't get very far because no one has been able to solve that. As for my personal problems, I have not any new ones or any that would provide much to talk about.

CGS: Well, what about the old ones?

PT: Oh, those have been cleared up.

CGS: Cleared?

PT: This is one problem I object to. About this medical library—I don't know why they advertise all these books downstairs and then, they won't let us read any.

CGS: Maybe it's advertised for the staff. But have you asked anybody for a special permission?

PT: I did and she said I had to see you and when I asked you, you said I had to see the librarian, so there is no out anywhere.

CGS: It seems to me that—did she say "ask your doctor?"

PT: Yeah.

CGS: I think she might have meant the Administrator. I believe on occasions, he does check out a book for a patient that is interested. You might ask him about it.

PT: Well, I have to admit that I am getting a little tired of reading encyclopedias, I might do, I might read some Freud's writings. They only have one book on psychology over at the OT shop, whenever I can start on that that would eliminate the problem. I have had a psychology course and I don't remember doing too well in it. I thought I might brush up on it. They dealt more on the problem of labor relations—how to get more work out of the employees and still keep them happy.

CGS: Umhm.

PT: For instance, if you had an assembly line, thirty people working on it, how you would keep them from getting tired just doing the same thing every day and still keep them turning out the goods. I don't remember any conclusions either. They treated it as rather a minor subject so I wouldn't get too much out of it.

CGS: What would you be particularly interested in finding out now?

PT: Well, I don't know. I just want to know what people are thinking in the field. Not that I am planning to set up an assembly line anywhere, but just the fact that I am not allowed to read them is a little annoying. The same thing happened down the town library. They wouldn't let me take out any books because I didn't have a card there and they wouldn't let the nurse take them out I was with, because she was only going to be in town for three months and she was classified as a non-resident.

CGS: Won't they let you obtain a card?

PT: I think they said the way you are supposed to do it is to get the librarian here to go down there and get them. However, I have plenty of stuff I can read down at ———— to take out, so it's not the crucial problem, however, none of it deals in psychology, which seems to be the important field to me. It's just as if I belonged to the Chess Club, which has a large library of chess books and they wouldn't let me take any out if I wanted to keep up with what everybody else is doing by reading them.

CGS: Maybe you feel you are not getting enough from me?

PT: I wouldn't say that you haven't given me enough; however, to get all the cases and background of the theories of Freud by reading him directly is not what I could get from you unless you just read it to me. Maybe she wouldn't object if I just went down there and read in the room? You think that would be possible?

CGS: No, I think that ruling that was set up goes for downstairs too. It's for the nurses and the doctors. Why do you feel discriminated against? People look down on you. They have to be taken down a few notches like the fellow you set as an illustration last time, or a couple of times ago. Maybe this is again along that same line of feeling that inequality here.

PT: Well, I don't see the point—if nobody else is interested in the book, why shouldn't they let us read it. If there is a large demand for a certain book I wouldn't take it out, but I don't think that's the case here.

CGS: Well, I am not sure they won't let you take it out if you work through the Administrator. You'd be responsible for the book and if he is willing to do that, it's alright with me, but I guess it does bring out the old feeling of comparison and envy and resentment about it.

PT: No, it's our money that's paying for those books—I don't see why we shouldn't be allowed to use them. I don't think there is much demand for them among the patients. I might be an exception to the rule.

CGS: Your money is paying for books which they won't let you use!

PT: In so much as they have decided to buy a new book, they take it out from a fund, which is presently paid for primarily by the patients.

CGS: So is our salary. And if I buy a car, it's paid for by the patients and it doesn't mean they would use it.

PT: Hm, it's true.

CGS: You don't think the staff should have a library?

PT: No, I can see the value of it. I suppose you can always say, why don't you go out and buy these books yourself if you want to read them. That would be an answer. I could do that. Build up my own medical library. Well, that was just a point, it didn't really worry me.

CGS: Well, maybe there is some feeling that you are not getting what you are paying for.

PT: I think you are doing everything in your power to make our lives better, with what you have to work with and that's anything to turn out in my favor.

CGS: Maybe there is something in psychology that you wanted to check on—on Freud, maybe you wanted to see if I knew anything about it.

PT: It's just a feeling that as long as I am here, I might as well learn as much as I can about the easiest subject to teach. For instance, if I were in a canoe factory, I'd want to read up on canoes. I am in a psychological hospital, I want to read up on psychology, that's all.

CGS: The easiest subject to teach?

PT: Not the easiest subject to teach but the one, let's say it would be easier for me to get the information now rather than ten years from now when I wouldn't be so closely associated with psychologists. It is far easier to learn when there are people around who know something about it, and you are alone. Just as when I went to Engineering School, I learned engineering because they had a lot of people who knew a lot about it and found it easy to teach us that, whereas if I tried to learn engineering right now, I would have a tough time. They just don't have the books here, they don't have anyone who could explain it to me.

CGS: It is very dubious that you would learn something about yourself by reading psychology.

PT: No, but I could certainly apply it to other people, in my contact.

CGS: What's on your mind today?

PT: Well, nothing at the moment. I can dig up something if you want. There is only one suggestion in the Patient's Planning Committee Suggestion Box at ———, which indicates to me that there is not much on anyone's mind, over at———. And the box has been sitting there all the time. It was a suggestion about fixing the tennis court; so it's a little tough for me, to come up with some ideas. When you say "what's on your mind" that means I should have some ideas about the hospital and I am trying to show you that it is not easy to have ideas.

CGS: Well, I thought maybe there might be something that you wanted to bring up and had not gotten to it yet. You talked about going to the movie in which they seemed to be doing a lot of shooting and a good bit of violence and then you mention the library and that you are not allowed the use of the library that is there, they only tempt you by putting up notes on the bulletin board, about books, and so on, but don't give you access to it. You are interested in psychology, in Freud.

PT: Of course, I can just sit back in my room, play cards with myself all day long, if you'd rather have me do that. I don't think that would lead anywhere.

CGS: If I add those things up, does it mean you want to know something about the psychology of violence?

PT: No, I don't think that's part of what we are supposed to talk about.

CGS: Well, in a way, it's a factor of your life.

PT: I think it would be too large a factor in my life to discuss. I am reasonably able to take care of myself, and people don't generally take it out on people who can take care of themselves. They take it out on people who can't take care of themselves, who are afraid of them. For instance, you wouldn't walk up to a girl's heavyweight boxing champion, hitting her in the jaw for fear what would happen to you, so that doesn't worry me so much.

CGS: You mean as far as people are afraid of you, they won't do violence to you.

PT: On the other hand, there is the example of those dogs that are running around all the time. A couple of dogs about six inches long, everybody comes up and pats them on the back, and the big dog will come along, about three feet long and everybody stays away from him. It just isn't as cute, let's say, as the other dog and he probably has some resentment because everyone is paying attention to the little dog; so it doesn't seem to pay for the dog to be able to take care of himself. So that my idea may be all wet, I don't know. Of course, you might say we are not going to try to psychoanalyze dogs, so that subject is out.

CGS: You are the big dog or little dog?

PT: I was thinking of the big dog. Everyone seems not to be afraid of the little dog so they just are real nice to it, yet the other dog probably comes from a good family, there is nothing wrong, but no one pays any attention to him, because he is an older dog, bigger and one might not get the pleasure out of stroking his head or his back as they do to little dogs. (Pause.) I don't know of anything outstanding in my mind, to be talked out.

CGS: How would you feel about people being afraid of you?

PT: I would feel very lonesome.

CGS: And the same with you being afraid of people?

PT: I might feel very lonesome.

CGS: And you do.

PT: I haven't looked at it that way. I think that a moderately friendly attitude is a good attitude to take, (inaudible) it drives other people away.

CGS: Umhm.

PT: You should know how I feel about this learning of psychology, you certainly taught enough people psychology, being here, and if they said, "How can I apply this to myself," you wouldn't know the answer any more than I do. I have noticed it at school now, they are giving correspondence courses which indicate that you can learn a subject by yourself if you just apply yourself diligently to your work. Sitting in class and listening to the teacher who primarily gives his material from books written by others—why couldn't you get the same learning by reading the books yourself? The work I have done over at the canteen has helped me a lot because I know how to mix concrete which I didn't know before. Saw how much it takes to lay so many square feet of concrete. There are lots of things you have to know when you are a cost estimator on a building project—how much it would take to do certain tasks. This experience of reading of prime authors' works on it would help later on. I think psychology is an important field and the value to me would be more if I spent my time doing that than wasting my time, since I can't be employed now, I might as well use all my time to getting ready for the day when I will be working again.

CGS: Well, that's what you are working towards. (Pause.) Well, come back to the shooting in the movie, and so on. What feelings of violence have you encountered in yourself?

PT: I have been angry at myself, sometimes, unnecessary things I have done, violent, (inaudible) myself with them.

CGS: This is recent?

PT: No. In the past. That's what you meant when you said "what have you found in the way of violence towards yourself."

cgs: I didn't mean necessarily toward yourself, but within yourself. Feelings of violence toward others.

pt: I have noticed one thing when reading all these various books; most of them seem to have violence as one of the main factors in them. A book just doesn't seem to get written if it is not about some war of some kind going on where people have something to think about rather than their routine lives. Although there are exceptions, no doubt, but; for instance, "Gone with the Wind", was centered about the Civil War. "Lydia Bailey," which my mother worked on before, was about the war in Haiti in 1796, and the one I am reading now, "The Spider King," it's about at the end of the Hundred Years War, back in the 1400s. You just can't seem to read something that doesn't have something to do with violence. Evidently they put it in there as a sort of a way to make a book exciting whereas it would be dull otherwise.

cgs: See you tomorrow.

pt: O.K.

Denial was a prominent feature of our sessions at this time. The patient wondered why on his admission to the hospital he had been placed in a ward where he might be injured by those other disturbed patients. I learned that he did not want to tell some of his thoughts because they were "indecent" or "incoherent." By consistently focusing on instances where he was concealing his thoughts and feelings, dents were made in this move toward a generalized denial. He presented himself as a model patient, one who brought in his dreams and reported the events of the previous twenty-four hours. Such efforts to please me were interpreted as being similar to his attempt to be a model boy for his mother. While he made vigorous efforts at keeping silent about his resentment toward others, I gradually began to hear how he was discovering instances of his rudeness toward some of the hospital personnel. Approaching a markedly obese employee, he commented, "Travel is broadening," and he referred to a stout nurse as "blimpo." Recognizing this in himself, he seemed genuinely astonished saying, "This isn't like me."

Two general categories of reasons for concealing parts of himself during the hour sessions were: (1) he believed that he could get out of the hospital if he could convince me he was all right, and (2) he was afraid that he may have a harmful effect on me. As a result of our discussions, he made excursions into being more open with me. This openness was at first primarily in the direction of disclosing dreams. One particular dream was concerned with his sexual participation with a mermaid who was helpless because she had no arms. This theme of the female sexual partner being made helpless became a prominent feature of his later fantasy life but at this time it was manifest only in dreams. In the same hour he was able to tell me that prior to my vacation two months previous to this, he had been all set to enjoy not having his hours, but after a week of my vacation he had felt a longing for the hours. In the next hour he spoke of another patient whom he considered to be homosexual. He wondered if I thought he was homosexual because he played chess almost exclusively with men. He described an actual previous homosexual experience of his own and went on to develop the idea that much of his dating was to prove to his fellows that he was not homosexual. He also voiced some of his uncertainty about his ability to perform heterosexually, conveying his feelings of being threatened by heterosexual participation together with his concern that attachment to me would be considered homosexual and therefore unacceptable.

As the time for his move to outpatient living was approaching, we began to see further manifestations of his separation anxiety. He had a dream in which I had asked that he come to his hour twenty minutes early and had said we would have the hour in the hospital building where he was living. He came for the appointment; however, I wasn't there but in the next room. He left and I was very angry. Later in the dream, people started throwing stones at him and he awakened very frightened. During this period of therapy he made complaints about the high cost of treatment. After returning from a search for a room in town, he remarked how nice and warm his room was in the hospital. In an hour three days before moving out he appeared to be rather guarded. Upon inquiring I learned that he was thinking that if he had plans to run away, it would be sabotage to tell me about them. I replied that it would be the wisest thing he could do so that we could understand more about it. He said that I wouldn't care anyway. I would just get another patient. "You didn't know me before a year-and-a-half ago so you wouldn't care."

He had a dream in which he had to move a huge pile of weights on a cart with ball bearings. In our discussion about the dream he felt weighted down by responsibility. He had a razor now and must tell himself not to cut his wrist. This led him to tell me about his auditory hallucinations that had occurred a year previously, in which women's voices told him to jump out of the window, put his head under water and drown himself, or to castrate himself.

In the next hour, his conflict about therapy was highlighted when he felt no need to be in treatment but he also had thoughts that it might be a good idea if he could see a doctor for the rest of his life. He questioned his right to continue to see me forever, thereby preventing someone else from seeing me. This brought up a discussion about his brother's appearance on the family scene. He was thus reliving the situation with his mother in which his exclusive relationship with his mother had been shattered by the appearance of his younger brother. The act of moving out of the hospital was a concrete indication to him that our relationship would some day come to an end.

Many of his plans were efforts to achieve independence from other people. His father had always filed the patient's income tax return. The patient became afraid that his father would make a mistake; therefore, he began to make out his own tax return. One feature of chess that appealed to him most of all was that it did not involve a partner. Responsibility for a win or a loss was strictly an individual one. Another example of his attempt to be independent was his plan for dating several girls concurrently so that he did not feel rebuffed if one of them turned him down. When his hospital roommate made him a present of a book, the patient arranged through one of the nurses to reimburse the roommate.

In discussing his wish to obtain a job in order to be independent, we discovered that for him independence was, in part, equated with being masculine, a sign of being more like other people, and a way of not needing his therapist. A warning that we should not be taken in by this came in the form of a dream in which he was acting in a play, "trying to impress some other guy what a good actor I was."

The second psychological test was performed twenty months after the patient's admission.

COMPARISON OF RORSCHACH TESTS

The patient was retested on this date primarily because his improvement clinically had been very marked and we were interested to see whether this would be shown on the projective techniques.

On the second test the diagnostic impression is still clearly that of a manifest schizophrenic psychosis.

The most obvious difference between the two tests is the great increase in number of responses on Test No. 2 (thirty-six compared to fifteen on Text 1). Since the total time has scarcely increased at all (Test 1: twenty-two minutes; Test 2: twenty-four minutes), the larger production on Test No. 2 suggests that the patient is freer both to allow associations to arise in his mind and to express them in words.

The second most striking difference is the increased liveliness of the record (Pure F per cent on Test 1: 87 per cent; Text 2: 65 per cent). The patient seems to be more flexible in his ability to respond to various aspects of the environment. He can let himself go more and put more of himself into his communication with others.

In this process of increased communicativeness one gets a clearer picture on the second test of the paranoid quality of the patient's thinking. This is shown particularly as a need to fit every aspect of a situation into an arbitrarily chosen "meaning" with a strongly autistic flavor. Whereas on the first test the patient's mental process might be called "blocked" and "disintegrated," putting things together, but the organizing principle is inadequate. This shows up in several ways: (1) He *forces* things together without developing a significant relationship. (2) He seems to think he has formed an integrated structure when all he has actually is a series of isolated entities loosely strung together. (3) If it suits his emotional needs to form a causal or logical connection between two entities, he does not exercise any objective critique about forming such a connection but simply does it arbitrarily. This last point may be obscured by a tendency toward expressions of self-doubt and self-criticism, but these are often badly misplaced.

PROGNOSIS

Fair.

This is made solely on the basis of this test disregarding, insofar as possible, knowledge of the patient's actual progress.

Two years after beginning treatment the patient enrolled in a post-graduate course at a local university. This enabled him to continue keeping himself busy in an effort to avoid feelings. However, sexual feeling and feelings of depression would intrude into his awareness.

In therapy the emphasis continued to be on pointing out his defenses such as his effort to prevent the experience of rebuff by first rejecting the other person. For example, he told a student nurse he had been seeing that he would not miss her when she completed her affiliation and had to return to her home school.

At this time there was evidence of his identification with me. The patient began to interpret some dreams of a student nurse and commented on how easy it was to be a therapist. He offered to see my patients for me if I became ill.

As a result of consistently focusing on his defenses against feelings, together with his more active dating experiences, the patient began to be more aware of sexual feelings. Concurrently he had a series of dreams involving violence. As he reported his associations, I noticed the sequence of topics involving sexual feelings and violence as illustrated in the following examples. On one occasion he was commenting on how satisfying his life was at the present time. He had everything—an apartment, a car, a television set, school, cats, girl friends, chess, and "even my hours." The only thing missing that he would have in marriage was sexual intercourse at regular intervals. From there he began to wonder if anyone would care for his cats in the event that something should happen to him. "Supposing I should be killed in a car wreck? Would the police go to my apartment and feed the cats?" In another hour he had been referring to an episode of necking with a girl. Immediately following this, he mentioned that he heard an airline advertisement on the radio. A plane belonging to this airline was bombed by a youth whose mother was a passenger.

A session with the patient is now summarized in some detail in order to illustrate the patient's growing awareness of feelings toward his therapist. This session occurred two-and-one-half years after the onset of the treatment. In the first part of the hour he described a number of his recent activities. He had purchased a rug from money he had received as his veteran's disability compensation. He allowed himself to buy the rug because it was the government's money, not his. He had had some difficulty in cashing the check because he did not have an account with a bank. He had also been busy working on his chess game. He described a letter he had written to his girlfriend in which he had been careful not to mention people so that she would be likely to do the same, and he would thereby avoid hearing about other boyfriends. They had planned not to see each other for six months, and he wanted to tell her not to go with other boys. There then followed a description of how he had consistently used a certain chess opening in order to become proficient with its use. The only problem about this was that the opponents study your opening, prepare their defense, and "lay in wait for you." After this, he mentioned a number of disappointing experiences: a correspondence chess opponent had taken back a move; his television aerial was broken and he had a makeshift solution by leading a wire to a screen; he burned his hand grasping a hot pot while absentmindedly clasping a pot-holder in the other hand, and he had broken a bottle while trying to dissolve powdered milk on the stove, using inadequate utensils.

After hearing this report of self-destructive behavior, I asked if he were mad about something, but there was no answer. I added, "Possibly your girl friend?" No reply. I asked why he made it so difficult for himself. He then compared his apartment with my office, pointing out that it was just as well equipped. I said that I didn't attempt to prepare meals here. This seemed to get nowhere, so I switched abruptly and said, "If you are content, that is the important thing." He then enumerated many of the discontents he felt about his present living.

After this he recited his version of a "Fight Song," which he had planned to enter in his college's song contest. This song made reference to scratching out somebody's eyes and similar expressions of anger, the implications of which he was unaware at the time.

He then told of a dream in which the usher in a theater had shot him in the right hip while the usher was in a gun battle with another man. A girl was also shot. When the patient came out of the theater, he saw Hitler and Mussolini in a car. The patient then hailed a German taxi, which would not wait for him.

In his association to this dream he told of his father's warning that he may be shot by mistake if he came home late at night. This was apropos their discussion about a prominent family in which the wife accidentally shot her husband. I pointed out that he had felt threatened in the dream. He said that automobilies threatened him; they may run him down. I wondered aloud about a previously discussed equation of gun equals penis. He thought that sounded homosexual, but said nothing further about it. He pointed out that my name is German and that the taxi that would not wait for him was equivalent to my ignoring a packet of letters he had given me to read. These were letters he had written to his parents while he was in service.

He spoke of my plans to cut down my caseload of patients in order to take on more administrative work and added, "You may take over all the administration and I will not be seeing you at all any more." I said, "I guess that does threaten you." There was a pause and he asked, "Would you like a Life Saver?" I accepted it from him. He said that the idea that he is homosexual is farfetched.

He continued by saying he didn't like losing in chess to ———. As he pointed out, this person had the same last name as his fiancée (at the time of his breakdown), and he added, "I lost to her." I questioned what he meant by losing *to* her. Hadn't he lost her? He explained that maybe he said "lost to her" out of his feeling that she left him because he was something terrible and that she had won by not being married to him but to someone else.

I suggested that being emotionally close to a man may be some-thing he thinks of as "homosexual" or "bad." He said that he had lived in fraternities and had male friends, but he liked to "size up a guy" before being friends with him or before becoming closely related to him. "He may take a poke at me." That was the end of the hour.

It is my impression that in this hour he became aware of feeling threatened by a positive attachment to me, which he felt might bring harm to me (as indicated by his offer of a Life Saver) or harm to him (as indicated by his need to "size up a guy"). His labeling the attachment "homosexual" was giving it a culturally disapproved stamp, which would account for his feeling of being threatened.

Toward the latter part of the third year of treatment and on into the fourth and final year, the themes of dependency and castration anxiety became especially vivid. How these themes were dealt with in the treatment will concern us in this final portion of the discussion. The conflicts about dependency and the acting out of castration anxiety will be illustrated with examples from his daily life, his dreams, and in the transference.

In the beginning of an hour during the end of the third year of his treatment, he asked why I had become interested in psychiatry. I did not answer his question; rather, I asked for his thoughts in connection with the question. He spoke of having read in the *Wall Street Journal* that engineering and business administration were two of the top three professions in demand. When he did not receive an answer from me, he complained that another patient's analyst talks about himself. I replied that he must feel left out of my life. The patient then said, "You cannot like somebody unless you get to know him." I asked what he wanted to know. His next associations had to do with money and his impression that I went into psychiatry because it "pays well." After some comments that psychiatry is "inefficient" because it could not be adapted to assembly-line methods, he focused on his concern about his own career. He had forgotten much of his chemistry and had doubts about his business course. As he put it, he felt he was "in-between—like a dog who chases two rabbits and doesn't catch either one." I then said that maybe his question is whether or not he wants to be in business. The patient then described how he had selected accounting as his major when his advisor, in listing a series of possibilities, remarked that he probably wouldn't want accounting. The patient's impulsive choice was based on a negative reaction to his advisor's suggestion. Such a negative choice was also evident in the transference.

An example of negativism in the transference occurred when he avoided eating meat altogether for two weeks after I suggested a more balanced diet to correct a digestive disturbance he was having at the time.

In this hour he related a dream during which he was threatened by a steak knife. In his associations he described the movie "Carousel," in which a man falls on his own knife. After this he revealed his own concern that he might cut himself with his butcher knife. Here the elements of self-destruction, or more accurately, destruction of an introjected mother, continued to be present in a dissociated way. Examples to be given later will show the extent to which such impulses were acted out and then integrated.

In the next hour the following day, the conflict of his doing something for what he wanted out of it as opposed to his need to oblige others was prominent. He had wanted to purchase a mechanical rabbit for his cats to play with, and thought that this was "silly." He then thought that if he wanted it, he ought to get it, remarking, "That is what mother would say." He described a television program about parents who expect their children to do well in school and how this was parallel to his own situation. He spoke of his talking this way as "junk." After this he told of writing letters to keep on good terms with the people to whom he was writing and that the content of these letters was a waste of time. There were additional examples of his conflict about wanting something and having to pay the price for it.

To him, the dreams he was reporting and the things he had to say seemed without value. The implication was clear that in these hours he felt he was not getting anything out of it for himself.

I summarized the instances in which money and paying a price were a concern: (1) in his dream in which he had to pay to see a girl, (2) in his concern about how much it will cost to go on a date, (3) in how he pays to see me, and (4) in his concern about the cost of the things he wants. I went on to point out the way in which he thought in terms of money as a way of avoiding any personal feelings about another person. By "paying" he freed himself from any obligation. I reminded him of the example where he had paid his roommate for the gift of a book. This was part of the way in which feelings of dependency could be avoided. Money became an insulation from emotional attachment to people.

The third hour in this series occurred just before the patient was to leave for a week-end visit with his parents. He had been speaking about his girl friends and his thought that maybe he was looking for something impossible—an ideal woman. While talking about his engagement and his first admission to the hospital he remarked, "I don't see any reason for going to the hospital, frankly." I asked if he was now ready to get some information about how he got into the hospital. He seemed reluctant about asking his parents, thinking that this might lead to a discouraging talk, and he didn't want to go through it now. Then, after a pause, "Maybe it's best." I asked, "Is there some feeling that as long as you don't find out how you got into the hospital, it will not matter?" He replied, "I don't think I can stand it." I asked, "What do you envisage?" He answered, "Suppose they said that a week before you threatened to kill yourself. It would be very degrading and humiliating. They wouldn't want to tell me, and I wouldn't want to hear it." The discussion then centered around how in the past his mother would break down at the mention of his brother's death and how the family could not talk about his sister's death. Thus he was identifying with his mother's apparent fragility when he thought of himself as being unable to face a discussion about a tragic event in his own life.

In the hour following his weekend visit home, he described his conversation with his mother. Instead of learning that they wanted to break up his approaching marriage, he heard about his own doubts concerning marriage. His mother tearfully related the events leading up to his hospitalization. On one occasion he had said he would wash the dishes but when she volunteered to help, he became angry and said he didn't want any help and threatened to throw a chair.

From this and other information he concluded that he must have felt "pretty lonesome" when he proposed and he thought that in marrying a Catholic he would be forced to have his children become Catholic and he didn't want this.

He expressed considerable objection to my urging him to ask his mother about this since she had already given most of the information to the hospital upon his admission. He felt "betrayed" by me and spoke of it as a "low blow to have me find out something you already knew" but then added "Maybe you were right to have me find out for myself."

From the time of that weekend visit and thereafter he never again used projection and denial in discussing the events preceding his hospitalization.

In the next hour he mentioned his feeling of relief on not having hours over the weekends. He felt burdened with the task of thinking up "light and airy things" for his hours. I then made a connection between this and his not wanting his mother to get upset by what he told her. He said that he hardly ever told her anything significant, and that everything they talked about seemed so inconsequential. He then described his "rebellion" over the weekend visit when he refused to eat eggs and ate only his cereal, whereas formerly he would try to please her by eating everything that she cooked for him.

In the subsequent months the patient showed a recurrent activity that was considerably under the influence of primary process i.e. primitive, prelogical, unrealistic thinking. This activity consisted of cutting his own hair with the clearly self-destructive result of giving his hair the appearance of a plowed field. Each hair-cutting occasion was preceded by some kind of disappointment, frustration, or other depressive experience.

Just prior to the first occasion of cutting his own hair, he had been rejected by several girls he was dating. Instead of feeling rebuffed or depressed, he experienced compulsions. At that time he expressed fears of leaping from a theater balcony. He made sure that he kept the cap on his fountain pen so he would not absent-mindedly stab himself in the arm. The difficulties with girl friends, loss of several chess games, and similar disappointments in his life culminated in the haircut. When he discussed his thoughts about it, he emphasized his effort to be able to do everything for himself. He didn't want to pay a barber, and he thought he could complete college on his own without instruction. During crises he often practiced talking to his cats instead of talking to me. He considered it a weakness to patronize barbers and analysts. These attitudes were illustrative of his strivings to avoid dependency.

A similar series of disappointments resulted in the second episode of cutting his hair. Our earlier analysis of his defenses of the denial of his needs and desires made many of these disappointments prominent at that time. As his pathological defenses were rendered less effective, his needs became more apparent. He was less distant from people and became more assertive with girls while on dates, and consequently was more often frustrated when they refused him. With this freeing of his sexual impulses, there were increasing castration elements in his dreams. In one dream, for example, he was on his way to a fraternity house where he wanted to go to bed with a "loose" girl friend of another man. He looked for her and then went over to another fraternity house where they thought he was the guest lecturer.

He attended the lecture. He dipped his hand into carbon tetrachloride and was told it was poisonous and that he had better take his fingers out. This was one of a series of dreams occurring in this period where he never quite reached the sexual object.

Just before his second self-administered haircut, he had told me that his cat had been killed, one of his girl friends was cool toward him, and a second girl friend announced her engagement to someone else. He attempted to take the sting out of these events by saying that he was thinking of getting rid of the cat, anyway, and that he no longer had to worry about his children being brought up Catholic since these two girl friends were both Catholic and were now out of the picture.

We saw an additional example of how he insulated himself from feelings when he described the way he spent money and paid his bills. He said that doing these things was "like a game, like Monopoly. I used to like that game." When I took up this way of dealing with so many of his experiences and said that I thought he must be concerned about having his feelings break loose, he was reminded of a dream of his car breaking loose and careening down the mountain. All he could do was close his eyes.

Since this dream came to him as an association to my comment, it had much more meaning for him than if the comment had followed his report of such a dream.

The above developments were followed by a change from remoteness to greater assertiveness with a new girl friend. Fortunately, she was able to respond to him, and although there was no attempt at genital intercourse as yet, there was greater physical intimacy. She was also more open about telling him of some of her objections to his behavior. For example, she pointed out his contemptuous attitude toward girls and also observed that he would crack a joke whenever the discussion became serious. Coming from her, these confrontations had more validity than when he and I had discussed them in the hour.

At this time he told of a dream in which his female cat was beaten up by her lover. He was erotically excited by the dream. He thought the dream pointed out his concerns linking sex with danger. These concerns included both the harm that might come to him as a result of sexual activities as well as the injurious results to his sexual partner.

Then in an hour just before the third episode of cutting his hair, he told a joke, which one of his current professors had told in class. The joke was a definition of "African Roulette." A man goes into a hut where there are six Negro women. All are "cocksuckers," but one is a cannibal. This joke reminded him of how his girl had put her head near his penis and he had the wish that she would take it into her mouth. He then thought that if she bit it, the only thing he could do was to hit her. We discussed examples of his repeated concern about danger to his penis. He then told of a dream in which he was going to Africa and his parents warned him about infectious diseases and the natives. Continuing on in the dream he was trying out his screwdriver several times. Then he was on a familiar road and saw his brother in a bus and realized he wasn't dead after all.

In his associations to this dream he said that his parents have deterred him from doing many things he would have liked to do. The screwdriver reminded him of his mailbox, which fell down. I asked him how he spelled "mail." He thought a moment, laughed, and said it was my dirty mind. Of the reference to his brother's death, he thought he might look up a *New York Times* of that date to see if there was any article about his brother. This was his way of obtaining more information about another family tragedy that had been shrouded in secrecy.

In the above example we see how his ambivalent feelings toward this girl became prominent as he became more intimate. Following an evening when she was quite cool toward him, he returned home and gave himself another haircut.

After this latest girl broke off with him, he found himself passing two cars on a narrow road and he had to pull back quickly when another car came out from a side road. He didn't know why he was taking such chances since he really was in no rush. He talked about passing the car as not giving a damn, after discussing a dream from which he concluded that it showed how lonely and frustrated he was.

RORSCHACH TEST

The patient was retested on this date primarily to discover whether or how the Rorschach would reflect changes that are observable in his behavior.

The present test, if taken by itself, would be considered by most, if not all, Rorschach workers to be that of a schizophrenic patient. Whether or not a psychosis is *grossly* manifest could be an open question but that schizophrenic thinking still takes place in this patient seems clear. There is no evidence, however, of serious distress at the present time. The patient seems to be in good humor. The test shows that he is an intelligent person, imaginative, and original. But his perceptions are so distorted and they take account of so little of the complex, real elements of the blot that a very strong trend toward autistic thinking is suggested.

In comparing this test with the two administered to him on previous occasions, it is clear that the first one represents a much more serious degree of disorganization than either the second or the third.

It is also clear that the patient's productions on the first test are much more impoverished than on the last two, both in quantity and in quality. At the time of the first test the patient was markedly blocked,—either quite unable to think of *anything* that the blots reminded him of or very slow in making associations. It was as if his mental processes were inefficient and grossly hampered. This was borne out by the impairment shown on the intelligence test. The earned I.Q. of 112 was clearly not representative of the patient's superior capacities.

On Tests No. 2 and 3 the patient functioned much more efficiently. His speed of production doubled on No. 2 and remained at this level on No. 3. He produced the most quantitatively on No. 2 (R 36). In No. 3 he seemed less willing to spend time looking at the blot (T24 to 14), so that the quantity drops (R21), although the speed remains the same. I am not sure of the meaning of this increase followed by decrease in quantity, but my impression is that it is associated with a change in the patient's attitude toward test and tester, which can be described as follows. On No. 1 the patient felt and was relatively impotent and incompetent. In No. 2 he was much more competent and was making a rather conscientious, serious effort to put forth his best. On No. 3 he was feeling still more competent, even a little cocky, and did not bother so much about putting forth his best. In a test full of so much pathology, this attitude suggests a rather brittle defense.

In considering the quality of the patient's productions, there is a steady increase in liveliness from No. 1 to No. 3. This is particularly true in the increased perception of human movement (0 to 1 to 3). This slow but steady increase in the perception of human movement with a steadily improving clinical course was found also in Dr. ———'s patient, Miss ———. With regard to the other elements of liveliness in the test (other types of movement, color, shading), the big change came between No. 1 and No. 2.

On all the tests the patient has given a few responses that have a humorous quality. They are clearly schizophrenic, but unlike the autistic responses of many schizophrenics, they strike the listener as communicative of conscious whimsy. This quality is clearer on No. 2 and No. 3 than on No. 1.

On Test No. 3 oral themes (food, open jaws, teeth) emerge in significant quantity, which has not been true on either of the other tests.

On Test No. 2 the patient showed a strong tendency to "organize" the blot in an autistic fashion, that is, to force every aspect of it into an arbitrarily chosen meaning. On Test No. 1 there was less ability to organize in any form. On No. 3 the need to "organize" and find "meanings" seems less compulsive.

On No. 1 the patient perceives only one of the ordinarily seen "popular" responses. This is characteristic of severe psychosis. On No. 2 he sees

9, which is a good normal amount. On No. 3 he sees only 4. This is a quite low number and fits with his slightly cocky and less earnest approach to the test. It is a little bit like a declaration of independence from doing what is expected of him. It must be hoped that this is a phase of his development toward real independence rather than a largely defensive maneuver.

In the months that followed there were many examples of his growing awareness of his derogatory approach toward women. This occurred when he felt inferior in a social situation or when he had some feelings of jealousy. For example, he looked at his girl friend and thought of her as "dumpy" just when she had turned away from him to talk with someone else.

In another session he told about how he had come to an hour more than a year previously and had carried a banana in his pocket as if he had an erection. He thought at that time that I was curt with him and disapproving toward him. From his thoughts about this, I made a transference interpretation of how he thought his father might disapprove of such a bold display of sexual assertiveness. This was followed by his decision to enclose a letter to his father rather than just send the financial statement that his father had requested. As he gained greater freedom of expression with me he became more collaborative with his parents—having neither to avoid them completely nor to conform to what he thought were their expectations.

There were many occasions where he could see himself repeatedly expressing hostility when his own narcissism was threatened by failure, criticism, and frustration. Along with this there were successful attempts at working through his castration fears and loss of independence in relation to women. As a result, his pathological need to dominate women, render them helpless, or humiliate them decreased. As he mastered his hostility he was able to be more considerate and tender. Along with this he was able to participate successfully in intercourse. His relationship to his parents became one in which he was independent of and respectful toward them without feeling rebelliously tied to them. He enjoyed visits with his family and once commented to them, "You are not half as bad as I tell Dr. Schulz you are."

In going over his plans about marriage and discontinuing treatment, he brought up a dream of running away. He was able to interpret this and talk about whether or not he was running away from me with his feelings of needing me.

He eventually married a nurse whom he had dated for a year and a half during the latter part of treatment. By mutual agreement we decided to discontinue therapy four years after we had begun. He subsequently obtained a job and set up a home with his bride.

DISCUSSION

This first case presentation was selected to give an over-all view of the course of therapy from its initiation through to its termination. The patient's course of treatment readily lends itself to three separate divisions: (1) the period of acute psychotic disturbance; (2) the intermediate "obsessive-compulsive" phase; and (3) the final phase of integration of affective experience and working through of conflicts to the termination.

The Overtly Disturbed Psychotic Phase and Identity Reconstruction

Erik Erikson's concepts about identity, identity diffusion, and identification are a useful frame of reference to conceptualize the course of treatment with this patient.[2] During the treatment, there were many events that pointed up this patient's fragile sense of identity, together with our attempts to reestablish his identity. My early summary of my "opinion" of him, in addition to other attempts to understand what he was experiencing, were probably perceived by him as evidence that I knew what he "was" at that particular moment. In this way, I was able to confirm whatever flickering awareness he had of his own self-impression. This is in contrast to another possible approach of attempting to talk the patient out of his feelings of despair or to persuade him that after all he is a "nice person." His attempt to reassure himself that he was a man by fighting like a man had become a stable form of identity during the years of hospitalization. He felt his identity to be threatened in several ways. This was expressed during the disturbed period in a concrete way when he was reluctant to give up his fingernail trimmings because these were part of himself. Much later, there were to be parallel concerns when he thought that he would have to give up his own habits and be forced to take over those of others.

Erikson's initial phase in his concept of identity formation for the infant is in the "trust *vs.* mistrust" crisis.[3] Certainly in the work with this patient, the initial phase was dominated by his mistrust and suspiciousness. He was reluctant to reveal information about himself and extremely cautious in his replies. On the other hand, there were elements of trust: for example, he had told me more than he had told others; or after initially refusing appointments he then asked when the schedule would be. These elements of trust were vital in eliciting a response of encouragement from the staff when they were faced with someone who had earned a guarded prognosis after two years of chronically disturbed behavior. As the psychotherapist, I experienced this spark of trust from him as the same feeling of emergence of another being as a person that I felt with each of my children. In the early weeks of infancy, when smiling directly in response to my efforts to reach them, they become real persons in their own right. This is quite relevant to Erikson's comments about identity formation. He writes, "its roots go back a way to the first self-recognition; in the baby's earliest exchange of smiles, there is something of a self-recognition coupled with a mutual recognition."[4]

Federn has conceptualized severe regression in schizophrenia in terms of loss of ego boundaries.[5] Consistent with this concept we view the basic threat to the ego as the return to the stage of predifferentiation resulting in an obliteration of the self. For this reason, the deepest root of identity is the feeling of separateness (but relatedness or security) experienced by the infant. This feeling of separateness gradually emerges in an atmosphere of maternal love and trust. An essential ingredient in the clinical setting of the deeply regressed schizophrenic patient and the staff is the "mutual recognition" referred to above. It is not enough that the staff see the patient as a person. The patient must also convey his own response to this recognition in order that the flicker of identity occur. The optimistic feeling that the nursing personnel had about my assignment to the case was one element that might have facilitated this with this patient. They felt that this patient closely resembled a previous patient who had made an initial striking improvement (see the case in Chapter VII).

In retrospect, it appears to have been a crucial difference that the female nursing staff was able to respond with "mutuality" in this final hospitalization where this had not occurred in previous hospitals.

In most psychiatric hospitals at the time of the onset of his illness, the custom was to employ male nursing personnel in men's disturbed wards and female personnel in women's disturbed wards. Thus, this setting with female nurses and nursing students was somewhat unique. The advantages of using female nursing personnel in men's wards were easy to identify. Their presence, in itself, had a constraining effect on the behavior of the patients. Their more typically feminine concern with the attractiveness of the physical environment effected a change in the appearance and atmosphere in the ward. The fact that they added another more natural dimension to the patient's opportunities for relationships was recognized in retrospect. Recognition of the real therapeutic potential of men nursing personnel on female wards has been slower. State laws that require that female patients have female nursing personnel in attendance have often been interpreted to mean that they may not have male nursing personnel. Female nursing personnel, even today, tend to cast the male nursing staff into the role of a "strong arm" used to control combative behavior in patients. They do not utilize the potential of the male nurse with female patients to provide another dimension in relationships.

The next psychosocial crisis referred to by Erikson is that of "autonomy versus shame, doubt."[6] According to Erikson, shame involves being exposed in a self-conscious way. An early manifestation of such feeling of exposure with this patient was portrayed when he avoided answers to my questions by saying that everything would be televised tomorrow as though he felt completely transparent without a sense of privacy. In order to support his autonomy, I attempted to convey respect for his needs as well as preservation of my own. For example, when he requested "a half hour to think it over," I agreed. On the other hand, I set an example by insisting on my own autonomy in limiting the extent to which I would answer personal questions and by defending myself when under physical attack from him. My confidence in myself and the job I was doing, vis-a-vis the patient, was also instrumental in reducing his doubt about me as a therapist and of himself as a patient in therapy. We are convinced that the patient's use of the therapist as a model during these stages is a very important aspect of the treatment. The patient tends to identify with the staff around him. The personnel who are mistrustful and doubtful about themselves make it difficult for the patient to be other than mistrustful and doubtful about himself.

An early clarifying transference interpretation relevant to his sense of autonomy occurred following my interview with his mother. Here we could understand how much of his intense resentment toward the nursing personnel and myself as intruders—"like living in a goldfish bowl"—was a direct carry-over from his feelings about his mother.

Another device that was important in the autonomy issue was the change in the lock on his seclusion room. The seclusion room door lock had been arranged so that it could not be opened from the inside but could be opened from the outside without a key. In this way the patient could be placed in his room and the door pulled closed quickly. With this one-way locking arrangement the patient could be locked in and anyone from outside his room could enter. However, when the lock was turned around, the patient could exit at any time he wished. But only those with authorized keys could enter. This mechanical rearrangement to the seclusion room made a considerable difference in the patient's sense of security and privacy.

If this patient were being treated in our hospital today, "his room" would not be a "seculsion room." We have come to feel that assigning a patient to a seclusion room tends to perpetuate his disturbed combative behavior because it conveys the message that the staff expects him to need this type of control. However, this same type of arrangement of the lock could be used either in a seclusion room or in his own bedroom.

At the next crisis of "initiative versus guilt" Erikson conceptualized the developmental task of healthy self-assertion without concomitant guilt that cripples such assertiveness.[7] Obviously, guilt won out during this patient's identity diffusion. The preponderance of guilt was apparent in the first interview when, in speaking of his brother, he said, "I didn't kill him." Other early examples of guilt were his warning that he and the therapist better stay apart because he might kill the therapist, the voices telling him to castrate himself, and his blunders when about to win in chess. He was indeed filled with conflict about his aggressiveness. Frieda Fromm-Reichmann placed a special emphasis on this aspect of schizophrenia. In commenting at a staff conference about this patient, she said:

> I was warned that it would be better for me not to go and see him when he first came without being first sure that he wanted to see me. So the first time, he said, "She had better not come, I'll knock her head off." The second time, he said, "No." The third time, I said, "Well, if he were uncomfortable, we could have him packed but I would want to see him." As I came—he is a very tall fellow—and he looked at me, put his hand on my head, and said, "Oh, you're such a little thing. Come in." And then, after a few minutes, I felt quite comfortable and he seemed comfortable. We discussed his treatment and how things went on the ward, etc. The other contact was just last week. He usually comes up from his hour to the ward when I leave the ward after having seen my

patient and I am a little reluctant to be shutting the door, and here are the two of us, and especially now when he is looking banged up after his fight. But I did it. I opened the door, and he said, "Do you think it is right for me to be here now on the ward with you?" As though he had to tell me, "Look, I am entirely not a dangerous fellow." So from these contacts it makes me feel that the main thing is really his own fear of his own hostile side.[8]

That the patient's aggressiveness was a problem to him as well as an immediate problem to us was our treatment orientation. We attempted to convey to him that it was a problem, to get him to acknowledge it, and to take some responsibility for it. If one can persuade an assaultive patient to request a sheet pack in order to control his assaultiveness, one has then made the first step toward his assuming some responsibility for his behavior. Needless "heroics" on the part of the personnel, in which they expose themselves to danger in the face of the patient's assaultiveness, are apt to unnerve the patient rather than convey some sense that the patient can be trusted. Therefore, the use of pack, the seclusion room, or additional personnel are important adjuncts in dealing with the patient's assaultiveness.

The staff, however, must not be trapped into using these measures to reject the patient. Such a patient is usually rejected by his peer group and the staff can reinforce this rejection by too quickly isolating him from his peers. A patient-staff meeting that was called to discuss the assaultive behavior of one of the members of the group began with the generalization that he was too sick to be a part of the group. In time the discussion got around to the fact that everyone was, at least, a little afraid of the patient. A frank discussion of their fear by both patients and staff reduced the tension that each had been experiencing alone. Once the tension was reduced, the group began to explore what it could do to include the patient in the group. The suggestion came from the group that the excluded member be invited to join the meeting. When the patient joined the meeting, there was a frank, if a bit awkward, discussion of his effect on the group and their effect on him. Everyone in the group was then sharing the responsibility rather than leaving it to the patient to control himself, or the staff to control him.

The use of the seclusion room should relate to the patient's assaultiveness and attempt to control his behavior or to decrease the amount of stimuli coming toward the patient. In this way, seclusion becomes a specific technique directly related to the patient's problems rather than a "punishment." For example, a patient had been wandering into other patients' rooms on the ward and, as a consequence, was placed in seclusion. It might have been better to have had a hall meeting at that point to discuss with other patients what they could do about such a patient's wandering into their rooms. The other patients' rooms could be locked or someone could go along with the patient and point out whenever the patient entered a room other than her own and explain that this was off limits. A similar misuse of seclusion occurred when a patient would isolate herself and fail to make any contacts with the personnel or other patients. Seclusion prescribed for such a patient only aggravated the situation by further isolating her.

An extremely hyperactive patient, such as a manic or an acute catatonic, can be helped to control his hyperactivity by being placed in a sparsely furnished room and provided with simple diversional material such as charcoal and paper. To leave this type of patient completely alone, with nothing to do may, however, tend to increase the panic.

With these disturbed patients the space and time aspects of the interview are important. They are alert to any minor changes in the rearrangement of the furniture or to variations in the place where the interview is to be held. Once, when the therapist was five minutes late to a session, the patient responded indignantly, "You're five hours late!"

One must be careful about taking at face value some responses, such as his initial rejection of participation in psychotherapy with the therapist. It is very difficult for these patients to acknowledge any positive alliance that might threaten them with risking feelings of rejection, humiliation, and abandonment. One must listen for the other side of the message, such as when this patient requested a schedule for his hours.

Sometimes the question is asked whether psychotherapy should be attempted during an acute phase of disturbance with these patients. While it does not seem immediately relevant to always try to interpret the genetic-historical roots of the patient's conflicts and defenses, it certainly seems important to concentrate on the here-and-now of his behavior. It isn't so much a question of whether therapy should be attempted but what the focus of such psychotherapy should be. His angry, assaultive alienation of other people was the predominant interference of his relationships all through his hospitalizations and was therefore the immediate thing to be dealt with. The fact that this assaultiveness might have related to his anxiety about attachment and tenderness would not be interpreted at this point. The surface content of the patient's behavior as communication must be acknowledged rather than always attempting to find something latent or hidden behind whatever the patient presents. Such responses on the part of the therapist and the staff are more in the nature of confrontations than they are interpretations. In this initial phase of treatment the patient is confronted with the manifest behavior rather than with some interpretive explanation of what lies behind that behavior. Such a forthright investigative approach differs from a more superficial supportive therapy that uses avoidance and denial. In that it does not recognize the patient's conflicts, the latter is not really supportive and thereby does not assist in dealing with these conflicts.

We speak of the staff's "reactions" rather than "countertransference" in our attempt to look at the range of feelings among the staff. Anger is a very natural initial response when one has become the target of verbal and physical abuse. The freedom to feel this anger and then discuss it in staff meetings enables the staff to put their feelings in the proper perspective and thus prevents an unwitting sadistic response. Through a discussion of their feelings the staff can identify what in their behavior may be provoking the patient, and what aspects of the patient's behavior may be unrelated to his immediate environment. It is seldom an "either/or" proposition.

In dealing with the impulsively assaultive patient, it often seems that in the time it takes to get the patient to the seclusion room, the episode is over. Deciding to leave the patient in seclusion for a few hours at this time, however, can have the useful effect of helping to reduce the tension in the other patients and personnel. The prolonged use of seclusion, or the insistence that patients and staff cope with the behavior on the ward can have the effect of alienating the patient from the group.

The following description taken from the nursing notes is typical of the manner in which this patient's impulsive assaultive behavior was handled:

Shortly after breakfast he came out of his room clad in his undershorts. He said a few words to another patient, then picked up a chair and threw it across the hall. It did not hit anyone. The male aides quickly put the patient in seclusion. When his lunch tray was taken to him he seemed quite calm and was very pleasant to the nurse. He ate all of his lunch. About 2 p.m. the nurse went into the seclusion room to talk with the patient about his behavior of the morning. She pointed out that there was a tea dance in the Activity Building that afternoon that he had planned to attend. He expressed an interest in going and said he felt he could handle himself appropriately. He showered, dressed very neatly in his blue suit and went to the tea dance accompanied by a student nurse. He seemed to enjoy it very much.

Physical care is a vital aspect of the medical treatment. During this acute period, the patient requested an examination by the therapist for what he thought was a hernia. Fromm-Reichmann, in supervision on this case, indicated that such patients wish physical contact, and, at the same time, are frightened about the homosexual implications of such contact. She suggested that, instead of examining the genital area, the therapist merely touch the patient on the shoulder and indicate that we would have an internist or surgeon examine the patient concerning the complaint. Touching the patient permitted partial gratification. Incidentally, it was discovered that this patient did have a hernia that subsequently required repair. One of the most frequent mistakes made by young residents is to dismiss all physical complaints as "psychosomatic" and therefore not worthy of further diagnostic investigation. One can call forth dozens of instances such as a patient who lay curled up in a "fetal position" of "regression" and refused to come to her appointment. Only later did the doctor on call discover on rounds that this patient had an acute appendicitis. These words of caution are perhaps most importantly directed to the nursing staff, since they are generally the first line of communication about such complaints. Of course, if the nurse doesn't call the doctor's attention to the patient's request, and/or condition, the patient may never be seen by the doctor or may be seen only after considerable delay. Nurses seem to want to be protective of the doctor on call and the clinical administrator, and are thus apt to err on the side of not relaying such complaints to the medical person who should carry out the examination.

A patient's physical problems can be an important channel of care by the nursing personnel. After this patient was scratched in a fight with another patient, he was talking with the nurse about how he had failed. He seemed to request a tremendous amount of reassurance. He followed the nurse into the treatment room where he wanted to have his face looked at, and asked questions concerning the possibility of scars, how deep his wounds were, and whether his eye was involved. They talked together for about half-an-hour while the nurse took care of his face. At first he was quite depressed and tense but gradually as they talked and as she looked at his face he seemed to relax, joke, and become more sociable. As they walked out, he thanked her quite profusely for the attention she had given to his face. Another nurse was concerned about preventing a narrowing of his relationships to a few nursing personnel. She reported that while taking him downtown to obtain glasses she pointed out other people with whom he could talk and consider doing things.

During his floridly psychotic period, the nursing personnel were intimately involved with this patient almost continually. He received a great deal of physical contact in the form of help with bathing, dressing, and occasionally spoon-feeding. As he became less psychotic he handled his physical needs quite competently without assistance and maintained a guarded aloofness from the nursing personnel. There then evolved a period of several weeks during which the patient had a large number of minor accidents. He sprained his ankle, caught his finger in a door, stubbed his toe—almost daily he had a complaint that required the nurses' ministration. The personnel were beginning to classify him, jokingly as "accident prone." It became evident that, at this point in his illness, this was his way of maintaining his contact with female nursing staff and gratifying some of his dependency needs.

Tranquilizers were not in general use at the time this patient was in his acute period, and the question naturally occurs as to whether they would have been used in current practice. We are inclined to think that we would have postponed recommending tranquilizers since the patient did seem to be steadily moving in a direction of responding to the program without such medications. It is difficult to know to what extent the tranquilizers might have accelerated the process or, on the other hand, may have slowed down the understanding of the patient's inner struggles. Certainly in our experience it seems apparent that electroconvulsive treatment, insulin shock therapy, and lobotomy work toward obliteration of such understanding rather than facilitate the working through of the conflict in treatment.

THE MIDDLE PHASE OF TREATMENT

To return to Erikson's sequence of psychosocial crises, we next come to "industry versus inferiority."[9] We would think that this aspect of psychosocial development was particularly prominent during the post-psychotic, obsessive-compulsive period. The patient kept himself busy with projects all day long, successfully excluded feelings from consciousness, and tended strongly to deny any need for treatment. This period began approximately nine months after his admission to the hospital.

Although he was very busy at this time, the patient participated in many of these pursuits in an essentially passive manner showing little or no enthusiasm. He guarded himself against experiencing inferiority feelings by having many "irons in the fire" at the same time. Failure in any one or two activities could be quickly passed over by rapidly shifting to a third, fourth, or fifth interest. This meant, of course, that he really didn't become involved with any one thing or any one person to an appreciable extent.

After a long period of analyzing his defenses and the consequent emergence of his feelings, he was able to be more active in his choice of what he wanted to do. His identity became strengthened. He was able to take greater risks in the selection of a course of study that was of interest to him. His choices were then more likely to be based on what he wanted to do rather than on how he could avoid failure.

At this time, identifications by the patient with his therapist were quite prominent in the form of his giving interpretations of their dreams to student nurses, offering to see the therapist's patients for him, and selecting a course of study in graduate school more along the lines of the therapist's newly acquired administrative duties at the hospital.

The question was raised by Eissler[10] as to whether the same technique could be used to treat the patient during the acute phase and also during the postpsychotic phase ("the phase of relative clinical muteness")[11] in psychotherapy. Dr. Fromm-Reichmann commented on John Rosen's plan to bring the patient out of the psychotic phase and then assign him to other therapists to complete the work during the more quiescent phase. She took issue with this approach and felt that the same therapist was able to continue with the patient throughout the entire course of treatment.[12] Her view was confirmed by the work with this case. The postpsychotic phase of therapy with this patient was conducted in a setting more closely resembling a traditional psychoanalytic approach. As soon as he was able to have his appointments in the office, he used a couch with the therapist seated behind. The patient was seen four hours weekly up until the final nine months of treatment, at which time he was seen three hours per week. Free association on the part of the patient was expected with

a passive listening attitude from the therapist. Eissler concludes the
following:

> Although techniques have been devised to undo, at least temporarily,
> acute schizophrenic symptoms, it is highly debatable whether the modi-
> fication which the schizophrenic ego so impressively shows can be altered
> by psychoanalysis. The psychotherapeutic techniques which are applied
> most commonly in the treatment of schizophrenics do not add sub-
> stantially to our knowledge and understanding of schizophrenia, since
> most of them disregard the clinical fact that the problem of the therapy
> of schizophrenia is essentially the problem of undoing an ego modifica-
> tion.[13]

The theoretical assumptions upon which Eissler's caution is based
seem to center around the notion that in the acute phase the therapist
must be involved in so many parameters from the basic model of
psychoanalytic technique (". . . a technique which requires interpretation as the exclusive tool").[14] He becomes too gratifying of the patient's
psychotic and neurotic needs to be able to shift back to a more frustrat-
ing position. The resulting analysis and working through of the transference is thereby prevented—according to that view.

Some therapists complain that patients seem to go through the
motions of doing things well in order to get out of the hospital or to
deny their illness. We think it a mistake to undermine such activities
on the part of the patient. These can be important steps. It gives the
patient a chance to develop a sense of accomplishment, self-esteem,
and identity, as well as a chance to overcome certain fears and uncertainties. However, at the same time, the therapist and others should
let the patient know that they realize that he is not recovered and
that there is still much to be done even though his outward behavior
indicates adjustment to the routine and gives the outward appearance
of recovery. Incidentally, this is also important in relation to the patient's moving out of the hospital for aftercare treatment. It can be
a very significant aspect of the treatment program to convey to the
patient the realization that not all is completed. The move out of the
hospital is just one more step. It does not mean that the patient has
now solved all his problems and should be free of conflict. Such is,
after all, not the goal of treatment in any case since conflicts are part
of the lives of all human beings. The question is how he deals with
such conflicts.

Having worked with this patient during the acute disturbance of
his florid psychotic production, the therapist was in a better position

to understand what was being denied by his defenses in the post-psychotic phase. This was an additional reason why therapy can be of value during the acute phase when the patient is seemingly unable to make use of such therapy. An example can be illustrated in the manner in which this patient's dreams were extremely helpful in the treatment.[15]

As the patient emerged from his psychosis he began to report his dreams. The increasing frequency of the dreams corresponded to a decrease in the disturbing symptoms in his waking life. We found these dreams to be similar in content to his psychotic expressions of thought and behavior. In this way his dreams could be more easily understood by a knowledge of the patient's behavior during his disturbed period. Over forty years ago, Harry Stack Sullivan replied to William A. White's formal discussion of a paper by Sullivan with the following:

> I would add that in the early stages of acute psychosis, these patients are frequently unable to distinguish that which transpires in sleep and that which is transpiring in psychotic reality. As they improve and suffer less from, you might say, dream experience in their waking life, the dream begins to reappear in sleep and to be formulated in fashions intimately relating to their prevailing problem. As they become convalescent, still psychotic but much more comfortable, then most of the abnormal material is dealt with in sleep just as it is in the psychoneurotic. The dream at first is indistinguishable from the waking psychosis, then it tends to become more poignant and finally it takes the place of the waking psychosis if the problem is not wholly resolved.[16]

We would like to concentrate on the following three themes of his psychosis: (a) Violence and Fear, (b) Depression, and (c) Identity Diffusion (in the sense that this term is used by Erikson).[17] These themes reappeared in the patient's dream content.

Violence and Fear

This patient had been given shock treatments at the two hospitals to which he was previously admitted, largely in an effort to control his physical violence. This violent behavior continued for several months after his latest admission. It was the patient himself who was finally able to make it understandable when he said, "You know, I might be as afraid of you as you are of me."

During the first part of his hospitalization, he was concerned about being attacked by rockets from Berlin. Many times he was afraid someone was trying to poison his food. In one of the early hours, he wondered if the therapist carried a gun. During that hour he pulled a knitted cap over his face and placed his hands behind his back saying, "Shot at sunrise." This theme of violence and fear was most prominent in his dreams and persisted for about two years after he had ceased to have much concern about it in his daily life.

His second dream, which occurred about five months after his admission, was typical. A small boy was jumping up and down in the air to a height of fifteen feet. Rockets and buzz bombs were coming across the city. He awakened, frightened.

In many of the subsequent dreams, he was frightened by guns being pointed at him, people throwing stones at him, fire threatening him, someone dynamiting a school, railroad wrecks, automobile crashes, fights and duels with knives, and guns and saws.

In one dream, which occurred two years after the start of treatment, a jeep was on fire. The army came to put it out by repeating magical phrases that didn't help. The patient asked in the dream what was the idea of the army trying to put out a fire with magical phrases. This perhaps gives an idea of his estimation of the therapist's usefulness to him at that time.

Another recurring typical dream was his being shot at by someone with a gun. He was shot in the right hand and then, still in the dream, found he was locked out of a room, naked. Here we can clearly see how his dream life portrayed much of what went on during his psychotic period although while in his waking hours he was unaware of this violence.

Depression

During the early weeks and months of his hospitalization, he made frequent attempts at self-destruction. He heard voices telling him to castrate himself. Three weeks after admission, he took a table knife and outlined a circle on his abdomen down to his groin, saying, "This is what I need." He thought that his therapist told him to jump out of the window, and he attempted to do this. Within the first month he tried to twist a shirt around his neck. On several occasions, he spoke of his hopelessness.

After the acute phase of his psychosis had terminated, most of the prominent features of his depression temporarily disappeared, both from his waking life and his dream content. The only manifestations were his occasional struggles with his compulsions to throw himself in front of a bus or over a theater balcony. He was also concerned that he might stab himself with his fountain pen or a kitchen knife.

Two-and-a-half years after beginning treatment, the patient began to report dreams of the following nature. In one, he had a business failure by owning something that was going bad, such as a dying horse, in another, he was on a sinking submarine. He tried to crawl up the ladder and fell down. He also discovered worms in his pocket. There was a long series of dreams portraying frustrations of various kinds. For example, winning a car and never seeing it, drinking coffee and finding it to be cold, or discovering he had a lowered credit rating.

As he began to report more and more of these dreams, he became more aware of how depressed he actually was.

Identity Diffusion

As with all persons disorganized to the degree of psychosis, this patient showed manifestations of severe loss of his sense of identity. A month after admission, he said to the nurse, "Nobody likes me anymore. How do you know my name is ———— (giving his surname)?" Later, he spoke with an artificial English accent, which he said he had adopted from another patient. This may be taken as an attempt at restitution in an effort to locate an identity. In a dream occurring a year after his admission, residuals of his identity problem appeared. The patient stated that in this dream he had gotten a job and was given an identification card "which told who I was."

His confusion as to whether he was male or female was one aspect of his identity diffusion. At one of the hospitals in which he had previously been treated, he had expressed doubts about being able to function as a man. Once he shaved his arms and said he wasn't supposed to have hair. In one of his hours, he was illustrating something and prefaced it by saying, "If I were in a Miss America contest . . ." At another time, in calculating his proper weight for his height, he did this on the basis of what would be the normal ratio for a woman.

This sexual confusion cropped up again in some of his dreams long after he had made the previously mentioned statement. We illustrate this with the following two dreams. In one he was sitting in his mother's chair at the dining room table. His father was in his regular place, and there were two strangers present. In the other dream, "I am a mother bird looking for a place to lay eggs. Two grandmother

birds tell me the place is no good so I don't get to lay eggs there."
Here we see examples of the patient's self merging with that of his
mother.

This obsessive-compulsive period lasted for about one and one-half
years. The main link, for himself as well as for his therapist, with his
intense psychic struggles was by way of this vivid dream life. The fact
that this content continued to come out in his dreams was a measure
of the effective therapeutic relationship that was operative. In this
way, the dreams served as an effective communicative link for both
patient and therapist in integrating massive dissociated aspects of his
personality.

TERMINAL PHASE OF TREATMENT IN THE PSYCHOTIC

This final phase of treatment includes a period when feelings and
conflicts came much more into awareness after the analysis of the
denial and obsessive-compulsive way of dealing with his anxiety. This
period of therapy would correspond roughly to Erikson's "Identity
versus Identity Diffusion," which is the psychosocial phase corresponding to adolescence.[18] With this patient, the final phase was characterized by a resurgence of feelings, rebelliousness, and, at the end of
this period, his growing attachment to a particular girl. In the category
of feelings, he was experiencing anger, jealousy, sexual feelings, and
attachment.

There are probably few reported cases of termination of the treatment of a psychotic patient. The therapist's confidence that it was
unlikely that he would become psychotic again was based mainly
on his greater awareness of himself, his problems about being close
to people, his conflicts over hostility, and his actually having made
some change in his way of relating to people. It seemed that there was
room for further change as there would be with anyone, but he had
made a good beginning. He certainly had shown a greater tendency
toward catching onto things going on within himself, and he was
interested in his own dreams and not merely content to recite them.
There were many things that gave the impression that he was assuming control over the running of his life.

It is important that dissociated aspects of the personality be reintegrated. One example of the type of integration of psychotic experience occurred when he approached his mother about what had
happened during the onset of the psychotic period. This put an end
to his delusional misinterpretation of the events. It enabled him to

see the episode, as she described it, as an understandable outgrowth of what he had known about himself and his life, which was reconstructed during treatment. Moreover, it allowed him to find out that requesting this information from his mother was not destructive toward her. She was therefore not as fragile as he had anticipated because of conflicts about his aggression. In this case, it would be comparable to Freud's recommendation that a patient, at some point in treatment, confront himself with his phobia, experience the anxiety, and move beyond it.[19]

There are several questions that arise about the topic of patients being discharged from the hospital and the program of aftercare following discharge. Certainly not all of the treatment need be completed while the patient is in the hospital. In fact, life outside the hospital can present certain problems that facilitate the progress of further therapy. The staff is often in a quandary as to what criteria to use to determine when a patient can leave the hospital other than his suitable behavioral adjustment. We consider it essential that the patient at least have some grasp of how psychotherapy can be of help to him and therefore have some insight into the definition of his problems, what the main conflicts are, and how he can work on these after he leaves the protection of the hospital. Contrast this with the middle-aged alcoholic woman, for example, who, although perfectly calm and "well adjusted" in her behavior, begins to acknowledge that her problem is "alcohol," that alcohol has gotten the best of her, and if she would only stop drinking, then she would be all right. While this is perhaps true, it is a very meager understanding without any reference to why she resorted to the use of alcohol in the first place and what her particular psychological problems are that would contribute to her resorting to such a "tranquilizer."

Many times the question arises as to which therapist should continue the treatment after the patient leaves the hospital. This is sometimes dictated by the need for the patient to return to his home town or another location quite distant from the hospital. We have often tried to overlap the period so that the new therapist and the patient have some time to become acquainted during the transition. The question is sometimes raised as to whether it is advisable for the patient to return to the referring physician who was treating him at the time that hospitalization became necessary. Often, when patients seem determined not to return to this doctor, the decision is based on some unresolved transference feelings that center around the crisis that led to the admission. We have found that when the patient resumes with an interview or two, such apprehensions are resolved and the patient and doctor are able to continue work following hospitalization.

This patient's contemplated marriage at the end of treatment also illustrates a number of problems with the hospitalized patient. There is, first of all, the large question of major decisions occurring during the course of therapy. The guiding philosophy used here was to have the decision rest with the patient, but all facets of the decision that could be thought of would have to be considered and worked out in treatment. For example, there was the obvious conclusion that the patient was timing the marriage to coincide with the termination of the therapy. This would mean that, rather than experience the loss of the therapist, he would merely exchange him for dependency gratification toward his wife. We felt it would be sufficient if the ramifications of the decision were thoroughly worked out and explored in therapy. The decision would then be his to make.

The patient became acquainted with his future wife while she was a student nurse affiliated with the hospital. This raises the question of the staff's involvement emotionally with patients as well as the rather complex issue of romantic involvements between patients and personnel. Doctors have become sexually involved with patients, both inside and outside of hospital settings. Such acting-out on the part of the doctor unequivocally ruins his usefulness as a therapist with the patient. Certainly, there have been a number of social and romantic involvements between patients and members of the nursing staff. Some of these have resulted in marriage. Generally speaking, we feel that when a member of the nursing staff becomes too socially involved with a patient, her ability to be therapeutically helpful to the patient is impaired. This cannot be our primary reason for objecting to a member of the nursing staff dating a patient, for then we would have no objection if she dated a patient who was on a different service from the one where she has direct clinical responsibility. The primary reason is the erosion of the nurse's professional role. At the time that this patient was hospitalized, there were two or three other patients at the same hospital who were also dating student nurses. It is of interest to note that during this period of time, knowledge of the activities of these other individuals was common in the hospital community. The instructor of nursing, however, was not in any way made aware that this patient had been dating students, and in fact, was quite surprised to learn that he was to marry a former student. There were probably several factors to account for this. One, he seemed respectful enough of everyone concerned so that he handled it in such a way that it never became common knowledge. In addition, he did not have a history of acting-out type of behavior in contrast to the other patients.

It is difficult to know of any completely satisfactory way of dealing with the problem of socializing between patients and staff. If one takes a judgmental, disciplinary approach to this problem, it is forced underground. An important useful approach is to try to help the parties involved understand all of the ramifications of their association. The staff member must be helped to see more clearly what needs of hers or his are being met by the patient, and, in return, the patient must understand how he is using his relationship with the staff member in a dependent way or in a hostile way, and, specifically, how it might be an acting-out of something from the transference in the treatment relationship.

Our current approach is to try to prevent romantic attachments from being acted upon in any way during the patient's hospitalization, with the belief that this most often interferes with the treatment and that such matters can best be dealt with after the person leaves the hospital. This would fit in with Lewis Hill's admonition that ". . . 'sleeping with' was something which people who were well could think about."[20]

To carry Erikson's chart through the next phase "intimacy versus isolation," which is as far as it will be carried here, this patient's decision to marry at the end of the treatment and his ability to go ahead with this decision without having a psychosis, as he had done once before, is an indication that his choice for intimacy had won out.[21] Certainly, the course of this treatment represents a justification for not settling for reorganization on an obsessive-compulsive or denial or other compromise level. Dr. Fromm-Reichmann came to feel that formerly in the treatment of psychotics the goals were much more modest, the job being considered complete if the patient could reach some kind of schizoid level of adjustment outside the hospital and obtain some satisfaction. She revised this to feel that many of these patients could go on to lead a full normal life with all of its conflicts, sorrows, joys, responsibilities, achievements, and disappointments.

POSTSCRIPT

At the time of this writing, twelve years have elapsed since this man terminated treatment. During that time, he completed his work toward an advanced degree. He has done well in his work and has required no further psychiatric treatment. His marriage has continued satisfactorily. His wife describes him as a devoted father to their two children—a long, long way from lobotomy.

NOTES

1. A shorter version of this case was published in German. Clarence G. Schulz, "Identitat und Genesungsprozess im Verlauf Einer Schizophrenen Erkrankung" ("Identity and the Recovery Process in a Schizophrenic Reaction"), *Psyche*, Stuttgart (December 1961).

2. Erik Erikson, "The Problem of Ego Identity," *The Journal of the American Psychoanalytic Association*, IV (1956), 56–121.

3. *Ibid.*, pp. 75f.

4. *Ibid.*, p. 69.

5. Paul Federn, *Ego Psychology and the Psychoses* (New York: Basic Books, Inc., 1952).

6. Erikson, *op. cit.*, p. 98.

7. *Ibid.*, pp. 99f.

8. Frieda Fromm-Reichmann, Staff Conference, April 7, 1954.

9. Erikson, *op. cit.*, pp. 83f.

10. Kurt R. Eissler, "Remarks on the Psychoanalysis of Schizophrenia," in Eugene B. Brody and Fredrick C. Redlich (eds.), *Psychotherapy with Schizophrenics* (New York: International Universities Press, 1952), p. 148.

11. *Ibid.*, p. 110.

12. Frieda Fromm-Reichmann, oral communication, 1952.

13. Kurt R. Eissler, "The Effect of the Structure of the Ego on Psychoanalytic Technique," *Journal of the American Psychoanalytic Association*, I (1953), 148.

14. *Ibid.*, p. 131.

15. Some of the discussion on dreams appeared in an unpublished paper. Clarence G. Schulz, "Psychotic Thought Content Compared with Post-Psychotic Dreams of a Schizophrenic Patient," presented at Chestnut Lodge Symposium, October, 1956.

16. We are indebted to Dr. Milton E. Kirkpatrick for the manuscript containing Dr. Sullivan's comments.

17. Erikson, *op. cit.*, pp. 77ff.

18. *Ibid.*

19. Sigmund Freud, "Turning in the Ways of Psychoanalytic Therapy," in *Collected Papers* (London: The Hogarth Press Ltd., 1924), II, 400.

20. Lewis B. Hill, *Psychotherapeutic Intervention in Schizophrenia* (Chicago: University of Chicago Press, 1955), p. 38.

21. Erikson, *op. cit.*, p. 80.

CHAPTER III

Confusion as a Defense

CASE PRESENTATION

This account covers a period of slightly less than four years of treatment of a single woman in her middle twenties, who is a college graduate, a secretary, and a nursery school teacher.

When first seen, this patient's posture was somewhat rigid, she held herself in an angular way, and her coordination was awkward. Her facial features were angular and tense, with the corners of her mouth turned down. Yet, she had the potentiality of being a rather attractive looking young woman. There were long pauses in her speech, and she showed obvious blocking. She tended to think over her replies and was not at all sure that she really meant what she was about to say. In the first session, she said, "I do not know who I am." She said that she would hear others saying things that reminded her of something in herself. Quite characteristically, she related many things going on in her environment to herself. If one of the hospital personnel made some comment about her own children, the patient would feel that this other person was saying that she was a child or they were reminding her of her experience of teaching children in the nursery school. She wondered whether a drama on television was put on for her benefit. She also described a feeling of being hopeless and recalled thoughts of suicide from her past. She mentioned what she called "memory shocks," which were flashes from her past that would suddenly engulf her. Auditory hallucinations came through like "grating static from a loudspeaker."

Following her graduation from college, she took a secretarial course in order to obtain work. She held a job for two years. During that time she dated and was living with a roommate, but things gradually became difficult for her. Many of the difficulties seemed to center around loss or separation from various people. A friend of hers had to leave the country because of visa problems, and she lost a boyfriend to a roommate, which was very distressing to her. She felt like killing this roommate, and then developed fears that the roommate would kill her. On one occasion, she became frightened when the roommate was peeling fruit with a knife in the kitchen. She thought that the roommate might use this knife on her. She broke up with this roommate and moved back to a women's dormitory, where she felt very lonely. At that time her daily routine of being expected to go to work was the mainstay of her life. She felt the schedule of expectation to appear at work as an anchor or pivotal point for her. It prevented a great deal of confusion and disorientation at that time. When the woman she was working for didn't come to work, the patient felt that she was on her own a great deal, and without such supervision she felt truly lost. Seeking help, she went to the emergency room of a general hospital and was seen by a physician who suggested that she go home and get psychiatric care.

She contacted her mother, who flew to her and found that the patient's living arrangements were chaotic. At her mother's suggestion, they took a trip to Europe, which proved to be a very unhappy trip for the patient. She felt quite threatened. She thought that her mother was encouraging her to be friendly with the taxi driver they hired in Italy, and she began to be concerned that he might make sexual advances toward her. Upon returning home, she lived with her parents and entered private psychotherapy, which continued for the two years prior to her admission. During that time she took sailing lessons, attended some evening courses, and worked as an assistant nursery school teacher. She was troubled by sexual feelings and was disturbed when she helped little boys go to the bathroom. At times, instead of acting like a reliable parent, she felt that she was becoming too dependent on the youngsters. The better behaved children almost seemed to her as though they were her parents. While the teacher she was assisting was talking to someone else, the patient, who was working on some papers after school, called out in a very pleading tone, "mother." This was rather upsetting to the teacher. As a result, the patient was not rehired. This was an additional stress for her.

The patient's parents became dissatisfied with the course of her treatment. When the doctor seemed not to respond to their requests for a consultation, they made an arrangement to have her admitted to a clinic for diagnostic tests, with the specific purpose of getting her out of treatment. It was from this clinic that hospitalization was recommended and her treatment with us began.

The patient's adoption at the age of four months was an especially significant aspect of her early history. For the first four months of her life she had been in a foster home. At the time of the adoption, the mother noticed that the infant was banging her head on the crib, but since she was being raised according to a schedule, she was allowed to cry it out and was picked up only at the appointed time.

When the patient was two-and-a-half years old, the family moved because of a change in the father's work. After the move they made arrangements to adopt a four-year-old boy. This youngster did not get along with his and the patient's adoptive father, and also treated the patient very badly. She recalled one incident where the boy broke her musical teddy bear, and in remembering it, she felt quite sad. The boy was living with the family only conditionally, and after a year he was returned to the agency that had placed him for adoption. Years later the patient still carried a picture of this foster brother and had one in her billfold when she was admitted. The patient was generally a compliant child. In fact, the social worker assigned to her case was quite impressed by the report that the family would make long motor trips and the patient would not request to go to the bathroom for hours at a time. Highlights from this past history that stood out in contrast to this general attitude of compliance concerned an episode that occurred when the patient was ten years old. She became angry at a neighbor boy and broke a bowl over his head. The cut he sustained required sutures. In junior high school she became associated with a group and started to date. Later in high school, after this same group became involved in petting and sexual activities, she left the group. Between her sophomore and junior years at college, she spent a summer in Europe. The girl friend she was with became sexually involved with another student traveler, and the patient became quite shocked by this behavior. She herself was involved in some petting but never had sexual intercourse. After her return, she wanted to go to a coeducational school, but her father would not permit this. She followed his advice to continue in the college where she had been enrolled.

To return to a description of the treatment, in my second session with her, she presented a markedly different appearance from our initial appointment. Changeability was characteristic of this patient throughout the course of her treatment. In this second session, she was much more coordinated, seemed improved, and was able to talk about her confusion although was still unable to give much of her history. She said, "I pressed the vapor button," meaning that she pushes things away from her that she does not want to remember. In her remarks about the various people who lived with her on the ward, she would make puns of their last names and find hidden meanings in their names. She thought the whole confused situation was a type of drama that was being put on for her. She felt that she was at the mercy of other people's actions as though she were a puppet. Everything reminded her of her past—"I am a part of every one of those people up there." She thought of the main building as a tombstone, and that she was dead. In the subsequent appointments, I found that I was unable to get much at all from her in the way of history. She seemed very confused, often silent, and remote. I then shifted to focusing more on her current experience. At the end of this second session, she politely said, "Thank you, Doctor. Have a nice weekend."

The initial psychological tests were reported as follows:

PSYCHOLOGICAL REPORT

The patient was seen in three sessions in my office. In the first session, she was gracious and cooperative, though it took an obvious effort for her to dismiss her suspicions and keep her attention on the task at hand. She spontaneously talked a bit about this, commenting, for instance, with some wry humor that "oh sure, she is good at mental arithmetic, but her trouble is she always thinks the problems have double meanings." In the next two sessions, she was much more confused and withdrawn, and testing became a painful chore for both of us.

Wechsler Adult Intelligence Scale

The patient functions at the dull normal level, which is grossly below her basic superior capacity.

Her functioning fluctuates from moment to moment. At times, she lost track of what she was trying to do, seemed abstracted, and probably was having auditory hallucinations. At times she seemed unable to establish contact with the ordinary common-sense answer or to recognize it as correct even if it occurred to her. A moment later, her responses would be concisely exact.

One notable aspect of her functioning is how hard she does try to think straight and to criticize and improve her performance.

Prorated	I.Q.		Weighted Score
Full Scale	85	Information	14
Verbal Scale	89	Comprehension	10
Prorated Performance		Arithmetic	10
Scale	81	Similarities	10
		Digit Span	6
		Digit Symbol	—
		Picture Completion	7
		Block Design	7
		Picture Arrangement	4

Projective Techniques
(RORSCHACH, FIGURE DRAWINGS)

The tests display a severe chronic schizophrenic psychosis.

The Rorschach is terse, intense, violent. There is some development toward translating the conflict into cosmic symbols, but this is less marked than one usually associates with a condition as deeply ill. The patient still retains a direct, human orientation (for example, *people* knock their heads against a wall, yell at each other, have the rug pulled out from under their feet).

There is also, however, a hint of movement in the direction of hebephrenia. This shows itself grossly in the patient's drawing of a person. Her image is of the barest kind of smiling clown—with an electrode implanted in its head.

PROGNOSIS:

The active effort and fight, the preservation of some significant reality about people and their struggles are good prognostic signs. The prognosis must be guarded, but perhaps it shades into fair.

When I tried to find out what went on over the two-year period in her previous therapy, she described it as "being in a swamp and hearing a voice." That was all she could say about her therapist. Meanwhile, in her own thoughts, questions seemed to constantly barrage her, such as, "Where am I in space?" "Where am I in time?" She wondered whether she had known her roommate before. Was another patient on the ward a classmate of hers? These questions would go on all day long. The patient herself suggested that maybe she thought of these things to feel more familiar in a strange situation. She described how she went to the hairdresser and noticed a woman with gray hair. It reminded her of her previous therapist's gray hair, and she thought maybe that this strange situation at the hairdresser gave her some feeling of connection and familiarity with her past. I found this interpretation of these events quite surprising and felt encouraged.

About a month after starting treatment, another patient was hurt when bumped by a loom in the occupational therapy shop. She expressed surprise that she enjoyed this. She had never thought of herself as enjoying someone else's misfortune.

When her parents visited her after six weeks, she commented "we played solitaire." The parents presented themselves as rather helpless and asked for all kinds of advice about what to do and what to say. It appeared to me that there was a similarity in the patient's taking cues from her environment and the parents' looking for guidance, cues, and information. This first visit by her parents began what turned out to be a long period of education and support for them by the clinical administrator, social worker, and myself. They complained that when they asked the patient what she thought of her roommate and what she thought of her doctor, she simply said, "I don't know." They felt this was antagonism and stubbornness on her part. When I pointed out that it might be quite difficult at this point to say what she thought of these two people, they seemed able to grasp and accept this. The patient had very little to say about her mother. She described her father as a person who always wants things right and to make everything right. For example, he always emphasized how well-built their house was and how the foundation was built correctly.

At this time, the patient's hospital roommate became physically quite ill. The patient cried during her appointment as she was thinking about the roommate. I responded by commenting on how upsetting this must be to her and she said, "No, I don't care at all. Maybe it was me who is sick and not her." With that, she seemed to be quite confused about who she was and who the roommate was, and who was the sick person. It appeared that the confusion served to dilute the feeling that she was having about the roommate. To be unclear about it made it easier for her to deal with the feelings about the seriousness of the roommate's illness.

In sessions about two months after the beginning of treatment, there were long silences. I would try to question her but any direct attempt seemed fruitless. I waited for quite a long time and then made various speculations. I said that she may be afraid that if she told me what she was thinking she would be giving up part of herself. She said that she didn't know to whom she was talking. I replied that that in itself might make her reluctant to talk. After a while, she told me that she "passes out." This turned out to be a blanking out for varying periods of time. I said that there might be something protective about this, similar to passing out to relieve the pain of a severe physical injury. She asked, "Do you mean it's good?" I replied, "Well, it means also that you are unable to hear, talk, or do things about the trouble that causes so much emotional pain." I came back to the point of finding out to whom she was talking and I said that, in a way, we would be looking at that question for the next several years. The latter part of this phrase jolted her. She came alive and began to talk seriously. She said that she hasn't been able to figure herself out.

During the next appointment, she was silent at first and finally I said perhaps she was concerned that if she talked, then I would use this information against her in some way. She nodded in a somewhat absentminded way and then finally she asked, "How long did you say I was going to be here?" I replied, "Several years," and explained that not all of that time would have to be spent as an inpatient. These things took a long time to work out. She said, "I cannot do it." I told her that I thought that this was the best way that I knew of bringing her to a life where she would not be overwhelmed by her conflicts, fears, and anxieties. She was thoughtful and said, "I have so many conflicts that I am torn apart. I do not know what I am." She then got up to leave the room, saying that she could not stand it. I prevented her from going out the door and kept my hand on her shoulder. She sat down and cried. After a while, she then withdrew from me, talked about not trusting me, and mumbled something about pushing me away. In the next appointment, she made a comment about going on to the next psychiatrist, and, after more silence and my mentioning again her going on to the next psychiatrist, she said, "You are too much mother for me." She then talked about my ripping her and her family apart, and about how her previous doctor had ripped her apart.

She described a fantasy in which she said that she thought of hitting the "sputnik." This she described as "something in the paper that leaves a vapor trail." Then this vapor trail seemed to be a person on top of her. This was all rather vague. When I asked about it, she confirmed that this being on top of her was in a sexual position. She then said that this vapor trail became a man who turned into her father, and, strangely, she became one with this person.

The following episode is one of the few instances in which we were able to document clearly some of the details of the working of her confusion. In this incident, the patient was on her way to the canteen with a student nurse. As she was walking along with this nurse, she felt as though she were three or four years old. Then, feeling like a little child, she looked at her hand and found that she was carrying a card addressed to the alumnae of her college. This began to stir her to the point where she almost became panicky because she could not see how a three-year-old child could graduate from college. The incongruity of this almost drove her into panic. She looked at the student nurse in a pleading way, wanted help, and felt that the student could not help her at all. Following this, she developed the idea that her previous therapist had sent her this card just to upset her. With this explanation, she calmed down. I thought this was a very clear example of how her paranoid projection would operate to furnish an explanation and reassure her in the face of anxiety. Following our discussion of this, she began accusing me of being behind all of the panic and said that I had made her feel like a kid at that moment. I then pointed up her suspiciousness about me as occurring right after she had begun to make something quite clear to me. She was able to see the sequence of how her paranoid idea about me occurred just after her anxiety resulting from our mutual clarification. I felt that a major step had been accomplished.

I was able to use such a sequence in a predictive way. For example, jumping ahead to an incident that took place about six months after starting treatment, we were examining some of her feelings, particularly her sexual feelings, toward one of the male aides. This seemed quite clear to me, and both of us were talking about how much clearer she was. At that point, I made a prediction that she would do something to put distance between us again and try to erase this feeling of getting close to me. Then, toward the end of the appointment, as we were leaving, she asked, "Dr. Schulz, did you understand anything I said today?" At first, she was baffled when I recalled my prediction but then was able to laugh with amusement.

As the patient became less confused and more integrated, her anger became more overt. During a visit by her parents three months after admission, she threw a wastepaper basket at her father. She also began expressing more anger and discouragement toward the hospital personnel. In one incident, she was afraid that she was going to run away if she were escorted to the canteen by a student nurse. Before leaving the ward she picked a fight with the student, became very angry, and then was not allowed to go to the canteen. In this way, she provoked an external control over her impulse to run away.

As mentioned previously, her condition during appointments would vary considerably. At one point while describing her confusion, she related, "I don't even feel I am here. Yes, I know I am sitting in this chair but I do not feel my mind is here." It was at about this time that I moved into a new office in another part of the hospital, which was being remodeled. She was upset when she came over to the office and soon had to leave. I found that during such upset periods I was unable to inquire into the cause of the upset. On the next day, she returned to my office and appeared composed and talkative. I asked her what had happened the day before. She complained about all the confusion. There were workmen finishing up the work in the hallway, and we had to step around these people. She had been reminded of the time that her parents had built their new home. People kept running up to her, asking her what color wallpaper should be in this room and would this color go with this item. She had felt really overwhelmed by the decisions that she was being asked to make. On that previous session, by the time she had entered my office, it seemed as though the walls were closing in on her and that her body was expanding to large proportions.

We discovered that my attempts to clear up her confusion would make her angry, and learned that this was closely related to her father, who wanted to make everything right. She felt pressure from me as she did from her father on those occasions.

In a session six months after starting treatment, she was afraid to come to my office. Consequently, I went to see her on the ward. I was waiting in her room, when she came to the room and stood in the doorway in a very tentative way. She didn't know whether to come in or not. Again, she seemed confused and somewhat disorganized. She spoke about changes. I could see there were two new pictures on the wall in her room. These changes, plus the ones in my office and the ones in herself, were perhaps what she was complaining about. She then spoke of suicide and the feeling that her lungs would collapse, and therefore she had best remain standing. We continued the session while she stood in the doorway and I sat in her room. She began to tell me of a dream, in which she was a house and someone had opened a window of this house. That was the end of the dream. Nothing more being said, I asked where the window was. She pointed to the area just below her umbilicus and didn't seem to know at all what this meant. She asked what I thought it meant. I told her that I thought this was some wish on her part for sexual intercourse. If she were the house and the window was located where she pointed on her body this might mean that the window was her vagina. She seemed to be

rather taken aback at this and said that she had had sexual thoughts
the previous day but she doesn't let herself think of sex. I then connected this with a possible concern about being in her bedroom alone
with me. She neither confirmed nor objected to that interpretation.

On another occasion, she described an incident where her roommate
was playing with silly putty by placing the putty on a newspaper,
taking an imprint from it, and then stretching it out to distort the
image. As she was watching her roommate do this, someone asked her
if she wanted to go to the ward upstairs to a party. She immediately
got the impression that she was being stretched out to the upstairs
floor and physically felt herself as thin as newspaper. She said that
there was no place for anything to come out. I got the impression
from this that all of her feelings were bound up in her. If she was
thin, there was no dimension to her and she had no real release for
her feelings. From this, we were able to discuss some of her anxieties
about going to the party upstairs on the men's ward.

In the seventh month of treatment, we had an appointment during
which she was confused, bewildered, slow in her movements, and almost stuck. She would not sit down in my office. I took hold of her
arm and she asked, in a very bewildered way, where her mother was.
When I said anything to her, she would ask, "What, what?" as though
I couldn't get through to her. As I held her arm she said she wanted
her arm back. I said it was still hers. She felt as though she were bump-
ing into things, into other people, cars and things. I asked her if she
felt enormous and she said, "No, like a little child." She wanted to go
out to the canteen to get some bubblegum. I went with her and she
was unable to cross the threshold of the door. I then took her back to
her room on the ward, where I saw evidence of her roommate having
moved out. This was the second roommate to move out within a very
short time and it was highly probable that her confusion and withdrawal were very much related to this. She agreed and said that she
felt very hurt by it. This second roommate was a temporary admission,
and the patient was reacting considerably to this separation. I connected this reaction to her brother's leaving, but it didn't seem to impress her. This appointment occurred just before I left for vacation.

When I returned, she described how she would lie in bed awake
in the morning and try to remember what had happened the day before. She said it was terrible not knowing who you are, where you are,
or what you have done. She complained of hearing voices and knocking sounds. At that time, while I was listening to all of the confusion

and what was going on, I began thinking that we might give her tranquilizers to help clear up her confusion. I suddenly heard her say, "I am well." I was quite jolted by this, but then laughed a little and challenged her in a somewhat kidding way. She then insisted that she was well. Upon leaving that session, I looked for her escort but she said she no longer needed one and could walk back by herself. I was baffled, and didn't know what this was all about. She returned to her ward alone. In subsequent hours, she seemed much clearer and able to discuss some very important aspects of her behavior. She spoke of intense anxiety that was near panic, causing her to laugh when she didn't feel like laughing. It was this laughter that gave her the appearance of being somewhat hebephrenic at times. She spoke of suicidal thoughts and then in a sentence later asked if she could spend the nights with her parents when they visited. They, in their characteristic way, wanted to know what they should do, what to say, and how to act. Her mother said, "We are dummies." That same day, the patient had said to me, "You are the doctor. You tell me what I am thinking." I connected the parallels in these communications and conveyed them to both the parents and patient.

COMPARISON OF RORSCHACHS

These Rorschachs show a dramatic movement in eight months toward the reestablishing of ego boundaries and ego functions.

The earlier Rorschach was in large part a series of single-word symbols. ("Fight!" "Evolution." "Split." "Confusion.") When asked, she could amplify, but mostly with scattered non sequiturs.

The second Rorschach is a flood of vivid, intense personal association. The significant thing is that the patient can now put it into words, and is now aware that it is her fantasy, and that she is talking about herself.

Confusion is replaced by doubting. The second Rorschach shows a running debate about whether things are friendly or malignant, fighting or protective, defiant or needful.

The patient still relates everything to her own inner struggle, but she makes much more explicit that that is what she knows she is doing. She is still preoccupied with questions of balance and intactness, external force and mysterious influence, being inextricably tied to someone, and with what she sees as potentially disruptive sexual impulses.

In essence, it seems obvious that the patient is moving toward a much clearer reality orientation, accompanied by a decided liberation of psychic energy.

The patient became much more communicative and expressive of her guilt feelings and her feelings of violence. She said that during

my vacation she missed me and was angry at me. She felt that she
was unable to work with me, and yet, at the same time, she felt that
I would give her room to breathe. She felt forced into a corner with
me, "You are my only way out of here." From this point, we were able
to go into much more of her own personal history and make connections between her sexual feelings and her anxieties. We were much
better able to connect past events with her current experience and to
integrate much of what had gone on in the past.

The following session, typical of this period, is described in detail.
As background, the patient had been increasingly clear in her communications and especially in recent weeks had been much more able
to give me a history of past events. She revealed conflicts, especially
about sexual feelings concerning boys, but also about almost any
kind of problem about her separation from friends. Also, of more immediate background was the fact that the patient went to a concert at
the local high school the previous night and that her parents were
expected to visit in two weeks.

On this day, the patient was in the group meeting on the ward
and had to be reminded to come to her hour. She was escorted to
the office. I asked her about the meeting, and she said that she was
thinking so much about the aide that she didn't know who was leading
the meeting and she could not pay attention to the meeting because
of her thoughts about him. She confirmed my speculation that these
were sexual feelings. Then almost immediately, in a very tense looking
way, with tears almost welling up in her eyes, she spoke about being
very angry last night. She said she felt as though she were going to
tear up the bathroom and she knew what ———— (patient from Chapter IV) went through on such occasions. This then led to a discussion
about the concert. She felt she was unable to hear a thing of what
went on in the concert and when she returned to the hospital from
the concert, she felt extremely angry. This began to build up during
the hour. She began pacing back and forth and crying "I have no
outlets, I have no outlets." She went to the corner of the room and
collapsed in tears. I went over to her and put my hand on her shoulder.
She was then able to sob out her feelings that at the high school she
felt just completely cut off from everyone. Even though someone had
escorted her she felt as though she were totally alone and unconnected
with anyone. This had reminded us of previously talked about occasions in the city when she crossed the park and felt so terribly
alone. Also, in the ninth grade a boy took her to a yachting club where
she felt alone because all the other young boys and girls were from

different schools. I continued to hold her hand and to embrace her gently during much of this part of the hour. She was quite receptive to this and quite appreciative of it. This was in contrast to other occasions when she was really quite reluctant to be involved in any kind of physical contact with me. During the hour, she was also reminded of a Jewish boy whom she had dated in college. He invited her to his apartment after they had been out to dinner and this almost drove her wild, as she said. She refused his invitation but the idea seemed to disorganize her. Then she talked about a neighbor who was a senior in high school when the patient was fourteen. She had a "crush" on him but her father would not let her go out with him even though he invited the boy over to the house and had long conversations with him. In all of this the implication was clear that sexual feelings were involved and the patient did not know what to do with these. She also said that she did not know where her self-worth came from, but it certainly did not come from her high school experience. She described how going to this concert at the high school reminded her immediately of the times when she was late to school. Her parents would have to drive her to school and she would then make a mad dash to get there on time. Many of these things came back to her and preoccupied her as she experienced the concert the previous night.

During the hour, she walked back and forth describing her loneliness. She suddenly switched to saying, "Dr. Schulz, I'm going to tear up your office." Meanwhile, she reached out her hand toward me in a way of inviting me to take it, which I did. A few minutes later, we were able to discuss how these feelings of loneliness just preceded the feelings of wanting to destroy and tear up things. She was able to confirm this and see how, on many occasions, this had served as a way of having aides come to her in an effort to control her on the ward. The patient also spoke of a boy friend whom she had been seeing prior to her hospitalization. She said that she felt extremely jealous of her roommate because she had been going with this fellow and she had had a lot of fun with him—"He was like the very devil himself." Yet, she felt all mixed up about him and was quite upset when he started going with her roommate. She said that she felt very much out of place with all people. It was as though all of the young people were "too fast" for her. The one boy with whom she got along offered to help decorate her apartment. It was as if he were really uninterested in girls. "When I left, it seemed as though I didn't know anyone and didn't understand anyone." She went on to elaborate how everything seemed totally unresolved when she left there. Her degree of disorganization was confirmed by her mother who said she looked like "a gangster" when she had her passport photo taken.

The parents' dissatisfaction in their communication with the previous doctor led to the patient's present admission. Having been alerted to these circumstances, the clinical administrator, the social worker, and the therapist made special efforts to work with this family. Her parents seemed to be quite reasonable, cooperative and willing, but there were hints of ambivalence in them from the beginning. Following the incident when the patient threw the wastebasket at her father, he made a statement to the clinical administrator, "We believe in you people and what you are doing 100 per cent." As he was saying this, he handed the clinical administrator a magazine clipping that reported that insulin treatments increased the speed of recovery of mental patients. Through repeated visits, it was noted how coercive the father was in his dissatisfaction with the patient's performance.

During their first year of contact with the hospital, her parents preserved an image of themselves as an honest, solid, loving family, who never quarreled. At about the end of the first year, the image changed when the mother, in a rather offhand manner, spoke of having "seen a snake" on the rug in the dining room. She became terrified when she knew there was no shadow or anything to account for this experience. Largely because of this episode, she went off on a trip abroad for a vacation. Since she was unable to persuade her husband to take time off from his work, she went alone. She soon received a distress message from him, giving her a week to return home. He had become upset, begun to drink, and accused her of having met someone else in Europe. She told the social worker that she was considering divorce but she could not "leave a sinking ship."

In a subsequent visit, the father alleged that we were keeping the patient too dependent, not giving her enough to do and not taking enough chances with her. He said to us, "She is as well as apple pie." In a meeting with the patient at that time, when he had stressed that she should be more independent, the patient replied, "That is a stupid masculine viewpoint," a response that brought a cheer from her mother.

However, the parents changed during all of this. On one occasion, twenty-one months after admission, they had a very good visit right until the end of the visit when the patient became quite angry. They felt that this was planned and that she could control it. However, the mother observed that the patient usually became angry on the day they were to leave. Thus, the mother was able to see how separation anxiety was being defended against by anger. This was confirmed by the patient in her psychotherapy appointment.

After two years of treatment, the patient was obviously much improved but the father was putting tremendous pressure on us to transfer her. He expressed his concern that the patient's telephone calls were becoming too much for his wife. He asked, "What would be accomplished if we cured her and killed her mother? I mean it seriously, not in jest." In discussing these telephone calls with the parents, it became clear that they could not stand her statements of wanting to be closer to them. The patient meant emotionally closer and they were taking it to mean that she wanted to be geographically closer. Therefore, they wanted to transfer her to a hosiptal nearer their home.

Two-and-a-half years after the patient began treatment, her father had a malignant tumor removed from his neck. Upon learning of the operation, the patient went to bed with a backache. When the father visited, he tried to avoid all discussion about his illness but became quite concerned about her backache. He demanded that specialists be called in. It became apparent that his own concern about his health was being denied and projected onto his daughter. It was as though she were more a part of him, in terms of her body, than he was of himself. As time went on, the patient was much better able to verbalize her wishes about the length of a visit and her desire to terminate it rather than end it by becoming angry or confused.

The patient made a successful visit home with one of the nursing personnel. This nurse noted how dependent the patient's mother seemed to be in her household functions. When the patient went out on a date with a family friend, the parents asked the nurse if it would be all right. The nurse indicated that they knew the young man and that she thought it would be a good experience for the patient if they thought it advisable. They gave their permission and the evening went well. When the patient returned to the ward after this visit home, the nurse noticed a visible sigh of relief on the part of the patient.

Three-and-a-half years after admission, the patient was placed on small doses of trifluoperazine, to see if we could decrease the periods of disorganization that she showed at times of distress. She seemed more stable, with less variability in her behavior and made a trip home by herself a month later.

The patient was maintained on a daily dosage of six milligrams of trifluoperazine. She became less afraid, more friendly, and generally more comfortable in groups. The patient moved into a "Halfway House," where she lived with other outpatients and from where she returned to continue her individual therapy sessions and participate in the day program of the hospital. She made plans to take a refresher course to improve her secretarial skills.

When I left the hospital staff, her treatment was continued by a new doctor. She continued her improvement and was discharged to return home nine months later. At the time of her discharge, she showed no manifestations of confusion, no inappropriate emotional behavior, no hebephrenic giggling, or extreme variability of mood. There were slight residuals of anxiety, slight emotional lability under pressure of change in her environment, and moderately easy fatigability.

DISCUSSION

EGO REGRESSION WITH SPECIAL EMPHASIS ON CONFUSION

Confusion in this patient served as a defense, in that it prevented a great deal of felt experience of affect. The patient described what she called memory shocks from her past. Schizophrenic patients are often terribly upset by memories appearing almost as vivid as hallucinations. Confusion is one way of clouding such experience, thereby providing relief. Not only the past memory but the experience of current reality itself can be disturbing. This patient described it when she was beginning to come out of her confused state. In a great deal of tearful anguish, she said, "Dr. Schulz, how would you like it if everything was unreal and suddenly became real—it's horrible!" Her confusion was variable. She seemed to move swiftly from disorganization to reintegration with a consequent changeability in her clinical picture. Such changeability makes it very difficult to assess the patient's capacity to assume responsibility at any particular time, and, consequently, it is difficult to establish consistent expectations.

Confusion served as a defense against a variety of feelings. Certainly, her confusion was a defense against her aggressive feelings. When she became more integrated and less confused, she expressed her hostility directly toward her therapist and subsequently toward her father. Similarly, confusion was a defense against sexual feelings. She would make tentative allusions to noticing the outlines of male genitals when looking at the aides' trousers but would quickly interrupt these perceptions with giggling and confused disorganization. Confusion against a sense of experiencing separation anxiety was a repeated phenomenon. She would deal with this largely by not knowing whether the event was happening to her or to the other person, when, for example, her roommate became ill. Identity diffusion as an aspect of her confusion is illustrated by the incident of her carrying the alumnae card and experiencing the irreconcilable discrepancy between being a college graduate and feeling like a young child.

Such patients seem to show disorganization of the ego in place of repression of the conflict. For instance, when she was traveling in Italy, rather than tolerating sexual feelings in her awareness or repressing the feelings altogether, she developed instead delusional ideas about her mother arranging for the taxi driver to make sexual advances toward her. The projection of such impulses is a primitive defense. In a similar way, she projected aggressive feelings when she became afraid that her roommate might attack her with a knife. She herself was angry with the roommate for taking away her boy friend.

Patients fluctuate in the amount of observing ego that is available to them at any particular time. One indication of the functioning observing ego is the ability of the patient to retain a sense of humor concerning himself. Dr. Dexter Bullard frequently emphasized at conferences the importance of the patient's sense of humor as a favorable prognostic sign.

The following incident illustrates the nursing staff's attempt to deal with the patient's confusion and withdrawal. After the roommate was taken to a general hospital because of her illness, the patient had an episode of upsetting furniture. When the nurse straightened up the picnic table, the patient straightened the rest of the furniture and told the nurse she had done this for attention. She had felt envious of the roommate because the roommate had gotten a great deal of attention because of the critical nature of her illness. She felt maybe she had to do something similar. She then went on to say to the nurse, "You know, I really hadn't got to know her very well; I really don't have much feeling about what happened; when one is here, one gets so involved with one's own worries and personal problems that one doesn't have time to think about the other person." She then went on to speak of the attention that had been showered on the roommate. She felt herself neglected and expressed a great deal of anger. When the nurse agreed that she had been neglected and that they were not going to let this happen again, the patient was taken aback.

This seemed to be an important turning point. At first, the nurses felt stymied because the patient gave people the feeling that she was thousands of miles away from them even though she was seated right next to the other person. When someone tried to reach out to her, she would block it with, "I am a camera" or some similar comment. This patient, prior to this episode, had been involved with the nursing staff in a "mutual withdrawal" type of interaction. Because she made few demands, she was easy to ignore, particularly when attempts to engage her were rebuffed. In rereading the nursing notes, one discovers that morning after morning this patient was permitted to sleep until she woke up, usually around 10 or 10:30. She would dress herself and come out to the nurses' station to ask for coffee. She would then take her cup of coffee and go sit alone in a corner. If she had been expected to be up and dressed for breakfast and to make her bed, this would have forced more interaction with the nursing staff. One can, of course, only speculate in retrospect, but our more recent experiences indicate that when expectations are clearly defined, the patients, by and large, meet them. We feel that a model of expectation that fairly closely resembles the expectations of life outside the hospital facilitates the patient's ego organization. It does place demands on nursing personnel. They can neither permit patients to get "lost in the shuffle" nor gratify their own needs to keep the patient dependent on them. The hospital world must have indeed seemed confusing to this already confused and disorganized young woman.

The occupational therapist had started to involve the patient in doing something when one day the loom accidentally collapsed and landed on the legs of both the patient and the occupational therapist. Because of her concern about her own destructiveness, this was followed by withdrawal and refusal to do anything at all with the occupational therapist for a period after that.

The occupational therapy worker continued to visit her on the ward once a week. Eventually, she was able to interest her in square dancing. The patient did quite well at square dancing and was even able to teach another withdrawn patient. This made use of her identity as a teacher.

Her confusion brought about many important technical problems in the individual psychotherapy with this patient. First of all, the patient's short attention span did not allow for any complicated state-ments. Responses had to be brief. It was necessary to postpone history-taking, since the patient seemed unable to go into this at all. It was important to let the patient know that the therapist was aware of how sick she was. One might think this would be devastating but actually it provided a realistic appraisal of herself. This occurred when her therapist spoke to her of the "years" of treatment required. It does no good to sugarcoat the estimate of the situation in an attempt to reassure the patient. It was also useful to the patient to confirm her accurate perceptions about the therapist. In this way, she was helped to sort out her distorted experiences from her reality experiences. On one occasion, when the therapist had strayed off in his thinking and his eyes were focusing on some point behind her, she noticed this and asked insistently, "Dr. Schulz, are you listening?" The therapist acknowledged that he had at that moment lost track of what she was saying and told her this. At the same time, he asked her to repeat what she had been talking about. The therapist must possess considerable confidence in his identity as a therapist to be able to acknowledge such a lapse in place of offering a pseudo-reassuring denial.

Physical contact is also an important way of helping a distressed patient cope with a massive amount of anxiety. While this would be contraindicated with a seductive patient of the character disorder variety, it can be very useful in the regressed schizophrenic patient. On one occasion, this patient had become quite anxious in the office and started pacing, saying, "I am going to tear up your office." When she came toward the table where the therapist had a dictaphone and reached out toward it, he took her hand and held it and touched her shoulder gently. She sat down and cried. She spoke of her loneliness and how this reminded her of a time when a friend had left her.

Another aspect of confusion is to look upon it as a communication. For example, another patient who "forgot" when he had his next ap-pointment arrived exactly a week early for the session. His confusion served as a communication of his need to be seen sooner than planned.

OTHER ASPECTS OF EGO REGRESSION

The patient showed evidences of regression other than the main one of confusion being focused on so far. She had many ideas of reference and tended to think of almost anything happening in her environment as communicating some kind of message to her. For example, when a tractor stripped its gears, she grabbed her abdomen and referred to

these as her intestinal sounds. The grandiosity involved in her omnipotent feelings of destructiveness was another aspect of her narcissistic
orientation accompanying profound regression.

Primitive defenses of denial and projection were also operative and
indicative of the early ego defenses. She would deny sexual feelings
and project them onto others, such as in the Italian taxicab incident.
By contrast, the psychological tests indicated a series of changes
toward ego progression and reflected the ego integration taking place
in this patient.

Massive sudden ego regression occurring in the newly admitted
patient can be a source of alarm to the family and the staff. Patients
who have had a tenuous integration outside the hospital may show
a massive collapse of defenses with total disorganization, regression,
and the need for complete nursing care. To be sure, the hospital situation itself fosters such a reaction since removal from the expectations
inherent in outside living no longer requires that the patient hold
together. Families sometimes get the notion that maybe the hospital
is "making the patient sick." Actually, this cannot be avoided in many
cases and it is probably well to inform the relatives in advance of the
possibility of this occurrence. While this phenomenon is probably
contributory to the cliché "the patient must get worse before he can
get better," such events should not become rationalizations for poor
treatment.

This patient had felt the requirement that she go to work as a
pivotal point in maintaining her hold on reality. The expectation that
she get up in the morning to arrive at work on time was an important
feature in preventing regression prior to hospitalization. Similarly, the
requirements of scheduled activities and work assignments within a
hospital will foster ego integration and tend to prevent any tendencies
toward regression. Such structure supports a fractured ego much as a
cast supports a fractured bone. Patients who are marginally holding
together will fall apart in a situation of total inactivity and absence
of expectation. The milieu program is a powerful force toward ego
reorganization. Some authors feel that these findings suggest that
psychotherapy is contraindicated in that it fosters regression while
the milieu therapy attempts to counteract such regression. While it is
true that psychotherapy mobilizes anxiety as a result of exploration of
defensive patterns, nevertheless, if skillfully handled, the dosage and
timing of such anxiety need not result in a large-scale regression. In
a unified combined program, the milieu component can facilitate inte-

gration and offset whatever disintegration forces might be resulting from the psychotherapeutic approach.

Often, the therapist and the nursing staff can become alarmed about a patient who is rapidly regressing before their eyes. There will be requests for heroic measures or the immediate prescriptions of tranquilizing medications when these might not yet be indicated. When the staff feels such a regression as a burden or demand, because of the dependency implicit in the regression, this might best be dealt with by giving the staff supervisory support to bring these aspects of their feelings into awareness. Often, personnel who are relatively new in their assignments, such as student nurses, will in some way feel that they have caused the regression and consequently experience a considerable amount of guilt. While we do not purposely set out to bring about a regression to such primitive levels, there is seldom cause for a reaction of alarm if the hospital has experienced personnel to handle such situations.

THE FAMILY AND THE TREATMENT PROGRAM[1]

During the years in psychiatry when these treatment cases were under way, there was a considerable shift in the attitudes of the staff toward the families of patients. In the early days, families were generally regarded as persons who were necessary to support the cost of treatment but who were otherwise more or less of a nuisance. With the concept of the "schizophrenogenic" mother, families were often thought of as evil and given to feel as though they were. Certainly they had no place in a positive way in the treatment program of the relative.

This present case illustrates some of the problems that can occur with the patient's family and ways in which these can be used to benefit the treatment program. At times the family has been thought of as involved in a homeostatic balance with the patient. Therefore, it follows that the patient cannot change unless the family changes. In a similar vein, it was thought that if the patient improved, the family inevitably became worse. Therefore, they needed help during the course of the patient's treatment. Such concepts still did not see the family as a positive contribution to the patient's treatment program.

Adult psychiatric work with hospitalized patients has lagged far behind comparable work in child guidance clinics. It has been a tradition for many years that the parents of the child be worked with at the same time the youngster is in treatment. This model has only recently been transplanted to the adult program, either in the form of social workers working with the family or a patient and family being brought together in family therapy.

Before going into some of the work with the family in this particular case, it might be well to enumerate the variety of problems that involve the family during the course of treatment. Sometimes, one member of a marital pair may threaten divorce during or prior to the emotional crisis that leads to the hospitalization. This creates the awkward situation of the spouse having to support the treatment of his partner when one of them expresses a wish to dissolve the marriage. Wedding rings of many acutely ill patients have been flushed down the toilets on the wards of psychiatric hospitals. Such acts, together with a refusal to accept visitors, bring about a spouse's severe emotional counterreaction almost equal to that of the patient. In other situations, battles between the patient's spouse and the spouse's in-laws have utilized the hospital as the battleground. The side supporting the treatment might insist on no communication between the hospital and their opposition. This, of course, is untenable in terms of treating the patient. Such a censorship interferes with the patient's ultimate attempt to come to some resolution of these differences. It is sometimes exceedingly difficult to keep the battlelines drawn so that the difficulties can be dealt with outside of the hospital arena and, therefore, free from the patient. Often the unsuccessfully resolved difficulties in the family lead to the removal of the patient from treatment. Such decisions have nothing whatsoever to do with the clinical indications of what is best for the patient, but are the results of power struggles within the family structure.

Another problem, especially likely to occur in a private hospital, relates to the family's commitment to treatment. There are times when families feel they are faced with the practical choice between the expenditure of large amounts of funds for active treatment programs, in the hope that the patient can be rehabilitated, and the more conservative approach of trying to limit the expenditures to a custodial program that will insure the private institutional care of the patient for the rest of his life. The parents correctly recognize that they will not always be around to care for the patient but more often than not such questions involve covert hostility toward the patient with an unconscious wish to prevent him from moving toward an active, independent life.

Dr. Harold Searles has pointed out how some member of the treatment team may come to fulfill the role of child of the parents of the patient. In this way, the therapist or the administrator may be seen as the son or daughter, replacing the patient who is taken away from them because of the patient's unsuccessful adaptation to his conflicts in living.

Patients who have no family or at least no interested family are a special problem in hospitals. This is more apparent among chronic cases where the family has moved away, lost interest, or disappeared, and, therefore, the link to the community is broken. Foster homes, halfway houses, and other devices have been used to rehabilitate chronic cases and thereby reduce the large hospital population for many state hospitals. Such cases are also to be found in private hospitals.

In troublesome families, one might ask why one could not just tell the family to remain away from the treatment arena until the patient has recovered sufficiently to participate usefully with the family and rejoin them. This is a very frequent recommendation by the medical staff but it often backfires. Relatives might readily agree to such a program to remain away for a period of say three to six months but will, more often than not, undermine the treatment program, either during this period or at its expiration. The old adage, "if you can't lick them, join them" seems to be a better way of dealing with such a family. Generally, it is more useful to bring the patient and his family together in an effort to understand the effects that they have on one another.

In this particular case, the father placed an enormous amount of pressure to have results translated into a change in his daughter. He particularly wanted to see her become more independent and active. The air was cleared considerably when he finally confessed that this was the first time in his life he had been helpless to do anything about a situation. In the business world, if he did not get satisfaction, he could fire someone or buy out the company or take some other steps that would alter the situation. Here, with a regressed, inactive, schizophrenic daughter, he for the first time found himself unable to change the static situation in front of him.

The lack of communication between the previous therapist and the parents led them to place her in another hospital for an alleged physical evaluation and from there to have her transferred away from the therapist. It was the circumstance surrounding the termination of the previous program of treatment for this patient that alerted us to the possibility that the parents might again become dissatisfied and transfer her.

We were impressed that the father was a self-made man who drove himself and everyone around him. His daughter had described him as a man who wants to make everything "right." In his pressuring, rigid way, he described "work" as the solution to his worries. Yet, in his outward appearance, there seemed to be a soft, accommodating quality about him that obscured the forceful, driving aspect of his personality. The mother seemed to be a person who was somewhat depressed in her appearance, rather quiet and passive, and frequently tearful. She was a person who seemed to have made an adjustment to the situation with her husband without offering any complaints. Together, they seemed to be compliant, agreeable, naive, and in need of help. On their first visit, they asked questions of us, such as, "What should we say to her?" How long should we visit?" "How should we act?"

Three months after admission, the father was assuring the administrator that "we believe in you people and what you are doing 100 per cent," and handed him the magazine clipping about insulin treatments. At that time, we did not point out the mixed message in his interaction with the administrator but dealt with it at its face value. In our current approach, we would be more likely to point out his sending a mixed message instead of responding to the content of the message by merely furnishing information.

Since these parents lived some distance from the hospital, their visits were rather infrequent and perhaps more "loaded" in intensity. When the father visited six months after the patient's admission, the administrator detected a covert and devious expression of resentment taking place between the patient and her father. There seemed to be a subtle, mutual coercion between them that was entirely unrecognized by the participants.

The patient improved. A year after admission, when she was going into her past history in a more integrated and detailed way, she still seemed oblivious of some of the connections concerning statements about her parents. For example, when they visited, she spoke of the visit and then mentioned, "I have a tremendous amount of hatred in me." When the temporal connection between these two statements was pointed out, she denied any connection. After this visit, she again had become perplexed and disintegrated.

The patient's mother seemed to count on her daughter to express the opposition she also felt to her husband. For example, the mother applauded her daughter's rejoinder to the father: "That is a stupid masculine viewpoint." The social worker spent a considerable amount of time with the patient's mother, who more and more aired the feelings of pressure that she experienced from her husband. When they visited the hospital, the parents were invited to come onto the ward to attend some of the ward meetings in which the patient participated with other patients. In this way, they could see at first hand some of the behavior of their daughter and how it was being approached by personnel, rather than receive empty-sounding reassurances from the clinical administrator and social worker. These meetings became a learning experience for the parents.

During a conference that occurred about twenty-one months after admission, the parents described a visit that was wonderful until termination, at which point the patient became angry with them. They felt it was planned anger on her part. The father, in particular, felt that she could "knock it off." However, the mother observed that the patient usually became angry on the day they were to leave. This was taken up with the patient in her individual therapy. She explained that she hated to come back to the ward while her parents went home.

In the example where the patient went to her bed with a backache upon learning of her father's malignant tumor, it seemed as though the patient obligingly expressed the illness that the father was denying. Their discouragement was expressed through asking why their daughter was tired. This seemed to be a direct link between her sensitivity to her environment and her ability to give expression to the unconscious aspects of her parents.

From this account it is obvious that the parents were engaged in concealment and displacement of feelings and attempts at naiveté with denial of dependent strivings, together with problems around aggression and the use of power in interpersonal processes. We attempted to give them explanations, to educate them, and most of all, to be supportive of them in expressing their feelings. These efforts were particularly directed toward the mother. They were able to talk about feelings of despair, impatience, and anger rather than act them out by removing the patient. In joint interviews with the patient, together with what they saw in the ward meetings, they were provided with a model for openness in dealing with the patient, which allowed them to be more free in their own expression toward her. In this way many feelings were brought out into the open for discussion. The patient felt quite reassured of their continued interest as demonstrated by their visits and the opportunity they provided for her to be away from the routine of hospital life during the latter part of the treatment. When one of the nursing personnel accompanied the patient on a weekend visit to her home, she received much information about the parents as she saw them in their own home environment. In retrospect, we thought that we could have been more actively interpretive in dealing with some of the communications on the part of the parents much earlier during the course of the hospitalization. However, the problem does exist of what to do with the anxiety that is stirred up by such visits. Sometimes a therapist, social worker, or clergyman in the hometown area of the relative can be a useful adjunct in such a treatment approach.

Therapists are often reluctant to join meetings that include relatives, social worker, clinical administrator, and patient. The therapist's participation in such group meetings requires that he broaden his concept of the area of responsibility toward the patient's treatment. Individual therapy hours then become only one aspect of the program. The therapist lends support to the clinical administrator and social worker when they have to bear the brunt of some of the opposition from the parents. Within a short time, joint interviews of this type can convey in a concrete form the treatment philosophy of the therapist toward the patient. Such demonstrations communicate much more than would lengthy conferences with the treatment team in the absence of the patient.

The entire function of family therapy in such cases is worthy of a considerable amount of research. In our recent beginnings with such a treatment modality, we are convinced that a family therapy diagnostic interview, early in the treatment program, which includes the relatives and the patient, is of enormous value. A single session can reveal prominent patterns in the family interaction that can alert one to problems to be dealt with later on. Such a family interview can point up defects in the assumptions and communications in the family patterns that should be of benefit in preventing and dealing with crises that come up during the course of treatment. Because of our limited experience, the value of continued weekly sessions with the family and the patient still seems to be largely unclear.

When the patient is an adolescent who will be returning to live with the family or when there is strife within a marital couple, these conjoint sessions seem to have more relevance than with other patients.

At present, when we use conjoint therapy, it is an adjunct to the individual therapy. Much is still to be learned about the types of pathological family interaction and the particular phase of treatment in which conjoint interviews are most useful.

IMPORTANCE OF EARLY INFANTILE EXPERIENCE

This patient was adopted at the age of four months. During early infancy, she was described as being engaged in banging her head. Many authors have speculated as to the importance of the early months and years of the child's life and their relationship to the cause of schizophrenia. Articles by Bowlby[2] and Spitz[3] indicate the importance of the constancy of the mothering experience to the infant and the aftereffects of separation anxiety and depression within the first year of life. It seems necessary that an infant of three to six months engage in a symbiotic tie with its mother in order to be able to develop an attachment to an object. Searles has stressed the importance of such symbiotic developments, especially in the recapitulation of the development of symbiosis in the treatment of the psychotic.[4] He finds that symbiosis is a useful occurrence in the phases of treatment of the patient and should not be viewed as something to be avoided. In treating the severely regressed patient, the therapist often goes through a phase of symbiotic relationship with the patient that was experienced in infancy but never worked through to the stage of complete differentiation. With this patient, the therapist went through periods of confusion, drifting, and reverie as he sat with her during her regressive experience.

We still do not know the nature of the constitutional and/or environmental influences that determine a later schizophrenic outcome. Hartmann has postulated a constitutional ego defect in schizophrenia. He specifically hypothesized that the person who later becomes schizophrenic is unable to neutralize his inherent aggressive drive from the beginning.[5] Ives Hendrik has pointed to ego defects developing very early in life.[6] Such a consequence leaves the schizophrenic with a significantly different kind of ego than that of the neurotic.

Work with psychotic children points toward two general types: (1) the autistic child; and (2) the symbiotically psychotic child. The autistic child seems unrelated to human beings and will react to a human being much as he would to a piece of furniture. By contrast, the symbiotic child, which seems to have developed further in his emotional development, will cling to the mother, yet will not have gone on to a period of differentiation from the mother. All of the patients reported in these cases had at least reached the symbiotic phase of development although presumably they had not sufficiently resolved their symbiosis.

A focus on the early infantile period and its relationship to schizophrenia has relevance to the treatment program in terms of the importance of gestural and physical responses that seem connected to the preverbal experience of the infant. For example, relationships with severely regressed psychotics can take place on the basis of swaddling the patient in a wet sheet pack, holding him, using physical massage, or nonverbal communicative acts by circle dancing or calisthenics when a patient cannot be engaged in a verbal interchange. One is reminded that an infant can be comforted by holding him, no matter what the particular cause of his distress at the moment, be he hungry, cold, frightened, abandoned, or whatever. He can often obtain at least temporary relief through being held.

Nursing care in the traditional sense involves much intimate body contact. Yet nursing personnel have a great reluctance to "touch" patients outside of the context of nursing procedure. Often this is stated in terms of how the patient might interpret a reassuring hand on the shoulder or even a hug as an angry attack or a sexual gesture. What seems to be of more relevance is the nurse's motivation. If the motive is to comfort a patient who seems genuinely in need of comfort, there is little likelihood it will be misinterpreted. The approach of verbal reassurance is much less likely to be effective.

Similarly, concrete changes in their environment can often directly affect schizophrenic patients. For instance, when the patient moves from inpatient to outpatient, he is apt to perceive this much more in terms of the approaching end of treatment than some abstract concept of that being the goal in the first place. Conversely, communications through concrete activities are often more effective, such as moving the patient to a more closely supervised hall or locking the door. The concrete, physical measures can be much more reassuring than a verbal explanation that he is in need of more intensive care.

These comments are not to be construed as regarding verbal psychotherapy as being a waste of time with the severely regressed patient. They imply that gestural responses, sitting with the patient, regularity of appointments, and so forth, might have more meaning than verbal reassurances at that stage.

CONFLICTS ABOUT AGGRESSIVE FEELINGS

Dr. Fromm-Reichmann emphasized the schizophrenic's fear of aggression.[7] It seems that every patient and perhaps every human being shows at least some degree of serious concern about the destructiveness of his aggression. This might be denied when the patient experiences it as a fear of other people's aggression, which turns out to be a projection of his own aggression onto the outside world. It is the omnipotent damage potentially associated with the aggression that gives the patient such concern. Common pathological ways of dealing with such aggression are to become catatonically rigid, to resort to some intellectualizing about it, to become confused and thereby render oneself impotent as well as unaware of the aggression, to withdraw from competitive situations that might bring forth the aggression, to discharge it by carrying out hostile attacks on others in a direct way, or to turn such hostility away from others and toward the self in the form of self-destruction and self-defeat.

These pathological responses to aggression are best responded to in treatment by accepting them, setting limits in relation to the aggressive potentiality, protecting those around the patient, including other patients and staff, and using tranquilizing drugs if the aggression becomes unmanageable. Aggression is not always simply a drive but, probably, a complex outcome of fear of helplessness, an attempt to keep distance and maintain a separateness of identity, and to cope with the anxiety of near-panic proportions.

There is still a considerable debate in psychiatric circles as to whether aggression is a primary "given" in every individual or whether aggression is the outcome of a reaction to frustration that is part of every human being's experience. Neither postulate need affect the way of treating the patient. If it is a primary given, it would still be the task of the ego to establish mastery and make use of such a drive. This then leads to the same kind of therapeutic approach that would be evident in the frustration theory. People misuse the frustration concept in an attempt to blame some outside source for their problem and thereby try to shirk responsibility for their aggression.

INTERRUPTION OF A TREATMENT RELATIONSHIP

It was necessary to transfer the psychotherapy responsibilities to a new physician when the patient's therapist for four years left the hospital staff. We place considerable emphasis on the importance of continuity in the treatment relationship of severely ill patients. If at all possible, the program of treatment should not be interrupted because of the assignment of the doctor to other areas of training or duty. Such reassignments are particularly frequent in residency programs set up with a "block system" of training assignments. For example, when the patient is admitted in May, the doctor breaks off treatment because he moves from the inpatient service to neurology, outpatients, or somewhere else in July. We recommend a "longitudinal" system whereby the resident carries inpatients throughout the entire three years but varies the size of his caseload according to the number of concurrent training assignments. This patient had had a sufficiently solid accomplishment in therapy, together with an established relationship with the other hospital personnel, to be able to negotiate the transfer without difficulty.

POSTSCRIPT

Following her discharge, the patient continued on medication and was seen by a psychiatrist every two weeks. She worked full-time as a secretary and got along quite well. We later received word that she was married two years after her discharge from the hospital.

NOTES

1. Parts of this section of the discussion were presented in an unpublished paper: Clarence G. Schulz, Michael A. Woodbury, and Elizabeth S. Palacious, "Is She Going to be Transferred?—Parents' Interaction with a Patient's Treatment," Chestnut Lodge Symposium, 1962.
2. John Bowlby, "Grief and Mourning in Infancy and Early Childhood," *The Psychoanalytic Study of the Child*, XV (1960), 9–50.
3. René Spitz, *The First Year of Life* (New York: International Universities Press, 1965), pp. 285–292.
4. Harold F. Searles, "Phases of Patient-Therapist Interaction in the Psychotherapy of Schizophrenia," *British Journal of Medical Psychology*, XXXIV (1961), 169–192.
5. Heinz Hartmann, "Contribution to the Metapsychology of Schizophrenia" (1953), in *Essays on Ego Psychology* (New York: International Universities Press, 1964), pp. 204f.
6. Ives Hendrick, "Early Development of the Ego: Identification in Infancy," *Psychoanalytic Quarterly*, XX (1951), 44–60.
7. Frieda Fromm-Reichmann, "Basic Problems in the Psychotherapy of Schizophrenia," *Psychiatry*, XXI (1958), 1–3.

CHAPTER IV

Negativism in the Psychoses: Warmth by Friction

CASE PRESENTATION

This patient was seen in individual psychotherapy for slightly more than three years in a very stormy relationship. She was a single girl, in her early twenties, whose course of treatment was characterized by (1) assaultiveness, (2) deep despair, and (3) an exquisite sensitivity that led her to have a hair trigger reaction in her relationships with those trying to help her, particularly her therapist. This presentation will focus on the early phase of treatment, which was so thoroughly characterized by negativism.

Her difficulties became manifest during the latter part of her high school years. The patient, an honor student and an outstanding athlete, began to have trouble concentrating. A tutor who was brought in to help her in mathematics explained to her family that there was nothing he could teach her since she knew the material, but for some reason, could not perform well on her examinations. She would frequently run away from home after a mild reprimand. Her mother thought very little about these events since her own adolescence was also one of turmoil. After the patient graduated from high school, she made a series of attempts at college, alternating with periods of hospitalization. Typically, she would spend a year in college and fail, become involved in excessive drinking, and have difficulties and crises, during which the family would be called and hospitalization recommended. She went to various sanitaria, where she received electroshock and insulin shock, group psychotherapy, and individual psychotherapy. These periods of hospitalization were characterized by a great deal of assaultiveness and combativeness on her part, by frequent running away, and some self-mutilation. This five-year period culminated in a hospitalization during which, according to her, she had been locked in restraints to a bed for three months prior to her admission to the present treatment program. Each time she was released from these locked restraints, she would set into motion fights, attacks, and assaults that would get her placed back in cuffs. Her clothes were slipped on under the restraints in order to transfer her to this hospital.

She was the youngest of four children and the only member of the family to have overt psychiatric difficulties that were clinically diagnosed as such. Her father, a farmer, tended to be a withdrawn and quiet man who was highly respected in the community. During the course of therapy, she came to see what a lonely man he had been and became extremely moved by this as she thought of him. Her mother showed episodic rages with physical violence. For example, when she had difficulty preparing the evening meal in their home, she would sometimes throw pots and pans at the children if they irritated her. On one occasion, when she became angry at her husband, she took his collection of rare books, heaped it into a pile, and burned it. During her angry outbursts, he, in turn, would often go off by himself and involve himself in his work. Occasionally, he retaliated with physical attacks on the mother. Sometimes, when there were fights during mealtime, the mother would leave the house and disappear. Later, the father would go out looking for her and would find her seated in the car. The patient described her mother as a very pessimistic person. For example, she was convinced that when the father made the flight to the hospital, he would be killed in an air crash. When the patient or her sister would come home from school and announce that they had a certain project, such as making costumes for a play, the mother's immediate reaction would always be that they couldn't do this, it would be too difficult. A particularly vivid episode in the patient's mind occurred when, as a little girl, she had been practicing for hours to accomplish a certain athletic feat, which she eventually accomplished. She ran into the kitchen, breathless, to tell her mother, who looked at her in a puzzled way and explained that the family was not athletic. The patient then thought back as to whether she had actually accomplished this feat and, having decided that she really had, she then began to wonder whether she was a member of the family or not. This brought forth a surge of doubt and uncertainty about her true identity. The patient experienced a similar sense of strangeness when her previous therapist made interpretations of certain unconscious processes operating in her. For instance, when she attacked him, he might say something like "well, you are really fond of me." Although this actually was an underlying determinant in the attack, she felt this was totally foreign to her and she would experience a sense of disorganization at such an interpretation.

When first seen in treatment, the patient was small, thin, of wiry build, downcast, and depressed, especially since she was sniffing from a cold and crying. Her uncombed hair was very long, hanging down over her shoulders. When she was depressed she looked rather ugly because a scar on her lip became very prominent and the facial muscles were drawn down. She was dressed in black pedal pushers and a black sweater. To me, she gave the appearance of a "Dead-End Kid." She said very little in the first interview, during which she sat turned away from me, sniffling and crying. She was smoking rather vigorously, tapping ashes about her on the floor without bothering to use an ashtray. Noise from outside the room seemed to easily distract her. She was silent and remained so after I asked what her difficulties were and what she considered her problems to be. We both sat in silence, after which she began to open up with an expression of her distrust and some tears. She indicated that she was afraid that if she "did anything" she would be "pinned down." By this she meant that she would be put in straps. She explained that, as a result of her running away and assisting another patient to run away, she was placed in restraints for three months. The patient emphasized that the previous doctors didn't give a damn about her. It was her helping the other patient—their alleged favorite—that had put her in restraints. I indicated that I hoped that if she had the urge to run away here she would first contact me, since there were usually reasons for such feelings and that we could then discuss them. She said that she didn't care and gave other evidence of severe discouragement. In subsequent hours, she came to my office and assumed a defiant stance, with slouched posture and one leg tossed over the chair, knocking ashes on the floor. My early efforts were directed toward obtaining her history. She chose to emphasize her life since high school.

In her sixth hour, we had our first real fight. The patient began with silence and asked why I did not "stare" at her. Other doctors used to stare at her in order to get her to talk. I told her that I was not so much interested in getting her to talk as I was in trying to find out why perhaps she felt reluctant to talk. In general, I thought it would be to her advantage to be able to discuss things. As I pressed for her history, she kept referring me to the record and clearly felt that I was lying when I told her that I had not read the record because I wanted to wait and get her impressions first. However, she did tell me about the time she cut her wrists while living in a boardinghouse for patients. This led to my asking about self-destructive behavior and self-defeating aspects in her. In talking about this, I tried to see if she had learned it from someone in her family. She was surprised at this question and wondered if I thought it was "hereditary." I said, "No, not inherited but I think sometimes these things are learned by children from their parents, grandparents, uncles, or someone close by." Although she did not answer the question, she thought it over, seemed surprised, and wondered why no one else had ever asked her this. She also said something about her mother being overattentive to details and that her mother was unhappy. To the best of my memory, it was at the time when we were talking about her previous therapist that she came at me with a heavy glass ashtray. I threw up my feet, which led to a scuffle in which tables, telephone, and ashtrays turned over. We ended up with her face buried in the rug on my floor and my being on top of her, pinning her arms at her side. This ended the struggle and after I caught my breath I released her. I invited her to help straighten up my office, which she did. I again pointed out that if she could not control herself she should let me know and we would meet in her room. She spoke about her previous doctor and the months wasted, and how doctors promise to go on but then give up.

There then followed a series of episodes of running away and fighting. Somehow, going into action seemed to be her way of trying to obtain relief. In a session at the end of the first month, she was talking about her previous therapist and complaining how he would disagree with her and tell her what she was "really thinking." As she described this in our session, she became very angry and started throwing cosmetic bottles and smashing glasses. It was apparent that if she would take up anything from the past it would actually be felt as something current and she would live it out. The cosmetic bottles were being hurled at me because she was at that moment misidentifying me as her previous doctor. Thus, the same feelings were coming out in the present relationship. About this same time, she described some of her previous hospitalizations and how, as she came out of her depression, she felt highly nervous, ran away, and picked up a man. She chose the "crumbiest crumb" that she could find, had sexual relations with him without any pleasure on her part, and finally returned to the hospital after a few days.

She spoke about an attack she had made on a nurse at the hospital where she had been treated previously. This nurse was one whom she especially liked and yet she beat her up. She also attacked a doctor who had taken a special interest in her and had taken walks with her. There were instances when, as she pressed for freedom, she would act in a way that would bring about further restriction. I talked with her about some of her dreams in which people would leave her and also her concern about my leaving. She said that none of this made sense because she really didn't want anything to do with people. "If I become attached to someone, I will commit suicide." If I had available time I attempted to meet her disturbance by scheduling extra appointments at her request.

In a session about two months after starting treatment, she was calmly dismantling a towel rack by removing screw after screw. (I sat and talked with her in an attempt to discuss her thoughts about what she was doing.) Soon, she had dismantled the entire rack and then began to poke out the windows by inserting pieces of the rack through the bars protecting the windows. This incident certainly indicated that early intervention was necessary in any kind of behavior of this sort. Many of the hospital personnel gradually learned the various cues and signals that would lead them to earlier intervention: as an example, the scar on her lip would become visible. In the following hour, when I brought up the incident of her dismantling the towel rack, she said she was hoping I would step in and stop her. She found it extremely difficult to discuss anything like that while it was going on. She said that her thoughts were just unavailable to her. She remembered that many times doctors insisted that she was holding back whereas she was completely blank and had nothing to say. Gradually, the episodes of anger seemed connected to her feelings about me as though I were like her father who was remote and distant from her. He was always retreating to his books or going off to work when there was trouble at home. She complained that if he did step in, it was always much too late.

PSYCHOLOGICAL EXAMINATION

Because of the escape risk, the patient was seen in her room. She was conversational and in a way warm with me. Her behavior was rational and appropriate for the most part, though several times she blew her nose on her bedsheet, with a glance that seemed to mix apology and bravado. Quite often she seemed confused about her personal history and geography, and seemed to assume that I must know everybody whom she had run into in previous school and hospital experiences.

She worked hard and seriously on the Rorschach, but refused to take any other tests. She especially insisted on not taking an intelligence test, on the basis that there is something wrong with her brain and taking the test would only rub it in. By the end of our contact together, I felt that she maintained her resistance more because she did not want to reverse herself than because she still had so much fear of the test.

RORSCHACH RESULTS

The test suggests an unsystematized paranoid schizophrenia in a person of lively intelligence and range of interests, who is vigorously struggling to regain personality integration.

The patient is concerned with whether her view of events is shared by others. Many of her responses are quite conventional. When she does come out with the bizarre and macabre, she knows it is and she is capable of suppressing what she does not wish to reveal.

The patient tends to be hyper-alert to small details in her environment and reads too much meaning into them. She shows some difficulty in synthesizing the elements of her experience into larger wholes.

The patient is easily stirred by outer events, without knowing what is agitating her and causing her difficulties. On the other hand, she is probably quite conscious of her own need to be liked and respected by others, but feels that this need humiliates her. If people do seem to like her, she seems to feel that this is only a prelude to their feeling that she is healthy and in no need of their attention; or else a prelude to their discovery that she is bad and not worth their attention. She seems to have to disillusion people quickly so that they will turn their backs on her now and not later.

The patient is preoccupied with sex, which she tends to see as a sad, sour failure, and even more preoccupied with some kind of cold, merciless violence that will pin her down. The test also shows some tendency for grandiose religious fantasy. There is a great deal of explosive potential, but also some ego strength that at least opposes it, though it is insufficient to master it.

PROGNOSIS:

Fairly good.

I saw her immediately after the psychologicals when she was painting colored stripes on the walls of her room. She was wearing pajamas and looked rather dirty. I commented on the vivid colors she was using, but she made no reply. She sat on the bed and was silent. After a while, I asked her how she liked the psychologist, but there was no answer. Soon she launched into a tirade that gradually built up into her breaking plastic glasses, throwing down the end table, pulling the shade off the roller, and smashing a toiletry bottle against the window. I stepped out of the room and got help. She fought a little with the female aide until a male aide arrived. As they were making arrangements to put her into a cold wet sheet pack, she said that it was all over. I accepted this and suggested we postpone the pack. The content during all of this was mainly a sarcastic mockery of comments that she had heard from people in previous hospitalizations. She quoted others as saying, "It's all an act. Why don't you control yourself?" "Everyone has problems," "It's just like having a broken leg," "You just haven't grown up," and "Just read when you're upset." Throughout this incident, she did not physically attack me. At the end of fifty-five minutes, she was discussing her outburst and sobbing, I arranged to continue for an additional hour. She objected mildly at first, saying that it wasn't fair to the person I was to see. She said that I didn't want to see her and thought that I must hate her. "The pay must be good." I said that it was all right. She then called me a liar. She frequently complained that her previous doctor understood her but that it didn't do any good. I made a few comments referring to her complaints and what she must have felt in the above remarks. It sounded as though people had turned away from her. I thought the entire session accomplished a great deal and told her this.

During these early weeks, I felt apprehensive, frightened, and frustrated. I was not aware of how furious I felt toward the patient until I had a dramatic dream. In my dream I was in a fight with the patient and struck out at her with a full swing. I awakened, having knocked the skin off my thumb by hitting my nightstand. From that time on, I remained cognizant of the anger her assaultive attacks evoked in me.

It is very difficult to describe how this tiny girl could be such a vicious and dirty fighter. For a while, we used cold wet sheet packs but she seemed so opposed to and resentful of them that they were discontinued. Three-and-a-half months after starting this patient's treatment, I first returned her kick. This incident occurred when she became annoyed by other patients who had come into her room and interrupted our session. She, in a very upset tone, suggested that we go to my office but I told her that I would not see her there. She seemed to feel criticized by this, then threw an empty glass on the floor, stepped on it, and left her room. As she did so, she slammed the door, thereby locking herself out, which made her extremely angry. When she returned to her room, in about ten or fifteen minutes, she came at me kicking and I kicked her back. After a few more minutes, she came at me when I wouldn't let her out of the room. She tore my shirt in the struggle. I threw her back on the mattress and then sat down. She rushed out of the room and on the way threw a cigarette at me, which burned a hole in my jacket. As she left the room, she shouted that "they" had never done *that* to her. She went out onto the porch and smashed windows in the door leading to the stairway. We returned her to her room, but any attempt to talk about this incident was unsuccessful. Finally, she left her room and didn't return. In the next session the following day, I was feeling rather discouraged because of the previous attack and this was apparent to her. She asked if I was depressed, and I told her that I didn't feel very good about what had happened. She said that her father would sell off more land and pay for the damages. I told her what the costs actually amounted to but that this was not the important part of it. She could not afford it in terms of her own self-respect. This hit home to her, and she voiced some of her feelings of hopelessness and suicide. I replied that I didn't know what to do, that I couldn't handle it by myself, nor did I think that she could control it by herself. I thought that perhaps together we could solve it and we then discussed the possibility of packs and sedation. The following day I arranged with the hall administrator, the patient, and the head nurse to discuss the question of controlling her behavior. In this meeting the patient wanted us to tie her down with straps, which we did not use. She said that she did not know what good the packs would do, since what she needed was a new brain. I replied that it would give us a chance to understand her problems and work on them, that her outbursts were interfering with our treatment and the pack was only a way of dealing with her upsets until she could change through our talking together. She again voiced her hopelessness and said that when I did not urge her to talk, she interpreted this as my not being interested in her.

The following incident conveys the intensity of this patient's combative capacities. One quiet Saturday morning I was seeing the patient in my office when she suddenly became anxious and upset and bolted from the office. She ran across the grounds to a parking area and, before I could reach her, threw a large rock through the window of my automobile. After considerable struggle, I was able to subdue her, and she was returned to the hall by a couple of male aides. Following this struggle, I met one of my colleagues at the staff mailbox area where, while trying to catch my breath, I related the latest incident. He listened for a while politely and then gratuitously explained that of course it was because of my fear of my own hostility that a man of my size could not control such a tiny girl. As we were discussing this, she suddenly appeared at the end of the hallway in the company of two aides. Upon seeing us, she picked up a chair and threw it through a window whereupon my colleague raced down to the end of the hall to assist in subduing her. Meanwhile, I calmly walked to the hospital switchboard to summon additional help. By the time I reached the scene, the patient had the colleague on the floor with her knee on his chest, pulling with all her might on his tie, strangling him in the process. The aides meanwhile were pulling on her extremities to get her off him. After hesitating a moment in self-satisfaction, I joined in to assist.

Eventually, in going over the various episodes of her attacks on me, we were able to realize that she often had noticed a wish to reach out and hold me just prior to the attack. The following is an example of this. When I was coming on the ward, another patient was being hustled off to her hour, assisted by an aide on each side, while my patient was coming out of her room for her appointment with me. As this patient and the aides rushed past between us, my patient felt like coming across the hall where I was waiting and taking hold of me. During the distance of the few steps across the hall coming toward me, she suddenly changed her feelings and began to assault me. It was only later that we were able to investigate this conversion of her attitude from an initial wish to reach out for me to feelings of anger toward me. This insight was quite a significant breakthrough in terms of a change in the assaultiveness. Taking hold of my hand or putting her head in my lap would now begin to take the place of assaulting me. Similarly, verbal closeness would threaten her. When I would begin to understand two consecutive sentences, a similarly close collaborative type of experience, she seemed to become quite anxious and frightened and would withdraw or attack. Each move toward a greater feeling of closeness to me or participation or involvement with me brought a counterreaction in her. As nearly as she could describe it, she experienced a tremendous amount of pressure. She felt that some great thing was expected of her and that she would be unable to live up to this. Consequently, I would then become disappointed in her. When I was disappointed in her I would leave her. She then saw me as becoming very distant physically and receding. While she was undergoing this anxiety, I would actually become somewhat distant in a reciprocal way after feeling quite close and collaboratively involved with her. She was extremely sensitive to this, and the subtle reality perception would confirm the delusional experience. At this point, I might seem quite tall to her or that she was shrinking. On the other hand, I might seem quite angry and menacing as though I were going to murder her and that she was becoming a nothing. Often, her way of getting herself out of this feeling of nothingness was to go into action—usually a violent outburst. She would then emerge as a person, even though a bad or evil person. Even if I wouldn't want anything to do with her, at least she felt that she was something and would thus avoid a feeling of nothingness. Often the nothingness could only be terminated as she heard the bits of glass falling about her and the various people grappling and tugging on her arms to put her into the seclusion room or into a pack.

She gradually began to be able to tolerate a degree of sense of separation from me. Prior to this, she was so subtly attuned to me that, if she were talking to me and I would perhaps glance down at my trousers, she would immediately react with a great sense of loss and separation, which would set forth a spiral of anxiety, despair, anger, and loss of control. Eventually, this changed so that I could scratch myself, yawn, or do almost anything without precipitating the whole flurry of activity. She also began to see me as a person who was separate from the past people in her life rather than reacting to me immediately through misidentification.

Initially, the discontinuity in her perceptions of people was quite striking. One afternoon she ran away. By the time she returned to the hospital, the day nurses had left and the afternoon shift had come on. There was a nurse on the afternoon shift who had just come to work at the hospital and whom the patient had never seen. This break in the relationship was enough to make her question whether she had actually come back to the same hospital and to the same ward. Similarly, in her own self-perceptions she would literally, during a particular session, within moments, change from feeling like a very young girl to feeling like a terribly old woman. The mechanism of projection was evident by her question, "Why do I have to say others think something instead of thinking it myself?" She gave as an example her thought "the nurses worry that I will commit suicide."

I developed into a more continuous person in her viewpoint of me.

Similarly, in my reaction to her, I began to feel less compelled to try to solve all of her difficulties by further extending myself. A particular example occurred after about six months in therapy when she set fire to a mattress. This was quite disturbing to me because of the implications of the destructiveness toward other patients. With the help of discussion with some of my colleagues, I decided not to see her and canceled our appointment that was scheduled right after this episode. I gradually paid attention to my needs and not so exclusively to hers. She expressed her reaction to this new development in the following note:

To SCHULZ:
1. In case of sick stomach—you LEAVE I'll only get nervous
2. In case of wanting to be close to you—LEAVE
   I might be scared and you might get
   hit (what would the neighbors think)
3. In case of tears—LEAVE It might make
   you feel human and that is enough to
   scare anybody
4. Banging my head—LEAVE The wall might
   fall down—it would hurt you (The
   hell with me)
5. In case of my loneliness—LEAVE and "sick"
   my worst enemy after me Then I'll
   be not only lonely but ferocious
   I'll run away and you'll be rid
   of me
6. In case I'm "o.k."—LEAVE Since I'm o.k.
   I won't need a doctor
7. In case I attempt murder or suicide—LEAVE
   I might miss my head (with a gun)
   or the noose might
   snap and I would either shoot
   you or land on your head
   which means YOU would feel pain
   Dr. Schulz must not feel pain.
   ———— must suffer alone—Always
   ALONE ALONE ALONE

Well Sir it all boils down to whatever I do I want NOTHING to do with you. You're a coward. You put everything on my shoulders Then why am I here if I can carry my own load. What are you for? To avoid trouble and confusion (my trouble your confusion) Don't come back.

RELINQUISH ALL HOPE YE
WHO SEE SCHULZ

It was at this time that I more consistently fought back and protected myself rather than trying to subdue her. This put us on a more nearly equal basis and shifted the exclusive focus from my superhuman efforts to her responsibility for controlling her own behavior. One problem about this soon became apparent. She would attack me to precipitate a counterattack from me and provoke me into abusing her. Once when we got caught up in this kind of exchange of blows in a seclusion room, I said, "You just want me to beat you up," and she shouted back, "Yes, that's what I want," and with that we both dropped our arms and sat down and talked about it. From this discussion came some history of many fantasies of wanting her father to attack her sexually.

A tremendous amount of depression came forth as the fighting, running away, and general action decreased. There was an enormous outpouring of grief that lasted for weeks and months. There were still occasional attacks but the amount of despair that she was experiencing was truly staggering. Her appeals for help from me provoked an equal amount of helplessness on my part in the situation and about all I could do was acknowledge this helplessness to her.

Ten months after her admission, the patient had a cough that worsened. I arranged for an x-ray, which showed that she had a left-upper-lobe pneumonia. This made me feel more useful to her as a doctor.

After an interview with her parents, I told her of some similarities between her mother and herself. I included the mother's pessimism, which seemed to run profoundly through the patient's life. At that time, the family was in the process of selling some land to provide funds for the patient's care. The mother was still predicting that the purchaser would not buy it even though it had been surveyed and there were other indications that he was going ahead with the purchase. She was pessimistic right up until the time that he signed the papers. Another similarity between them was the patient's outburst of temper, which has been described in relation to the book burning. The mother's leaving home when she became upset was similar to the patient's running away.

More and more, she began to participate in various work projects in the hospital, including assisting at the switchboard in the evening and working in the hospital canteen. This, too, precipitated a reaction that she labeled the "avalanche." When she first began to think about requesting permission to work in the canteen, she began to fantasize being granted this permission by the clinical administrator and saw herself working. Next, she envisioned being asked to move out of the hospital and becoming an outpatient. Afterward, the doctor would no longer be interested in her. Continuing the series of fantasies, she quits therapy and is terribly lonely on the outside. She is on the edge of the earth somewhere—quite panicky. The rapidity of these associations led her to use the term avalanche. She recalled that earlier in her hospitalization, when she was asked to come out of the seclusion room to go to the bathroom, she would experience a similar avalanche. It included remaining out of the seclusion room, exchanging the hospital gown for her regular clothes, returning to her room, moving to a less disturbed hall, becoming an outpatient, and living a humdrum life in suburbia without a doctor. By the time she had come across the seclusion room floor to the aides waiting at the door, she would be flailing away and be forced back into the seclusion room to end the avalanche. The threat of cure would require that she give up her individuality, her creativity, her flamboyancy, and her interest in people, to become a "cured, well-adjusted" person.

Almost two years after her admission, I returned to my home one late Sunday afternoon after a week's vacation. I was alone and found the patient seated in the den of my home reading the book *Exodus*. She was dripping blood on the couch from self-inflicted scratches and had been drinking champagne from my refrigerator. The previous evening the patient had run away from the hospital and spent all Saturday night away from the hospital. On Sunday she climbed through an unlocked window of my house. After applying first aid to these superficial wounds, I took her back to the hospital.

It was my impression that the patient was communicating a need for me, a wish to be close to me, to reinstate her conviction that she was still ill, and needed therapy. She especially tried to convey that she did not like my reducing the number of our hours from five hours to four a week, which I did upon my return from my previous vacation.

The following week was a difficult one for the patient. She cut herself, smashed windows, was angry and quite depressed, showed deep despair and suicidal thoughts, cried, and wanted to hold on to me during the hours. It seemed to me that she was quite anxious at the possibility of going ahead in life, of getting close to a male patient, and moving out of the position of "patient." She would then set into motion all those things that would reinstate the old familiar pattern of self-destruction, failure, and restriction. She would reject the other patient for fear of being rejected; she demanded her release for fear that her parents, soon to visit at the end of the month, would take her out; and she was quite upset when the nurses' notes said that she had had a good day.

Over the span of the next year, she showed a greater ability to tolerate the necessary absences of the therapist. One time when she ran away, she visited her sister, remained for a week, and fared well. A few months later, she visited her family in the company of a nurse.

She actually did become an outpatient for a brief period but returned when she could not face the loneliness. This was almost three years after beginning treatment. While living outside, she had a tremendous amount of competitive feelings toward her roommate. The latter seemed to be able to make decisions quickly about what furniture to buy and where to obtain it. She felt envious of the roommate's having been married and having children, which she felt she could never do. While I was on summer vacation, she became upset, demolished the furniture, and had to be brought back to the hospital.

The following condensation of a note written at the end of the third year of treatment further reflects changes in the patient. This was a note to me explaining that she had contacted the Director of Psychotherapy, because of her concern about me:

> I have worked with you for two years—nearly three and you have helped me in many ways—mostly just BEING there.
> But at this time I do not wish to see you as a *therapist*.
> I am feeling better and more worthy these days—perhaps it horrifies me to see you as a person with deficiencies and conflicts. You seem different and of course I wonder if I am different. I have told you many times I was close to you and so close it was like death—mine I suppose— one Saturday your face changed so violently I panicked because you seemed to be having despair, I worried about you. I was thinking of Dr. ———— who killed himself. I knew, I just knew I would never see you again and I considered calling the Medical Director to tell him you might kill yourself.
> I like you and I keep wondering *what is* this feeling of almost panic that strikes me when you seem different, or tense, or confused, sometimes just not there or in a daze.

(The note goes on to express her speculations that someone in my family is sick or that I am having a sexual affair or financial problems.)

About the affair it is none of my business except when jealousy over-whelms me to the degree that I may carry out perhaps successfully a suicidal impulse then it becomes your problem—or does it and if this is the problem *I* have to *deal* with it or *die* with it.

I can't change the fact that I am a woman with some intelligence and a little curiosity.

She had continued to work on her problems and was making plans toward specific training for a career when, for the first time in months during a regular session with me, she had an outbreak of rage during which she struck me in the face. This was related to my being a few minutes late because of a necessary consultation with a visiting doctor. My delay made the patient feel worthless and, hence, her violent re-action. Later on in the day, she requested an additional appointment in order to clear up some matters with me that were rather urgent be-cause she wanted to discuss these things with her administrator. Dur-ing the course of this discussion, she repeated the physical attack on me. It was at this point that I refused to go on in treatment with her. I felt that it was important to stick by this decision, primarily because I had had enough. I also thought this would back up my repeated warn-ings to her of the necessity to control her assaultive behavior toward me.

DISCUSSION

This discussion will concern itself with the following topics: negativ-ism, identity aspects, running away, externalization of conflict, "ma-nipulation," self-esteem, masochism, and dependency.

NEGATIVISM[1]

Negativism in the course of treatment of any patient is not unusual. The "negative therapeutic reaction" was described by Freud in his book, *The Ego and the Id*. Freud described how the patient, instead of benefiting from an insightful clarification in the treatment, would, in a paradoxical way, become worse. He attributed this to an un-conscious sense of guilt, which would be aroused when the patient should ordinarily improve and be benefited.[2] This was related to those patients Freud spoke of as being "wrecked by success."[3] Negativism in psychotic and borderline patients is frequently encountered and can be seen as present in each of the patients presented here.

In order to understand the basis of the negativism in the psychotic patient, one must look back to the early months of infancy. At this time psychologically the mother and infant are almost as one just as they were when the child was developing in utero. Largely through the child's development of its nervous system, together with experiences of gratification and frustration, it begins to differentiate as separate from the mother. At first, this experience of being separate is only fleeting and transient, with a return to the state of merging or fusion with its mother. The child's experience of hunger and other bodily needs being delayed in their satisfaction promotes a sense of separateness and distinction from the mother who gratifies such needs. Eventually, the young infant develops some sense of an object (the mother) as being "out there" in contradistinction to a dimly perceived sense of its own self (a body image). Through repeated experiences, these percepts come through to the young infant to be established in its experience as separate object representations distinct from the self-representations.

According to Jacobson's description:

> The baby's wish for oneness with the mother, founded on fantasies of oral incorporation of the love object, will easily bring about refusions between self- and love-object images whenever the child experiences gratifications, physical contact, and closeness with the mother. Evidently, such experiences of merging with the love object are always connected with a temporary weakening of the function of perception—i.e., of the awakening sense of reality—and with a return to the earlier, undifferentiated state.[4]

Eventually, if the child develops normally, there is established a reasonably firm sense of self as separate from object.

Psychotic patients seem to show a greater tendency toward fusion of self and object. Thus, when psychotic patients with such poorly defined sense of self move toward another person out of a need for dependency gratification, there is this threat of loss of separateness and a consequent loss of a sense of identity. Jacobson illustrates her concepts with a moving description of her encounter with a female patient.

> In the course of my talk with her, the girl—a pathetic, beautiful Ophelia clad in a torn nightgown—pulled me down to the couch where she had seated herself.

"Let us be close," she said, "I have made a great philosophical discovery. Do you know the difference between closeness, likeness, sameness, and oneness? Close is close as with you; when you are like somebody, you are only *like* the other, you and he are two; sameness—you are the same as the other, but he is still he and you are you; but oneness is not two—it is one, that's horrible.—Horrible," she repeated, jumping up in sudden panic: "Don't get too close, get away from the couch, I don't want to be you," and she pushed me away and began to attack me. Some minutes later, she became elated again.[5]

In the normal child at a later age than that described above, one can see the importance of the concept of "No" as used by the child in furthering its sense of separateness. At that time, the child almost automatically responds to everything with a "No" to the bewilderment and sometimes distress of the parents if they are not prepared for this. Similarly, a child, when being taught to correct a bit of behavior, for instance not to empty his cereal from the bowl onto the floor with his spoon, will often have to repeat the act once more before he conforms. This is a sample of negativism that reflects his attempt to preserve his own autonomy and to comply on his own terms. In a similar way, adolescent rebellion appears to be a variation on the theme of negativism in the soon-to-be-adult's attempt to declare his separateness from his parents. This reaction is apt to be especially pronounced when he feels a considerable amount of dependent need toward his parents.

The role of negativism in the psychotic has generally been accepted as a way of reestablishing separateness when there is a threat toward loss of ego boundary and loss of a sense of identity brought about by anxiety over moving close to another person. *What has not been so clearly delineated is the positive value of the negativistic behavior in maintaining a type of emotional closeness with another person while, at the same time, insuring a sense of separateness.* We have come to feel that negativism on the part of the patient is a defensive reaction to establish an identity; that is, the distinction of self and object. At the same time, the negativism becomes a way of gratification of the dependency need through what we term "being warmed by friction." In this way, the negativistic patient, through his abrasive contacts with the other person, establishes a transient kind of relatedness and, at the same time, builds into this relationship an attempt to maintain a separateness. These characteristics are found in other psychotic symptoms as, for example, the paranoid delusional system; however, in order for it to be considered as negativism, it must contain the quality of opposition. In his paper on "Negation," Freud indicated that negativism involved the aggressive drive.[6] "The passion for universal negation, 'negativism' displayed by many psychotics, is probably to be regarded as a sign of a 'defusion' of instincts due to the withdrawal of the libidinal components." Here Freud was emphasizing the aggressive component that gets split off and is so clearly involved in negativistic behavior.[7]

In this patient's psychotherapy sessions and in her contacts with others in the hospital, it became apparent that she would go into action in order to avoid the experience of anxiety. For a long time, the interviews were punctuated by sudden physical attacks and assaultiveness. At other times, she would refuse to enter into the interview situation. Defiance, mutism, attack, and many other forms of negativism were characteristic. As we were able to move from simply trying to control this behavior to an examination of what precipitated it, we found that a sudden physical attack and the resulting scuffle would terminate a feeling of "nothingness." These attacks were vicious and beyond her control. If the therapist seemed to recede physically into the distance at a time that he might be silent, she could make him real again with an outburst. The pattern soon emerged where she would attack every time a therapy session was approaching its termination. The appointments usually ended in mutual anger, with a feeling of physical pain and sometimes damage to person or clothing, leading to a continuation of feeling and thought about one another long after being physically separate from one another. In this way, the negativistic attack perpetuated the relationship long after the encounter was terminated. At times, she would attack when she felt emotionally drawn toward the other person with feelings of fondness. As she said, "If I become attached to someone, I will commit suicide." She found a modicum of security in her established identity as the most vicious patient and, in her view, the most hopeless patient in each of the hospitals she had entered.

Later on, when she began to be on the verge of any change for the better, she would experience an aggravation of her condition and this would be reflected in a return of her negativistic behavior. These were "negative therapeutic reactions" in a broad sense. A change for the better could be in the form of being able to come out of the seclusion room for an hour or being able to go for a walk or reaching some understanding about herself in therapy or—considerably later—being able to go downtown by herself and eventually to make plans to become an outpatient. No matter what the improvement, she would experience what she called the "avalanche." This rapid series of thoughts, which ended with her feeling a "nothing" would come in a flash, produce terror, and be quickly terminated by the sound of breaking glass or the pain of physical struggle.

Such oppositional behavior, whether in the form of refusal to eat, refusal to tend to personal hygienic needs, neglect of a reasonably acceptable personal appearance, or lack of participation in the broader hospital activities on any level, can be some of the most challenging problems to nursing personnel. Numerous techniques were employed in an attempt to control this patient's assaultive and destructive behavior. Cold wet sheet packs and seclusion were used. When it became apparent that she received some gratification from the physical contact involved in restraining her, attempts were made to provide physical contact in other ways. When nursing personnel observed that she was becoming tense, they would suggest a back rub. She was offered assistance with her personal appearance. Nurses set her hair and helped her experiment with different ways of using make-up. Doctors and nurses generally experience a sense of frustration when faced with their own impotence in trying to deal with this negativistic behavior. This patient was frequently permitted to withdraw to her room for hours at a time. Exhausted by their efforts to control her behavior, the staff found relief in her solitude and the opportunity to turn their attention to other patients. The identity of the nurse, physician, and others in the "helping professions" becomes threatened when they find themselves so ineffective. In some treatment programs, the staff respond with physical intervention such as tranquilizing or energizing medications, electroshock treatment, and even recommendations for lobotomy in such instances. On the other hand, if one understands the purpose of the negativistic behavior and the need that it fulfills for the patient, there need not be the pressure to try to change the patient. The problem becomes more one of accepting the negativistic behavior until something other than the negativistic channel can be tuned in and a relationship formed on some other basis. One could then feel that some of the patient's dependency needs were being gratified, although to the patient this is totally out of his awareness. One could also keep a respectful emotional distance with such patients until the readiness for closer collaboration was at hand.

It is important to see the complexity of this behavior and not dismiss it as mere "stubbornness," "manipulation," or "resistance."

Similarly, the psychotherapist—in his sessions with the patient who complains about his lack of progress or who criticizes the therapist—should recognize that this negativistic behavior should not be taken at its face value. In these instances, the therapist should not, for example, become defensive about the patient's criticism or agree with him about the lack of progress and then exhort the patient to get down to business in the sessions. Rather, he might look for whatever could have provoked such a negativistic reaction on the part of the patient and see, for example, that it was indeed the positive feelings for the therapist that led to such counterreaction.

So much of what is responded to by the staff as the patient's lack of readiness for a particular type of participation might better be looked upon as an aspect of negativistic behavior and an approach made toward trying to find a solution based on the information described above. Many patients who would be turned down for participation in the work program or be thought of as not ready for occupational therapy or not ready to engage in meaningful psychotherapy should be brought into these forms of participation much earlier than is often done. These patients could be helped to see the pathological aspects of such handicapping behavior and be encouraged to find more appropriate ways to deal with the anxiety and its accompanying sense of loss of identity.

Work programs for patients within the hospital are usually considered a step in the rehabilitation program that helps prepare the patient for assuming a productive role in the community outside the hospital. Under pressure to get the work done, or feeling compelled to get the work done efficiently, the staff often overlooks opportunities for very sick patients to assume a productive role in the hospital community. For example, the patient who can be relied upon to stack the linen quickly and neatly is more often assigned this task. The rigid structuring of work programs often interferes with providing work assignments that might be useful to patients. It is generally agreed that it would be useful to channel the aggressive energies of adolescent boys into shoveling snow. This, however, will not happen unless the boys have ground permission and the snow can be shoveled between 9 A.M. and 5 P.M. Various jurisdictional disputes will arise—the shovels are all locked in the maintenance shops, or it is the job of the rehabilitation worker to take the boys out. As a final obstacle, someone will wonder who will be liable if one of the boys falls on the slippery pavement.

During the time that this patient was quite negativistic, we attempted to channel this negativism into productivity. We felt some type of gross physical work would be an outlet for her energy and give her a sense of accomplishment that would bolster her self-esteem. At that time, the hospital's lawn furniture needed painting. Because of her episodes of combativeness and running away, we felt she could not be left in the paint shop unsupervised. We were able to arrange to have the furniture brought to the occupational therapy shop a few pieces at a time so she could work under the general supervision of occupational therapy personnel. She seemed to derive a great deal of satisfaction from this work. At one point, she jokingly remarked she had enough furniture to keep her busy for three years.

The difficulties encountered in working with this patient's negativism often overshadowed her capacity for warmth and sensitivity. For a time, she helped care for the patients on the geriatric ward. She made beds, assisted with the patients' personal hygiene, and read to them. When one of her peers developed a dermatitis on her feet, she assumed the responsibility for preparing the foot soaks.

Her capacity to relate to others in a very empathetic way was demonstrated in a moving way on a shopping trip into town with a male aide. The patient and the aide were refused service in a local restaurant because the aide was Negro. This was unusual at this particular restaurant and was attributed to a new waiter. The patient became very angry and knocked some dishes off a table near the door as they left. On the walk back to the hospital, she spoke of how angry she was and how she felt the aide should also be angry. The aide tried, unsuccessfully, to persuade her that he was not angry. When they returned to the hospital, she went immediately to bed and cried herself to sleep.

IDENTITY ASPECTS

The chronic hospitalized patient has a considerable stake in clinging to the familiar identity of being a patient. This is related to the phenomenon of dependency and "hospitalitis," but it involves much more than either of these. The threat of getting well and getting out of the hospital can lead to the concept of being a "nothing" as described above by this patient. It also raises the threat of competition with others that can be an unknown quantity to the patient. At least the patient is familiar with hospitals and has some sense of being able to compete on that level. At a recent ward meeting, one patient proudly proclaimed, "I'm the sickest patient in the hospital."

Relinquishing the role of being a "patient" threatens the patient's grandiose self-concepts. These will usually remain hidden unless they are particularly brought out by the therapist. Such grandiose goals are part of the patient's idealized concept of himself, and these will remain intact as long as they are not exposed to the light of reality. Such patients would prefer to preserve the image of being a potential Olympic competitor, opera singer, or great scientist rather than move out into the world where they might find that they are merely superior in performance.

Those of us who have never been chronic patients would ordinarily assume that life outside the hospital would certainly be preferable to a role of being a career patient. However, those patients who do make it from chronicity to living outside invariably go through a period of grief over giving up the identity of being a patient. There may be a long period of mourning and grief during the course of relinquishing such a role. The person can best be helped through this by being listened to and having the existence of such mourning acknowledged. Attempts on the part of the staff to treat lightly such expressions from the patient probably reflect denial of the staff members' own wishes to experience the dependency gratifications and security of identity that go along with being a patient.

Another patient who for years had clung to the escape clause via suicide plans experienced a great deal of anxiety and turmoil when she began to see the possibility that she might live. It was as though she would experience the same sense of terror when being "sentenced to live" as another person might on being sentenced to die. She felt as though she would be letting a great number of people down if she recovered and lived an uneventful life. She thought that she would be considered a fraud by those who had worried about her, had been concerned about her and, who, all along, thought that she was an emotionally troubled person. Of course, she had been troubled and their concern was justified, but this would all seem to be negated if she became an independent, functioning, self-reliant individual.

This patient also illustrates several instances of her need for verification of her experience or knowledge and its relationship to the sense of identity. When one of her previous therapists would bring up some factors operating out of her awareness, she would be terribly upset by this. It might indeed be true that her anger would be a reaction to her sense of fondness for another person but, at that moment, she was unable to look at these unconscious factors motivating her anger and would become almost panicky at such interpretations. Similarly, if the staff attempts to "sweet-talk" a patient out of her feelings of resentment, anger and what-not, the patient's identity is threatened by a lack of respect for what the patient is experiencing at that moment. This patient said that she appreciated it when others noticed her, even if she looked "crappy" and the other person said that she should wash her hair—"At least he notices."

A little knowledge is indeed a dangerous thing when a partially trained person dismisses the patient with the comment "It's part of your illness." Similarly, a misuse of the concept of transference is to tell the patient that she is angry at her mother in order to attempt to deflect the anger away from the staff person. It is essential to a person to have his feelings acknowledged and verified. A feeling is a feeling and it should not be labeled as something else. One patient's mother considered her child's expression of anger as an "upset." Whenever he became upset, she would then check back to see what he had eaten the previous meal and decide that he was allergic to this food that would be eliminated from his diet. One can readily see how such an approach would greatly warp his ability to accept the experience of anger into his awareness.

PATIENTS WHO RUN AWAY

It was this patient's repeated attempts to run away and also her assisting another patient to leave the hospital that led to her being physically restrained in cuffs for three months prior to her transfer to the present treatment program. The AWOL patient is a problem causing considerable concern. While the patient is out of the physical supervisory activities of the hospital, the hospital still has a responsibility toward the patient. The community becomes concerned when patients who require hospitalization are on the loose without authorization from the hospital. Relatives understandably are concerned about the situation and experience a great deal of anxiety until the patient is either found or returned to the hospital. Fellow patients resent the enormous amount of personnel time being taken up by the patient who runs away.

Within the hospital itself, such patients become the focus of controversy, with questions and accusations being made toward the nursing staff for permitting the running away or toward the clinical administrator for allowing the patient to have permissions sufficient enough to facilitate the running away, or toward the patient's therapist who may be viewed as not dealing with the patient's conflicts and problems with sufficient skill in the therapeutic sessions to prevent such "acting out." There might be an additional burden on the therapist if the running away is viewed as an expression of some unresolved conflict in the therapist that the patient is responding to and is taking action on. The nurses feel guilty even though they have not been accused of being negligent.

The adolescent patient with impulse control problems is the most frequent type of patient in this category. These patients are generally not confused nor responding to delusions and hallucinations and consequently are able to take care of themselves outside of the hospital. The main problem with them is their tendency to become involved in illegal drug usage, sexual acting out, or other forms of delinquency. The patient who causes more immediate and continuing concern is the one who is suicidal or confused and responds to hallucinations that tell him to run away.

We have become convinced that it is impossible to contain a patient in a hospital unless the physical setup is a situation designed as a maximum security hospital. Generally, this is inconsistent with a rehabilitative treatment program that fosters maximum responsibility on the part of the patient. The staff can provide some protection against such behavior, both in the physical setup and in being alert to cues, signals, and messages that patients give prior to taking off. The ultimate hope of benefiting such a patient is to get him to view the behavior as a symptom. This patient thought it absurd when it was suggested that she get in touch with her therapist when she had thoughts of running away. She thought this would be the last thing she would want to do. Eventually, however, she was able to turn to the staff for assistance.

The reasons why patients leave the hospital without authorization are varied. The patient may be confused, wander off, and not know what is expected of him. He may simply be "testing" the situation. There was one young schizophrenic man who explained that he was going with the group to the dining room, when, as they turned the corner, he decided to walk away from the group to see what would happen. Having once done this, he felt he must continue and he slipped away unnoticed. He went into town directly to the police station and explained that he was from the hospital, at which point he was returned. Other patients want to find out whether the people in the hospital care enough about them to come after them. Certainly, an exhibitionistic flare becomes a feature with many of the younger patients. They derive considerable attention when they tell other patients of their plans and even are prompted and assisted in carrying out such plans when they have the opportunity. They become "heroes" in the group when they act out the rebellious and negative feelings toward the hospital in this manner. Other patients will run away to provide some kind of distraction or diversion from conflicts and anxiety. The amount of excitement that fills a void of loneliness can be of considerable relief. There is a considerable discharge of energy associated with the whole process of planning and executing the behavior. Oddly enough, some patients run away in order to be caught. In such instances, it is clearly a message of needing to be further supervised and restricted for any number of reasons peculiar to that patient's dynamics. There is a frequent pattern of the patient's running away just prior to the absence of a therapist or other staff member important to him, whether due to holiday, vacation, or assignment elsewhere. Such patients cannot stand the experience of being "abandoned" and will leave before the important person leaves him.

The lack of intervention on the part of the staff can sometimes be quite dismaying. There was the incident where a patient with a suitcase in each hand was leaving one of the cottages at the hospital, walking slowly across the grounds. Two doctors, busily engaged in conversation, noticed her as they passed and one doctor commented to the other, "Isn't it nice to see Miss X outside today." On another occasion, a young patient shook hands with two attendants and said goodbye before he took off. On looking into this latter incident, an explanation was offered that all day long the patient had been "kidding" about running away. He had been skirting around the group acting as though he were going to run away, and finally everyone had become lulled into such a sense of false security that he was able to accomplish this. The whole phenomenon of the patient "kidding" about his intentions, whether these be suicidal, sexual, assault, or running away makes it very difficult for the staff to know when and how to intervene. This is best handled by viewing all kidding as a serious communication. It will stop the kidding. One patient on an intermediate hall made an offhand comment about wanting to set a fire and found himself moved to the locked hall so rapidly that he never again lapsed into such casual comment. The treatment relationship the patient has with the therapist can be a strong deterrent to running away. Among the devices used to prevent running away are such things as the locked unit, special escorts to appointments off the unit, or, in some open hospitals, special nurses assigned to the patient twenty-four hours a day. Another device in the open hospital is to put the patient in pajamas when he is apt to run away and thereby make the escape less likely. The strategic placing of personnel so that all traffic must go by a receptionist's desk or nurses' station is an additional form of control. Occasionally, some open hospitals will have a seclusion room available and will keep such a patient in seclusion for a while, and in that way physically restrict the patient from escaping. Almost all hospitals are reluctant to build fences or establish walls at the perimeter of the grounds to prevent people from running off. Such physical impediments tend to stigmatize the institution as being like a prison.

The families who collaborate in the failure of or delay in such a patient's return are also a problem. In such instances, the family and patient should be brought in for a frank discussion of the problem. Sometimes the family is easily talked into taking the patient on a "vacation" or in some other way not getting on with the treatment program by failing to return promptly to the hospital. This, of course, is a not so subtle undermining of the patient's confidence in the hospital by the family.

The "acting out" patient who frequently elopes from the hospital consumes a great deal of the time and energy of nursing personnel. Attempts to limit the patient's opportunities to run away often degenerate into a "game" in which the patient tries to outwit the staff. The frustration and anger the staff feel are expressed in the seemingly offhand remarks made at the time of an elopement. Remarks such as, "Did you hand him his suitcase?" or "Let's discharge him AMA before he returns" are commonplace. Nursing staff may behave in a way, which, in retrospect, facilitated the elopement. One patient left the unit when a group of patients was leaving to go to the occupational therapy shop. Even though this patient was not scheduled to go to occupational therapy, when the staff on the unit realized he was gone, they concluded he was there. They did not call the shop to verify this and, thus, the patient was gone from the hospital for an hour before his departure was officially noted.

EXTERNALIZATION OF CONFLICT

Externalization is present when the patient deals with an internal conflict by having someone outside of himself take one-half of the conflict and then enters into some opposition about this. This patient, for example, had considerable conflict about seeking help. She was longing for it at the same time she was extremely distrustful and could not bring herself to request help in a forthright and direct way. Instead, she was sullen, defiant, and rejected anything that was offered to her. As a consequence, those in the environment were reaching out in their efforts to be of use to her. With this arrangement, the patient had externalized the conflict so that others were offering the help and she was opposing such offers. It can be seen that this is related to the concept of negativism, although externalization does not always have the aggressive aspects of negativism. A patient might, for instance, be quite ambivalent about wanting to attend school. If he can get the staff to advise him to attend and even go so far as to urge and coerce him, he has thereby externalized one-half of the ambivalence and does not feel in conflict about it.

With such patients, it is necessary for the staff to participate in their half of the externalization process. They often must decrease the patient's anxiety, which results from the conflict, by taking a stand that they think will be in the ultimate best interests of the patient. This can be as fundamental as the stand for going ahead with the treatment program even though the patient, as far as he knows, is not in need of treatment. Similarly, the staff may have to participate in the externalization by setting clear-cut but firm limits and thereby relieving the anxiety and conflict within the patient. Eventually, however, one expects that the patient, through his understanding of this process, will be able to struggle with the ambivalence and eventually develop his own internal controls through identification with the staff.

A transactional or interpersonal frame of reference used exclusively by the staff in attempting to understand the patient's behavior can sometimes be misused by the patient and may foster the process of externalization. Such patients, in exploring the historical, experiential aspects contributing to their faulty personality patterns, might tend to blame their parents for being "schizophrenogenic" and thereby may externalize what might otherwise be a more internal struggle. If the staff, and particularly the psychotherapist, can include an intrapsychic frame of reference, the chances are that both the staff and patient will recognize the internal aspects of the conflict much earlier. Frequent meetings or other channels of communication between the psychotherapist and the other staff are additional approaches that may be employed in an effort to help the latter understand how the patient externalizes some of the conflicts and how the staff becomes drawn into such a process. They can then discuss other ways of dealing with these patterns to ensure the patient's developing a greater sense of awareness of the internalized conflict and autonomy in attempting to solve it.

What if we had it to do over again? Would our approach differ? In this case, the therapist set the tone for greater latitude in behavior and in retrospect might have moved in much earlier and for an extended period of closer setting of the limits. Certainly, the patient gave an indication when she was dismantling the towel rack that the therapist's questions and words were of no value. She needed direct intervention at that point. In such a situation, it is generally the role of the administrative and nursing personnel to set tighter limits on behavior than would be the approach of the therapist. However, the therapist's example is very influential in guiding the attitudes of the other staff, directly or indirectly. This sometimes leads to a considerable amount of resentment on the part of the nursing personnel, who feel that they are unable to take a laissez-faire approach to this behavior when they have to spend twenty-three hours while the therapist spends one hour with the patient. With this patient, the nursing personnel clearly delayed intervention during an attack upon the therapist in a treatment session in an effort to show him what they were putting up with most of the time. Actually, a divergent approach between that of the therapist and that of the nursing personnel might be quite justified but probably will not be successfully put into operation unless there is clear communication on a continuing basis about what is expected of each. It is difficult to know how one would approach the problem if he had it to do over again but this therapist, from the position of hindsight, would not have put up with that degree of physical attack by the patient if he were handling the treatment now. Perhaps his final decision to stop treatment was one of the most therapeutic things he did during the entire course of treatment. Obviously, it is difficult to be accurate about these matters, since the same patient cannot go through two different courses of treatment and be the same person at the beginning of each course. Therefore it is impossible to compare the effect of differing treatments.

"MANIPULATION"

Much of these complex processes that go on in a patient and have already been described under the headings of negativism and externalization have been dismissed as "manipulation" on the part of the patient by many of the staff. When used in this context, it has the quality of some willfulness, intention, effort to control the other person, and action designed to achieve certain selfish ends. When the patient is seen as a "manipulator," orders are often given to deal with such behavior promptly and severely.

One aspect of this, in addition to that already mentioned in the previously discussed topics, has to do with the patient's sense of helplessness. This helplessness is often completely disguised by an active attempt to master the environment or to give a sense of power in relationship with others. If the patient can be thought of as "manipulating" things, he is accorded a great deal of power and the helplessness is certainly disguised in such instances. The staff readily thinks in terms of manipulation in order to simplify the situation, to hold the patient responsible, and therefore to relieve the staff of the dependency needs expressed by the patient through his helplessness.

The entire question of the extent patients are to be held responsible for their behavior and the extent they are to be considered "sick" is a dilemma in psychiatry. This becomes especially puzzling for patients whose behavior and emotional condition fluctuates rather rapidly from one of considerable disorganization to one of reorganization and competence. With those patients who tend to remain rather chronically confused, regressed, and disorganized, these questions seldom arise. The situation is different with a patient whose behavior varies.

With sicker patients the staff can be rather sharply divided when the patient makes appeals "to be trusted." Sometimes the split in the staff is a reflection of certain internal divisions in the patient. In such a situation, the patient may unconsciously be setting up a certain small group of the staff who are considered to be "good" and usually a much larger group who are considered to be "bad." Efforts to solve this by everyone being "consistent" are usually doomed to failure. These problems are more completely illustrated by the patient in Chapter V. Only when the patient discovers how these factors operate and reflect themselves in the divided staff can the split eventually be resolved. The negative effects within the staff are meanwhile best dealt with through communication among those who are placed in both camps without the expectation that they necessarily should have similar attitudes toward the patient. This example in itself would be only one reason why the prescription of attitudes for staff members would be a difficult thing to put into practice even if it were considered to be desirable.

Searles has commented about the entire question of the patient's behavior being volitional as opposed to unconscious, by thinking of these polarities as being part of a continuum and that at any particular moment the patient may be utilizing previous unconscious mechanisms in a quite volitional way. He emphasizes that this might vary and fluctuate rapidly from moment to moment and, therefore, that the degree of the patient's control over this can best be assessed intuitively.

SELF-ESTEEM

As this patient came to understand more about the role of action as a relief of anxiety and as she could reach out toward the therapist and others, the tendency to action decreased and the intensity of her depression became profound. She went through prolonged periods of feelings of helplessness and despair. Out of this chaos there emerged a conflict of feeling and a need for another person, and the lack of any sense of predictability of constancy in her object relationship to the other person. She was afraid that she might be harmful to the other. In the case of the therapist, this included fantasies of causing him to have a cold, driving him out of his profession, taking him away from his family permanently, or even causing his death. She believed that she was fundamentally evil. To avoid needing the other person and thereby causing his destruction, she would have to first destroy herself. She was afraid if she became attached, the other person might find her unacceptable and she would then be a burden and rejected, and thus be alone again, or she might be dominated and enslaved by the other person. To be connected with another person would destroy her.

Everyone's feeling of self-esteem will at some time reach a low ebb. The patients described in these chapters are almost always subject to a severe sense of loss of self-esteem. Such low self-esteem reaches delusional proportions. What is not so frequently voiced by the patient, unless it is specifically sought out, is the opposite self-concept involving a sense of grandiosity with magical ego ideals. The unrealistic, idealized concept of what one should be becomes such a gap to what anyone could possibly be that the low self-esteem is quite understandable. Instead of the ego ideal being a useful goal toward which one can aspire and strive, although never expect to actually reach, it becomes a liability that serves no useful purpose. Another important source of one's self-appraisal is connected with the reflected appraisal of those with whom one has had important significant relationships. This aspect of self-esteem was emphasized by Sullivan.

Generally, it is of little value for the staff to attempt to "pump up" the patient's esteem. Sometimes a student nurse beginning her psychiatric affiliation will get caught up in questions such as whether or not she should let the patient win in ping-pong. Any contrived efforts are quickly detected by the patient and are disrespectful in that they do not give him credit for the ability to withstand losing. A patient is apt to develop a sense of self-esteem more from encountering respect from those about him, together with actual accomplishment, especially when some of the more narcissistic, grandiose, ego ideal aspects are brought into awareness via psychotherapy.

The entire question becomes exceedingly complex when one must also consider the patient's anxiety over competitive strivings and other handicapping patterns of performance. As described earlier, an active work program was arranged for this patient in the hope that some of her aggression could be channeled in a constructive way. Doing a job well, doing a job that needs to be done, and doing something for someone else are essential elements of any task that will bolster the self-esteem of the patient. These are the reasons why artificially created "work" can be detrimental to the patient's self-esteem. One assignment given to this patient was that of reading to the geriatric patients on a regular basis. This particular task, although it did not relate directly to the dissipation of her physical energy, did function to bolster her self-esteem. One patient was passively drawn into a dramatic play being put on by the patients because he vacillated between fantasies of total failure and grandiosity in his expected goals for the performance. As it turned out, he did a reasonably competent job and the acting was a boost to his self-esteem. In this connection, it is worth mentioning that some schizophrenic patients have considerable difficulty in acting in plays. A patient described how he was having trouble getting another paranoid patient to take the role of the villain. The paranoid patient had protested loudly that he was no villain and they could not force him to be a villain. As this patient pointed out, the paranoid patient had trouble in his sense of identity in separating himself from the role that was expected of him. This same patient who was describing this then went on to say that he certainly was not going to accept the role of a clown in the play since he was a serious, purposeful person, and did not want to be thought of as a clown.

The sense of worthlessness can be used secondarily in a defensive way as a protection against failure. If one considers oneself to be worthless or to have little ability, then one does not enter the competition and therefore cannot fail. At the same time, the patient can harbor the feelings of grandiosity and preserve these intact, since they will not be exposed to the light of reality. Similarly, a sense of worthlessness is also protective against defeating others and feeling lonely. The patient described in this case presentation won most of the prizes, trophies, and medals at her junior high graduation. She felt that such triumph brought forth the envy of others and left her feeling lonely. The loneliness of the schizophrenic patient occupied much of the thinking of Dr. Fromm-Reichmann in her later years.[8] It was certainly a frequent aspect of this patient's experience. As she described it, "I feel as though I've been run through an automatic washer with a glass front and all this time people are writing notes and watching—and wondering—and they're about to do something—climb in with me or let me out but nobody would ever climb in with me."

MASOCHISM

Freud in "The Economic Problem in Masochism"[9] extended his remarks on the "negative therapeutic reaction" referred to in *The Ego and the Id*. He pointed out that the masochist seeks punishment although he or she is largely unconscious of this. Masochism, according to Freud, is a complex psychological phenomenon that includes a reactivation of the Oedipus complex.[10] This patient's masochistic behavior manifested itself in the transference when she provoked the therapist into attacking her. She was able to connect this with sexual wishes toward her father. Similarly, her selection of the "crummiest crumb" she could find for sexual intercourse showed a connection between the erotic component and the self-directed aggressive component in her sexuality. While Freud connected masochism with the death instinct—on theoretical grounds—it would be a mistake to think of masochism in the clinical situation as a static "biological" tendency toward self-destruction.[11] It would facilitate the patient's understanding to view such behavior in its multiple aspects.

Robert Waelder conceptualized the approach of viewing mental phenomena in their multiple functions:

. . . behavior served several functions, or, as one might also say, that it was at once responsive to many pressures, or was a solution at once for many tasks. If this was so—regularly, as the principle of multiple function claimed at the time, or, at least very frequently, as Freud had suggested, and as I, on second thought, would prefer to say—then it followed that reality-directed behavior can be expected to serve instinctual demands, too.[12]

The infliction of pain upon one's self may take a variety of forms, such as cutting—as with this patient—burning, scratching, starvation, gorging, freezing, dermatitis, and provoked assault. Such masochistic behavior can fulfill the following multiple functions at one and the same time:

1. A definition of ego boundaries—a way of feeling alive.
2. An expression of aggression—a discharge onto the self.
3. A curbing of outward aggression—toward self rather than outward.
4. Dependency gratification—an elicitation of concern and care.
5. Superego gratification—self-punishment to assuage guilt.
6. Negativism (already discussed).
7. An act of mastery—bringing about actively toward one's self what one fears passively.
8. Control of others—"manipulation."
9. Expression of the staff's unconscious hostility—masochism as a component of the other person's sadism.

DEPENDENCY

The term "dependency," as currently bandied about in psychiatric circles, often has the connotation of an epithet. Even among patients, one hears the concern that they might be "dependent" upon the hospital or become dependent upon the therapist. Actually, dependency is an essential aspect of every human being's development and, in fact, characterizes the human species in its lengthy duration compared to that of other animal species. The problem generally for the patient and others of us is not that we are dependent but how we gratify our dependent needs rather than be frustrated because of conflict over our dependent tendencies.

Since dependency is a universal human process, we would expect to find it operative in the staff as well as in the patients. In fact, it is conflict around dependency and especially the denial of dependency that often leads people to choose a career in the "helping" professions. Those who are busy helping others can easily ignore their own dependent longings and yet, at the same time, they need the patient as much as the patient needs them. Simple observation of the neophyte student nurse, whose dependency processes are accentuated in the strange situation of a psychiatric affiliation, will often find her trying to be busy helping others and yet not knowing how to be of help. Such students will often resort to the familiar role of bed-making or other general hospital procedures grafted on to the activities of a psychiatric ward because they can feel secure in this type of helpfulness. The same thing applies to doctors who first begin their residency training in psychiatry. Here, they find themselves in a totally alien situation and, since one of their security operations is to be in the role of doctor, they will become busy prescribing medications, giving advice, or trying to tell the patient what is wrong with him. Such "helping" activities interfere with the most appropriate function of active listening. We see a comparable situation on a medical or surgical service when the medical staff feel helpless in the face of a dying patient and then perform heroic measures in order to avoid or at least postpone their feeling of helplessness.

In the work with psychotic patients, there seems to be a phase of depression, helplessness, and despair that follows the yielding of the defensiveness, which has kept the patient from experiencing such feelings. As he improves, he will often experience a strong undertow of dependency with the fear of regression to what one patient termed "inert passivity." As the patient cries out for help, the therapist is apt to ask himself, "What can I do?" The most therapeutic thing at that point is to be able to acknowledge one's own helplessness. If the staff can simply respond by an admission of their own helplessness in the face of the patient's reaching out and have faith that both can come through together and find a way, the patient can identify with the staff member's confidence about the ultimate resolution of the predicament. The patient can then avoid resorting to primitive defense mechanisms of denial, anger, and projection, and gradually work through this bleak period of despair, helplessness, and uncertainty.

In a similar way, personnel become dependent on patients and feel reluctant to see them grow up, much as parents would be reluctant and ambivalent about seeing an adolescent child grow away from them and no longer need them. By allowing himself to have such feelings the staff member is more likely to prevent unconscious obstacles to change in the patient.

Dependency processes appear to be central to the problem of the so-called demanding patient. There always seem to be those patients who explicitly or implicitly present certain demands to the personnel and eventually get to be thought of as a nuisance. The staff may feel equally burdened and called upon to do something about a passive individual who makes no verbal demands but communicates his requests by way of helplessness. Demanding patients can be grouped under the four following categories:

1. The highly verbal, insisting, or clinging patient.
2. The patient who acts out in a passive, helpless way and expects to be taken care of.
3. The patient who acts out in an aggressive, antisocial way, requiring intervention.
4. The patient with predominantly paranoid interaction involving those in his environment.

Each of these types is expressing unfulfilled dependency needs and, at the same time, excluding the awareness of such needs from his conscious experience. It is the action expected on the part of the staff, experienced in a burdensome way, that leads these patients to be labeled as "demanding." The extremes of response vary from the attempt to anticipate every need of the patient and to gratify it even before the signal is given to the opposite of not giving at all and expecting the patient to do everything for himself. An acute sense of timing is necessary when deciding whether to do things for the patient or to expect him to do things for himself. This patient returned late one night after several hours of unauthorized leave. She was tired and dirty. When the nurse suggested she take a bath, she protested that she was too tired. The nurse, feeling that a warm bath would help her relax, offered to help her bathe. She got into the tub and allowed the nurse to wash her. The patient then went to bed and slept soundly. The important point in this example is that her need was being met. If the nurse bathed the patient because she had some need to have clean patients or it was hospital policy to bathe patients returning from AWOL, the procedure would have probably antagonized the patient. Because the nurse offered the bath to help the patient relax, it had a salutary effect. The difficult therapeutic task for the personnel is to be able to respond to reasonable requests without condemnation in order to avoid reinforcing the disapproval the patient already feels about such needs. Meanwhile, the therapist in the individual sessions attempts to explore with the patient what is happening in such interactions and helps him to become aware of the processes and work through them.

Dependencies are apt to be highlighted at any period of separation. Again returning to the example of the infant, we can see that after the period of six months when the youngster has a clear recognition of his mother, he will react quite specifically to her absence. Similarly, this patient had a marked reaction to the termination of the appointments during the early phases of treatment. At first, this was disguised by her hostile assaultiveness, with declarations that she never wanted to see the therapist again. The patient usually experiences such angry outbursts as being preferable to any simple admission of helplessness, humiliation, or loneliness. During this period, a member of the nursing staff was assigned to stay with the patient for a period of time following each psychotherapy session. This seemed to dilute her feelings of abandonment and reduced her destructive behavior.

Any move toward independence is apt to reactivate dependency needs. In fact, it is well for the therapist to predict to the patient that as he makes a step forward this is the very thing that is apt to reactivate earlier processes in response to such forward moves. An example is the patient who moves from inpatient to outpatient status or any other similar extension of responsibilities. In this case, the dependency needs and the communication for intervention were acted out in an antisocial way. Just prior to moving out, another patient signed a prescription for some barbiturates and presented this at the local drugstore. When the druggist telephoned the hospital for verification, the communicative link was completed, and, as a result, the patient's plans for moving out were canceled. When this sequence of events was pointed out by his therapist, the patient said, "Well, I had a feeling I was getting better too fast." From this incident, by frank discussion, the patient was made more aware of his dependency needs, which he was unable to voice openly and directly. One could easily conceive of the therapist reacting by blaming the patient because he was disappointed in him for signing the barbiturate prescription, but that would only drive the dependency aspects further back into unavailability. In this case, the therapist approached the acting out in a spirit of therapeutic objectivity rather than blame. With such an approach, he could encourage a direct form of communication in place of an acted-out form of communication.

Sullivan's conceptualization, which he called the malevolent transformation, is a frequent phenomenon with these patients.[13] Here, the patient, instead of being able to express his dependent needs for tenderness in a way of reaching out and gratifying them, will anticipate rebuff and rejection. Then, acting as though this has already happened, he will counterattack with criticism toward the person who would be providing the gratification. A familiar story used in this locale to illustrate this process is that of the man who develops a flat tire on the country road and finds that he has a spare tire but no jack in his car. Surveying the landscape, he sees a farmer's house across the field and heads toward the house to borrow a jack. As he proceeds, he wonders whether the farmer will be home but then is reassured when he sees a light in the house. As he goes on further he wonders whether the farmer will have a jack. As he gets closer he notices a car in the driveway and feels reassured that since he does have a car, he probably has a jack that he could borrow. As he approaches he wonders whether the jack will fit his car, and, as he is about to knock on the door he has the thought that maybe the farmer will not even lend him the jack. At that point, when the farmer opens the door in response to his knocking, the man yells out at the farmer, "Keep your damn jack!" The patient described in this case showed repeated evidence of the malevolent transformation. One clear example was when she felt the need of some degree of comforting when frightened by two aides escorting another patient to her appointment in a forceful manner. Instead of being able to reach out to the therapist, by the time she had crossed the room and had become physically near, she lashed out in a physical attack. Certainly, every appointment was terminated with a phenomenon classified under malevolent transformation during the early phases of this treatment.

There are certain practical matters to be kept in mind when dealing with the dependency aspects of the hospitalized patient. With the outpatient in private office practice, it is customary to expect that the patient will make his vacation coincide with that of the analyst in order to avoid missing any sessions. When such a model is transplanted to the hospitalized patient, this can have rather disastrous results. One might think it would be well for the patient planning any trips or absences from the hospital to have those coincide with the therapist's absence from the staff, but the contrary is true. The patient derives a sense of needed support knowing that his therapist is available should he have to return to the hospital quickly. This knowledge is often enough to enable him to remain away and successfully negotiate a trip outside. With the hospitalized patient, one can frequently see that the patient will often try to schedule trips away from the hospital just before the therapist is to leave on his vacation. This is almost always a clear denial of the patient's dependency. An attempt is made to bring about actively, by leaving, what he fears passively in being left. The hospital milieu is important in its own right as a contribution to the patient's treatment and a reason for the patient to remain while his therapist is away.

Families often play a complementary role to that of the patient in the denial of dependency. With their concerns that their relative will become "institutionalized," they will often make unfounded allegations of lack of financial support in order to speed up the patient's departure from the hospital. Such attempts often boomerang in that the patient feels very much unsupported, with a reactivation of his dependency needs stirring up regressive processes. This insures his remaining in the hospital longer than would have been necessary had adequate financial and emotional backing been given in the first place.

The infantile dependent strivings of these patients are probably the single most important reason why the staff finds it difficult to continue the work with the patient "over the long haul." Staff despair can result in arbitrary limits as to the length of treatment of a patient in that particular hospital; the use of more drastic measures such as medications, electro-convulsive therapy, or others; the turning away from this work into that which is less burdensome; or the rather complete withdrawal into inactivity of a therapeutic nature with the patient and the fantasied hoped-for miraculous cure through biochemistry, pharmacology, or other research.

POSTSCRIPT

The following information spans the six years following the double assault that terminated treatment with this therapist. Her treatment was taken up by another therapist who saw her while she was in a wet sheet pack or with an aide present in the room. There was a parallel increase of control on the part of the nursing staff. Staff and patients were more resistant to her "tyranny." Finally, eleven months after transfer to the new therapist—while he was on vacation—she ran away and eventually returned home to her family.

She was subsequently hospitalized in a state hospital, where she was given shock treatments. A social worker was quite helpful to her and their relationship continued on a social basis.

She wrote her first letter six years after the above described treatment was stopped or four years after discharge from the state hospital. She has a good relationship with her family and is working. Two quotations from this letter make it all seem worthwhile.

> I still have ups and downs and periods of panic and despondency but am much more able to cope realistically with them and try to be useful and healthy and realize that I'm not unique and the only person in the world who has problems.
>
> I hope you and your family are well Dr. Schulz. I've thought of you many times and have wanted to write to you but was too damn scared.

NOTES

1. Some of the ideas in this section of the discussion were previously presented in an unpublished paper. Clarence G. Schulz, "Negativism in the Psychoses," part of a Panel Discussion on "Negative Reactions," at the Washington Psychoanalytic Society, 1964.
2. Sigmund Freud, *The Ego and the Id* (London: Hogarth Press, 1957), pp. 71f.
3. Sigmund Freud, "Some Character-Types Met with in Psycho-Analytic Work" (1915), *Collected Papers* (London: Hogarth Press, 1925), IV, 323.
4. Edith Jacobson, "Contributions to the Metapsychology of Psychotic Identifications," *Journal of the American Psychoanalytic Association,* II (1954), 242.
5. *Ibid.,* p. 251.
6. Sigmund Freud, "Negation" (1925), *Collected Papers* (London: Hogarth Press, 1950), V, 185.
7. *Ibid.,* p. 185.
8. Frieda Fromm-Reichmann, "Loneliness," *Psychiatry,* XXII (1959), 1–15.
9. Sigmund Freud, "The Economic Problem in Masochism" (1924), *Collected Papers* (London: Hogarth Press 1924), II, 262.
10. *Ibid.,* p. 266.
11. *Ibid.,* p. 267.
12. Robert Waelder, *Basic Theory of Psychoanalysis* (New York: International Universities Press, 1960), p. 57.
13. Harry Stack Sullivan, *The Interpersonal Theory of Psychiatry* (New York: W. W. Norton & Co., Inc., 1953), pp. 213–216.

CHAPTER V

Treatment of a Chronic Paranoid Patient

CASE PRESENTATION

This patient was in his mid-forties when he was transferred from a state hospital for treatment that was to extend over almost a five-year period. He had been previously hospitalized continuously for four years at several state hospitals, during the course of which he received twenty electroshock treatments and showed only slight improvement.

The patient was a distinguished looking man, whose large frame and rather proud posture, combined with his fairly neat grooming, made him look outstanding. His manner was one of immediate gracious openness and expressed an attitude of courtesy, deference, and extrovertedness. In speaking with him, it was apparent that he had an excellent vocabulary in addition to a strong paranoid orientation, in which he felt abused. He connected this in some way to the FBI (Federal Bureau of Investigation).

He asked in what city was the hospital located? When I told him we were just ouside Washington, D.C., he replied incredulously, "Oh, no!" He said he was told that he was going to be near Baltimore. I explained that the airport handling his transcontinental flight was outside Baltimore and that is why he was told this. He dismissed my explanation by saying that he had been purposely confused by the people at the previous hospital.

When I indicated to him that I was to be his therapist, he said that he didn't understand what that was and added that he was one of a group of gifted children who had been studied by a psychologist. He went on to add that there was no such thing as mental illness, only criminality and insanity. He thought that he was neither a criminal nor insane.

The early period of psychotherapy focused on his history during which he made many parenthetical allusions to mysterious events. For example, in speaking of his parents, he referred to the "murder" of his mother. The patient came from a prominent family, who were successful in business. His mother's first marriage ended with the death of her husband. There was one son, the patient's half-brother, of whom he was rather fond. The patient divided his parents into two distinct categories. He felt opposed to his father, whom he thought of as being Swiss, British, Germanic, Protestant, capitalistic, a member of the Chamber of Commerce, and Republican-Conservative. By contrast, he was much more closely identified with his mother, whom he spoke of as being Spanish, religious, loving, tender, liberal, Mediterranean, and clearly compatible with his own ideology. (Later in his therapy this sharp split was important in understanding his divided attitudes toward the staff.) He had an older brother who was successful in the family business and a younger sister, who, at the time of his admission, was also in a hospital for a chronic psychiatric disorder. On two occasions during these early sessions, when he had been somewhat angry and annoyed with me, he would call attention to my scratching my head or folding my hands behind my head and say that these gestures were very much like those of his brother. He seemed to link his brother with his father in one category, and his mother, his half-brother, his sister, and himself in another. His tendency to generalize and dichotomize categories was prominent. For instance, when speaking of the geographical eastern part of the United States, he would often link this with something Communistic.

The patient dropped out of college the semester before he was to graduate. While at college he took an active part in dramatics. The exact circumstances of his departure from college are in doubt, and it is not clear whether he was actually asked to leave the campus because of homosexual activities. After leaving college, he entered the family business for a brief period of time, which was then followed by a period of interest in the legitimate theater and participation as an actor. He achieved some success in this and later went into the movies, where he had several bit parts. At the end of this period, which covered about ten years, he married and returned to the family business. Although he was creative and contributed his artistic talents to the business, he bickered almost constantly with his father and brother. There were two sons from his marriage, which after eight years ended in divorce, when the patient was around forty. The marriage was a stormy one, and the patient showed very little interest in his children. He had an artistic male friend with whom he spent considerable time and gradually drifted away from his family and home. His wife indicated that among their friends was one group that thought of him as being odd, without talent, erratic, and without potential; and another group who thought of him as being artistic, inventive, talented, and having a great deal of potential. Thus, people were divided in their view of him as well.

Following his divorce, he fell while skiing and fractured some vertebrae. At that time, he felt that certain rays were being put on him and there was considerable paranoid delusional content to his thinking. Two years later (about four years before the present episode of treatment) the patient went to the White House and explained that he had been to the FBI because he knew that the CIA had been putting beams on him while he was in Switzerland. He was described as being quite suspicious and incoherent at that time. It was his attempt to see the presidential assistant that led to his hospitalization and subsequent transfers over the following four years.

It is difficult to convey the extent of this man's grandiosity and complex language. Perhaps some samples from his voluminous outpouring of notes can serve as illustrations.

DR. SCHULTZ

I have been serious and critical. I have wanted to help you. Perhaps I have.

I do not know you well. But if you want to as a matter of interest, good, ask me a question, directly, that troubles you about yourself and work and or etc. this Friday.

Just a suggestion.

• • •

Society of Jesus

_____

_____

_____

DEAR FRIENDS

Yet again, and again, and again.

We must eleminate the Infalibility and "Centrality" positions of the Roman Catholic Pope. This is immediately necessary as inevitably and truely just, true, right etc. Without this neither Christ nor The Holy Gost exist, are, etc and even Buddha cannot exit.

To our survival—our "immediate" survival and adjustment to survival as opposed to Communism and Criminality we must rid of the Infalibility etc. positions. (Do not except Italy)

Shall we allow Roman Catholics in high (or any) political authority in this country under present existing R.C. conditions—we shall not, must not, may not, etc. Examine what is happening, does happen when as now "we do."

And most important—and of grief surely but not alone for you—examine and state most truthfully—then shall we be rid of this ugly division, problem, whether or not, and even if not how far so, we, the United States, and allies by intention and or times in history actually subverted the Roman Catholic Church (group) into this position of Infalibility.

You know of the World Revolution and its intentions and strengths and weaknesses, etc etc etc. You know of the conflict between England and Spain, etc. You know something of our own (U.S.) history of Communist Conquest—we can and "do" say "Communist" here to illustrate.

And see what all of this has done to us *The United States of America* so far (,) as in this Administration—Do you not see that.

Dear men and women also who are our, YOUR, friends I beg you with all my love and understanding clear up this matter.

Have you no respect for Art, Science, Education, and reform of the law in this country and for Peace? etc. Certainly you do but are with us difficultly caught—

By whom?

Share this letter then with our best Universities and Churches

And ask God in any and all of His Trinity to be fairly impatient and loving with us

As always

• • •

———— University

———————————

DEAR FACULTY—each one of you individually—and so you will consult together and with others specially in great University and educational and Church centers—but also regard the fact that you are naturally and rightly deeply concerned for the Negro peoples and for the life and vitality of the South—

Let me pose a *most important* matter to you—without its corrections, reform, there can be no real and democratic life in The South or anywhere else in The United States—or elsewhere (but do not be *so* hypocritical as to be unfair—:

Whites   Blacks

The Blancos, as also the Negroes?, are engaged in a great and sustained effort to deceive themselves, and those they oppose, most viciously, by suggestion as in acceptance that Art and Religion are not one and the same thing. This is obviously maintained in the personnel, abilities, "genius," of many of the Church groups—Churches.

ministers priests

religious

Please consider this very seriously, most intelligently, and discuss it with The Church, and Universities.

Now also let me add—

You must make us the center central structure theme of your education history—that is the history of the identity of art and religion.

Also as is much the same but not yet so adjusted to be the same—the history of the great *religious* cultural lines of mans development and the history of religious conflicts and groups in this country

Do not be so stupid as to judge the Artists and The Church and let everyone else escape your attention—of course

This letter is not intended to be an exact studied word for word statement of ultimate authority—But it is clear and truthful and of more importance I am sure than generally comes to the attention of our educators, authorities, etc etc.

Please be kind enough to copy and send this letter to at least several of our best Universities and Churches (Catholic specially) and to our best Episcopal (Catholic that is) Monastic Orders—

We, I am, are so very much indebted to them for their having brought us to this point of recognition and responsibility.

Cordially

Your name and address was courteously given me by a negro man with whom I spoke.

•   •   •

Dr. ———

There is one boy who plays in the playground and the lawn who uses an ———— gun and a bow and arrow.—Good boy. Conceited. An irresponsible player at ball and leader with bow and arrow games and talking to adults—Also insolent with gun. Average (average good) intelligence. Nice looking stage now. He needs not a spanking but a serious, I say sever, talking to to be serious for long cause ahead, and decent—

Small blond boy spoken of before is thinking—selfish, also but different type.

Nice boys—Please attend—(At least then I know you are doing something) I hope

I would not under these circumstances tell Dr. Schultz—

. . .

DR. SCHULTZ

It is true for us to say as this morning "There are certain things I do not see."

But in truth and in justice this is not and cannot must not be so. I think I understand these things pretty well. Also I am OK

And you? And everyone else?

Could we go shopping in Baltimore you and I? I wish we could take a couple of days. And lots of others things

But what I want is to get out of here.

(Judicial)

Yes that Law system reform is important and I am clear that it must be done in this administration. Think how many people are hurt by the position of hypocrasy we are in on the immediately present desegregation matter. And that kind of hurt hits deep into the body of our faithful people. And beyond that?

Here is where the two connect.

We are in a period of Catholic revival so why try to pretend, or correct backwards—as is all *too* easy. Prejudice simply does not want to allow for or understand this matter—and even pretends to be frightened and to suggest that we have to accept R. C. Papal positions to suggest or show our understanding good faith.

I (as example) do suffer from abuse laid on the R. C. (and related) group(s) as if in correction. Yet I have most importantly suggested here as well.

From the beginning, an unusual feature in the therapeutic relationship was the extent of physical contact that this patient sought. He would begin every appointment by shaking hands and often wanted to shake hands at the end of the session. Additionally, his outward composure was in contrast to his mixed-up thinking and it was very difficult to understand what he was trying to say. When he would contrast his mother and father in the stereotyped categories, it would all be mixed in with other fragmentary content. He suddenly asked, "You understand, don't you?" and I replied, "No, I don't understand." He seemed taken aback and said, "Oh, I'll have to hug you for that." He continued talking and then a few minutes later he came up and hugged me in a Spanish embrace. At another time, he came over and wrapped his arms around my legs and lay down on the floor near my chair. On one occasion in the early sessions, he said, "I love you," in a way that did not seem to fit in with the context of his confused production. He spoke of his dreams as being "induced." In a bizarre way, he also described impulses going down the nerves of the various parts of his body. What were undoubtedly hallucinatory experiences, he referred to as "pictures" at the previous hospital. These were fragments of views of his son's head and another that had something to do with "mother's murder." These things were described as something coming from without.

His immediate attachment to me seemed quite prominent. This was in direct contrast to his rather isolated relationships with other people in the hospital. He tended to have very little to do with the nursing personnel, and, consequently, their notes were quite empty and stereotyped.

Psychological tests done soon after admission were quite informative.

PSYCHOLOGICAL EXAMINATION

The patient was seen in my office about three weeks after his admission. Four lengthy sessions were needed to complete the minimal testing. The patient determinedly tried to prolong the contact and cling to an audience. He verbalized that he welcomed any opportunity to get away from being a patient on a ward for a little while.

The patient was always meticulously dressed. His manner, though sometimes bizarre, was courtly and dignified. He put serious effort into the tests, except for the tasks of figure-drawing and story-telling, which seemed to be beyond his powers. Here he turned his evasion of them into a joke, going through the motions in a somewhat mocking way.

Wechsler Adult Intelligence Scale

The patient scores in the average range of intelligence. His performance, especially in the verbal tasks, is really not even as good as this, however. Quite often he automatically came up with a conventional answer, but elaborated it in a way that revealed how empty of meaning or distorted it had become for him.

The patient's present level of functioning represents a drastic loss. Initially exceptional ability is attested to by some of his responses, as well as by the report that he was one of Terman's research group of gifted children. (The criterion for this group was something like an I.Q. over 180.)

Gaps in memory, loss of judgment and flexibility, and a severe inability to think in verbal generalizations appear. Personal meanings tend to flood in. This was most striking when he defined "domestic" as "pertaining to the home," lapsed into what looked like a petit mal attack, and then shook himself out of it with the comment, "Oh *yes,* the little house of God."

The patient's grandiosity works well on some tasks. Impersonal problem-solving tasks, which for other patients often arouse flurried self-doubting, he worked at systematically and successfully, though at too deliberate a pace. When he must accept defeat (as in simply not knowing the answer to a factual question), psychotic processes promptly take over. Clang associations, perseverations from the whole gamut of previous questions, a general loss of conceptual boundaries (even to the point of including objects in the room in his response), and delusional preoccupations then run rampant.

The patient has some ability to identify the points at which his thinking has become disordered. Sometimes in the testing he would laugh and comment, "I ran that into the ground, didn't I?"

	I.Q.		Weighted Score
Full Scale	104	Information	14
Verbal Scale	109	Comprehension	9
Performance Scale	96	Arithmetic	11
		Similarities	9
		Digit Span	10
		Vocabulary	14
		Digit Symbol	5
		Picture Completion	9
		Block Design	9
		Picture Arrangement	7
		Object Assembly	8

Projective Techniques
(RORSCHACH, FOUR-PICTURES TEST, FIGURE DRAWINGS)

The tests reflect a grossly psychotic paranoid schizophrenic state. The patient's responses range from realistic and conventional, to bizarre, to dilapidated and primitive.

The patient's first prompt reaction is to deal with a situation in a quite ordinary, lively, straightforward way. But he cannot allow himself to stop there. He pushes on into a razzle-dazzle of pseudo-intellectual, aesthetic, social, historical commentary, like a parody of a highbrow little quarterly.

The patient is still actively struggling to maintain some personality organization. Some overt anxiety appears. The patient tries to control his emotional reactions by transforming them into cosmic struggles between good and evil, beauty and ugliness, etc., but there is considerable potential for impulsive outburst.

Lonely, sad, defeated feelings show through this patient's grandiosity more plainly than one often sees them. The patient seems to really feel that his days of glory are in the past, perhaps in some past long before he was born, and that everything has been crumbling and downhill ever since. Some of his preoccupation with aesthetics and such seems to be almost consciously a mere vacuum-filler. A trace of defiant mockery also seems to appear in it, as if he were saying "If you don't care whether I make sense, I don't either."

The patient must have felt all his life that everyone expected him to be odd and incomprehensible, perhaps that some people even esteemed these qualities in him. He is a person who in any mental state would be highly dependent on external structure and controls. Some of the dilapidation he shows seems to be not so much an inevitable internal development as a reaction to long situational neglect, "humoring," etc.

The patient is still aware of strong needs for affection and closeness, although he does not expect them to be satisfied. He is alert and sensitive to what goes on in an interpersonal situation.

A primitive kind of sexuality preoccupies the patient. He obviously is identified with his mother, and seems to think of himself as someone half-way between man and woman.

PROGNOSIS:

Guarded.

A month after beginning treatment, it was necessary for me to be away for a period of two weeks. When I explained this to him, upon parting he pleadingly asked, "You will be back, won't you?"

His fragmented accounts contained a considerable amount of sexual content. His dreams especially involved all types of homosexual and "perverse" activities, which he did not accept at all as part of himself but as something that was induced in him. When asked about the various aspects of his sexual life, he indicated that he had had several homosexual experiences beginning with an older church employee, who had seduced him. He had also been arrested as an adult because of his homosexual activity.

Grandiose, delusional ideas began to emerge in which he thought he was an important person who had discovered "the fact and the only fact that has ever been discovered." This fact was that art and religion are the same, and he referred to it as "the identity of art and religion." The patient had many grandiose plans for various religious activities, the building of monasteries, the establishing of ecumenical congresses, a mass that would be performed with jazz, and so on. (Incidentally, all of these things were present in his thinking before any of them achieved national publicity, such as the ecumenical councils and the "Jazz Mass.")

From his history he reported an alleged episode that occurred when he was eight years old. During a discussion at the dinner table, he told his family that he was going to be an artist and not a businessman. With this announcement, he said that if he had a knife he would plunge it into his chest. He thought the family seemed worried about this, but nothing came of it.

When he received a birthday greeting from his sister, he showed me the card and at the same time was quite critical of her. He then said something about how he wanted to contact the FBI and the Secret Service. I took a firm stand and admonished him not to do this. I warned him that this was impractical and would only get him into trouble. I then said that it was nice of his sister to remember him on his birthday. With that, the patient began to cry but then quickly stopped and came out with a flood of accusations of how the Secret Service was organized with the Justice Department. Paranoid ideas appeared to be used to turn off his feelings.

For the most part, I attempted to listen and to grasp the trend of his thinking. Repeatedly, I attempted to break into his many references to national and international problems. I conjectured that he possibly paid attention to these things to exclude the more immediate, everyday matters. This intervention on my part seemed to coincide with a change from his loving and benevolent attitude toward me. At that phase there were only minor kinds of criticism of me. He said that I was more of a farmer than a psychologist, my office was shabby, I seemed to resemble some people from his past whom he disliked, and that I should belong to the American Medical Association, since they would probably control my behavior. I reacted to his criticism by accepting it. Occasionally I would refer back to it, quoting him to himself, to convey that it was all right for him to have these thoughts and to express them. My strategy was to see if he could tolerate hateful feelings toward me as well as all of the alleged loving attitudes.

Three months after beginning therapy, he entered the office in a somewhat jaunty and dramatic way and said, "I'm going to give you Hail Columbia." This was then followed by a very mild reproach about not getting him out of the hospital. On one occasion, he referred to having poisoned cigarettes and that he wouldn't smoke these. He left them on the desk in my office but then several hours later he returned, became very much in need of a cigarette and asked, "Are these poisoned?" I replied, "No, as far as I know they are not." With that, he smoked it. On another occasion, he said, "I don't want to hurt you. It would frighten me." This confirmed for me what I thought was his tremendous need to dissociate a great deal of anger. During these early months I felt extremely pessimistic about the patient and noticed that I had a "research" attitude toward him. I was fascinated by the depth of his psychotic illness. This attitude of mine gradually changed when I began to think of his paranoid grandiosity as a way of compensating for feelings of inferiority, inadequacy, and the lack of accomplishment in his life. My speculation was confirmed when he openly cried and spoke of how desperate his situation was regarding his future. He added, "I am not grieving." After he dried his tears, I said, "You have a lot to grieve about." He started to deny this, but reversed himself and admitted that he did have a lot to grieve about.

In a subsequent session, he talked at great length about several of his ancestors, which was confusing to me. As he pounded his chest he talked about his grandfather who had gone off to the Civil War, which personified a civil war going on inside of himself. I commented, "I guess you feel this deeply." Tearfully he replied, "I do." He straightened up, and his tears quickly ended. He then spoke about his ex-wife and suddenly said to me, "If you don't do something, I will kill you." I was startled by this, coming from a man who had presented himself as being affectionate and loving. I spontaneously blurted out "Who, me?" Pausing, he quietly said, "No, that was just an aside," and explained how good and sweet-tempered he was. After he said how he felt that we were getting nowhere, I said that I felt quite encouraged. He paused, shook hands with me, and said that he was glad that I was encouraged.

More and more, I began to see how this man felt threatened and frightened practically all of the time. He began to talk about it and pleaded for assurance "They won't hurt me? They won't put something in my medicine and give it to me?"

On a beautiful spring day, we decided to have one of our sessions outdoors. When we were trying to find a place to sit down, I suggested that we sit on a bench in the sun. He replied, "Oh, no, that would look too much as though we were in agreement with one another." He seemed to want to preserve an image that he did not like it here and that he did not like me. At the same time, he was openly expressing feelings of wanting to be with me and wishing to spend the entire day together rather than just a one-hour appointment.

After six months, the patient was still isolated from many of the other personnel. He refused to go to a picnic with the rest of the ward.

When I asked him about this, he said, "I'm better off seeing you than eating steaks," and added, "I want to apologize for telling everyone you're such a poor psychiatrist." Noteworthy at this time was the patient's ability to allow me to interrupt his voluble outpouring. He listened to a twenty-minute summary of my thoughts about his image of himself and how he tended to exclude angry feelings. I said that this was done by his focus on international affairs and the large-scale plans that he had for the world. It was rather impressive to me that he remained quiet long enough to allow me to continue.

During one of his early excursions outside of the hospital, he went on a shopping expedition in the company of two aides. He thoroughly embarrassed everyone by trying on women's sweaters and pinching the foam rubber model at the brassiere counter asking, "Don't you have anything softer?" After receiving the report from the aides, including their abrupt termination of the experience, I tried to talk with him about it. In a very moving way, he replied emphatically, "Dr. Schulz, do you think your strength goes out to me when I'm out there? It does not!" We then discussed how, when he was with me, he felt some degree of ease but it remained right within the office. Outside he felt threatened, frightened, and distrustful of the people in the stores. He was concerned that they would put electricity through his body. During one session, he made one of his most sustained expressions of anger. Among other things, he called me a sissy and a dirty fighter. At the end of the appointment, I rose from my chair and stretched. He backed away and pleaded, "Don't hit me," as though he really felt frightened.

A year after beginning treatment, he spoke of feeling murderous. He was afraid of people and of some power that would destroy him and reconstitute him as a criminal who would then commit murder. He assumed that this would be the work of the devil. He described how threatened and fragile he felt. It was like being a newborn infant, he said, who required a lot of attention and care, and whose life could be snuffed out by strangling, being smothered in a blanket, or by catching cold. During this period, he was still isolating himself from the others. He tended to be by himself at the recreational center, where he would occasionally make a few passing comments of an uncomplimentary nature toward others. He walked through the Occupational Therapy Shop, but there was very little participation on his part except for an occasional derogatory comment. He generally remained aloof from the clinical administrator except to inquire about

how he could leave the hospital. The nurses' notes would be as stereotyped and as brief as possible, usually limited to three lines. The night
shift said, "Slept well," the day shift, "Usual day," and the third line,
"On the unit."

Attempts on my part to make interpretations or to connect his past
with the present would usually evoke the response from him that this
was "a lot of psychological rot." While he could speak of negative
as well as positive feelings, he was unable to simultaneously sustain
such mixed feelings toward a particular person. For instance, he said
he hated his father and then sometime later would speak of how he
loved the man. I would try to bring out something further about his
feelings of hatred. He would completely deny this and say, "I didn't
say anything about that." It had eluded him completely and was no
longer available to recall. This was also characteristic of his occasional
tender feelings toward me. Moments later, these feelings would be
totally dissociated and out of awareness.

A second Rorschach Test was performed two years after the first
test.

COMPARISON OF RORSCHACHS

These tests show some definite change in this patient. The thinking seems
to be less fluid, less arbitrary. The gush of grandiose, exhibitionistic,
autistic associations that so permeated the first test is largely gone. Although psychotic thinking is still very obvious, the patient is more
actively critical of his own thinking processes and seems to be making
much more of an attempt to communicate meaningfully to another person.

The current Rorschach shows less evidence of a potential for explosive
outbursts. Instead there is a milder, more open and pervasive dissidence.
The patient compulsively retracts and reverses and re-reverses these negative expressions, until he finally has them wound in a cocoon of paradox;
one must infer that his fear of his own destructive power is still intense,
but his projections are on a less distant and huge screen now. Instead of
God or devil, beauty or ugliness, one ethnic strain or another, he concerns himself now with the more immediate question of whether he likes
it or not. To be sure, he shows the same dogmatic belief in the rightness
and importance of his judgment.

PROGNOSIS:

Despite the clear gains he has made, the prognosis still appears to be
guarded.

After approximately two-and-one-half years of treatment, I became
interested in what changes might occur in the patient with the use of

a tranquilizer such as trifluoperazine. In addition to the changes mentioned in the psychologicals, I summarized the following clinical changes in my notes prior to starting trifluoperazine. The patient had developed a strong attachment to me. He had also begun to show confidence in some of the personnel and was friendly toward one of my other patients. His communication with me had been marked by considerable confusion, grandiosity, and delusional content. A very gradual increase in my understanding of his expressions occurred. He developed an increased ability to express feelings to me, both positive and negative, together with rather vivid expressions of his considerable sadness. There was a corresponding opening up in his communication with some of the aides. However, large portions of the sessions were very difficult to follow. He was almost constantly threatened by feelings of danger. Almost any change in his situation, or routine, or alteration of the schedule of hours, led him to become frightened and to ask for reassurance. He described how a bird flew against the storm window of his room. He thought the bird was trying to get in to help him since he felt terribly threatened by the personnel, the ward situation, and the room in which he lived.

From my notes of an hour just prior to the giving of the medication, the patient had been talking about the British and the Caribbean, and so forth. I tried to interrupt some of these digressions, telling him that I felt we should concentrate more on his own history and his life, particularly around his high school years, and that he seemed to be avoiding this. In response he did not tell me anything more of his life history, but instead came forth with fantasies about destructive impulses that he had toward other people and specifically toward me. He spoke, for example, of how he could come across a body that was mutilated and cut up, and how he might find me in this condition. He also talked about how he could put a knife through me. Later during that session, he described how his father, whom he referred to as "a crazy man," might put a knife in his son's hand and cause him to stab someone. He continued to show some attempts to make physical contact with me. He embraced my knees as I crossed my legs and then talked about the great sadness in his heart. In looking at me, he said, "My eyes are brown. They're not blue. They're brown. Of course, they're blue." He then went over to the mirror, looked at himself almost as though he were looking at himself for the first time, and said how terrible he looked and began to straighten his hair and adjust his clothing. (The patient had blue eyes and the therapist's eyes were brown.) This behavior led me to ask who he was. He then talked about how he had fired his brother from the company and gave the story a reverse twist from what it was in reality. He described how he had been "all broken up" and that he came to Washington to try to become straightened out. He then referred to how broken up he was physically, and pulling up his shirt and sweater he showed me his torso—saying something that indicated to me he had become physically disintegrated.

At about this time, the patient developed an infection of his feet and had to remain on bed rest. I saw him in his room rather than in my office. During one interchange, he asked me not to take my eyes off his. He said that when I did this, it seemed to feel almost as though I had left him. As we began to talk about this, he laughed, picked up a blanket on the bed and hugged it, saying, "Oh, I have given this a very bad name. I call him 'Boston Blackie' but he is my friend." I distinctly got the impression that, if I left him or if he missed me, he could then always have his friend, the blanket. This reminded me of how earlier in the course of his treatment he wore an expensive sport coat every day until it finally was in tatters. He spoke of this coat as a person whom he wanted to nuzzle up to.

We started the trifluoperazine with two milligrams in the morning and two milligrams in the evening. He refused to take it from the nurse. I came over, and, although he was quite distrustful, he finally accepted the medicine from her. While I was there, he talked about how he had done something bad. Each time we started to get into this topic, he would switch off and talk about religious issues or something else. Whenever I tried to bring him back to it, he would say that it was just too bad to speak about. Several days on this dosage seemed to bring about little change. He was talkative, as always, with characteristic conflicting statements, one moment saying that he liked me and the other moment saying he disliked me.

He said that he wanted to love me, but was afraid that I would hate him in return. He said he was concerned about people doing things to him. He gave me a note that he spoke of as a warrant.

These people (make) (want) a wall of burned trash and, as my mother has said, to protect their callous criminality. Please take this to the U.S. Department of Justice and say that I wish, I ask, I demand, as is just and right, my immediate release from these institutions and their vile pretentiousness. As well, show this to the press (signed with his name).

During this session, as he was talking about existentialism, he commented, "I invented the silly stuff." On that occasion, as he was looking at my eyes very intently, he said that my eyes were part of his mother. The way I touched my neck was more like his brother. Other characteristics of my face seemed to be various people he had known in the past, and I got the impression that I was a composite of parts of several people. The nurses' notes at this time commented that the patient was a little bit more sociable with other patients than he had been formerly. When one of my other patients became upset and cut himself, this patient became quite concerned about him and stopped by to visit with him while he was in a cold wet sheet pack in his room. I gradually increased the dosage of medication to see what the effect would be.

On the eighth day following the beginning of medication I entered the patient's room and found him in the bathroom getting ready to shave. When I commented cheerfully on what a nice morning it was, he replied, "Glad to see you this morning." He said that he would be with me shortly. He commented how angry he was and that he shouldn't be angry. When he came into the room, he stretched out on the bed. In general, he seemed to be more quiet in his movements and more subdued. He moved around less, not getting up and down from the bed and not going in and out of the room as he had formerly. I tried to continue the conversation about his anger, but his only response was a vague reference to how terrible it would be for him to be angry at me, and that it might be harmful to me, but none of this was said clearly. He recalled spontaneously that I had recently been making efforts to talk about his past life, so he explained that he had had a sad life and began talking about the nurse who was not good to him as a child. He began to talk about his mother and his grandmother, and how the latter told him how terrible doctors were. She had also informed the children about the British control system. When I tried to make a connection between his present fear of doctors and what his grandmother had told him, he seemed to laugh and felt that there was no connection. In a somewhat fragmented way, he spoke of some events from his past life at school, particularly around the time he was in the fifth grade. At times he cried, especially when he talked about World War II. In his confusion he said that he really wasn't in the war but he was in it, and that all of this violence and destruction was a terrible thing. When I left at the end of the session, he asked me to be his friend until I saw him the next time. At this same time the internist commented that the patient was much more cooperative with the medical attention to his feet than on previous occasions.

On the eleventh day after beginning the trifluoperazine, at the opening of the session, the patient almost immediately commented that I probably wanted to know about the pills. He said that it was a little bit confusing, sometimes they bring him a white one and sometimes two blue ones. He described certain changes in what he spoke of as depth perception. He gave as an example the phenomenon of lying down and looking at his feet. His feet seemed to be further away than normally. He said that his tongue felt different and that his speech was a little bit thicker. He did not say this in any complaining or paranoid way, but more as a rather clear, matter-of-fact description. In a subsequent hour, he spoke of how, as he tried to walk, he felt as though the bones in his ankles were going to crumble under him. He then spoke about some "deadened sensation" at times in his sexual feelings. Afterward, he talked about his former wife. On this occasion, as he began to ramble, he asked, "What was I talking about?" This was quite unusual for him. It was as though he realized that he was straying off the topic and brought himself back to it. He said that he actually felt somewhat more frightened, that he distrusted people, and wanted to trust me but that he could not be sure of me.

Two weeks after beginning the medication, he recovered from his foot infection and came to my office. He noticed a small metal watering pitcher on the shelf in my office and commented on this again as he had in the past, thinking that he had given me this and that he got it from Guatemala. This time, however, he also expressed some uncertainty about these ideas. He listed some of his past accomplishments, things that he had actually accomplished in the family business, but then he went on to talk about various other delusional creations of his. When he spoke about the Catholic Congress, he said, "I seem to be somewhat uncertain about this, just as I am about that pitcher." This was a different approach to matters about which he had been quite firmly convinced in the past. Although the topics were similar, I found that his communication had altered in a way that allowed me to follow him a bit more clearly and to be able to dictate a longer note about him after the appointment. I found myself listening to him more, whereas in the past my attention might tend to drift. During an appointment, he talked about how his mother and father died at about the time his divorce and custody proceedings were in progress.

I tried to determine the exact sequence, thinking that there may have been a precipitating factor here. He then looked at the watering pitcher and said that in some ways it was like the pitcher. He tried to think, and he just couldn't get it clear, and he didn't know. He did think that if his mother had lived, neither he nor his brother would have gotten a divorce. After this, he lapsed into something about mental illness authorities, the Z people, and a quite involved paranoid system. The nurses' notes at that time described how the patient had become more openly angry toward patients and toward the personnel. I tried to take up some of these instances with him, but he seemed unable to discuss them except to complain about these people at length. He then alleged that when he was born, his father had to be restrained to keep him from coming in, taking the doctor's instruments, and killing the new baby. He was now receiving seven milligrams of trifluoperazine daily.

Five weeks after beginning the medication, he handed me a paper saying the whole thing was outlined as to what had happened to him.

Attempted murder, kidnapping—attempted forced sale or buying——— and ——— (family company name) by examples, family interests and U.S. interests. Other surrounding level of serious crime and accomplished blackmail and jest. And ——— (college name) rating ——— (his name) actual and natural interests.

During an appointment the following week, he gave a somewhat more coherently organized account of his life. He said his mother had chosen his name, and that his father was so much against it that he felt disgusted whenever he had to write the patient's name on a check. He then spoke some more about his father, but this soon became enmeshed in a paranoid delusional element about Murder, Inc. and the Justice Department. In the next appointment, he spoke of the argument he had with the hall administrator, and I remembered from the nurses' notes that the patient had been quite furious with him. The patient would alternately agree that he had been angry and at other times he would say that he had not been angry. On one occasion during the session, he admitted that at times he felt violent and had felt this way since his divorce. At times, he was quite confused when he misidentified the hall administrator with someone from his past life. I brought up the possibility that when he gets angry, people from his past seem to be part of his present, and that much of his misidentification was similar to the thoughts about my being connected with the watering pitcher. He seemed unsure of this and didn't pursue the idea.

More and more, events began to enter from his past history. He once introduced a topic by saying that at times he wondered whether he was bad or not and described as evidence a car accident he had had in college. He gave an unusually factual, clear account, in contrast to some of his previous reporting.

One day as I was walking with another doctor, the patient came up to us and volunteered that he wanted to tell me two things that he was able to remember. I wanted the other doctor to hear the patient's comments about the medication since we had been discussing this at a seminar. In response to my asking, he explained that it didn't make him feel well, he was against medicine, and somehow he thinks less of me if he is taking medicine, and then added, "Besides, that is off this other topic." He then returned to what he had been speaking about when he had first met us. This was an unusual amount of alertness on his part. He showed a degree of attention and organization about where I had changed the topic. He not only caught on to this but was able to return to the things that he wanted to talk about.

About eight weeks after starting the medication, he again went into a rather grandiose, delusional preoccupation. He also talked about how he felt when he experienced people leaving him. He demonstrated by gesturing as though he were suddenly breaking the cord to my telephone. He agreed that this was the way he felt when our sessions were over and said that it made him angry. Then, as we discussed these mixed feelings of grief and anger, he suggested that the word "anguish" would describe the experience.

The occupational therapist noticed quite a substantial change in the patient when he returned to the shop after his absence when he was confined to his room with the foot infection. This time, he was still critical of many things she did but he spent much more time talking about his children and his past and she thought that much more of what he said made sense to her. It was still quite delusional but in some ways easier for her to follow. The nurses' notes also indicated that the patient talked with a great deal of increased clarity.

Two months after starting medication, the patient left with a group of patients for a two-week vacation at a cottage. Just before leaving, he was very suspicious and wanted reassurance that he would not receive electroshock. This came at the time of my vacation and meant an interruption of about a month in the treatment. Meanwhile the occupational therapist commented on how the patient was making considerable change in his participation in activities with others. He joined in frankfurter roasts and other eating groups. When they had a Japanese party, the occupational therapist invited him to help make some bowls for the rice. At first he refused, but eventually he helped mold and fire the bowls. This was the beginning of a lengthy association between the two of them. He worked with her in artistic productions, especially ceramics. The patient was then on ten milligrams of trifluoperazine daily and various members of the staff made comments on the change in him. For instance, when I was a few minutes late to my appointment with him, he asked another doctor if he had seen me around. This doctor was quite impressed that the exchange was appropriate and relevant in contrast to previous conversations that were entirely unclear.

Four months after beginning the medication, I urged the patient to get a job in the hospital canteen. He was reluctant but said he would accept a job in the laundry. It turned out that there was no job available at that time. He then sent me a note:

Dr. Schulz, please try to be fair with me. My motor is going fifty or sixty miles an hour. These other people's are ten to twenty miles an hour. Naturally, I will get into a crash under such conditions. Please understand (and then signed his name).

This note was significantly different from those quoted previously. It more clearly described the frightening situation in which the patient found himself. He went on another shopping expedition with the aides to buy clothing, and was much more cooperative this time, showing good taste in his selection of clothing.

The patient was scheduled to have extensive dental work performed under general anesthesia. After receiving assurance that he would not be given shock treatment, he went through the procedure well, and expressed his surprise that it was all rather painless. He began to tell me some of his thoughts about me outside the sessions. He clearly described how he was afraid he might do something to hurt me or destroy me, and that I did not realize this. He thought that in my position I could not conceive of the damage that he might do to me. I tried to find out how he reacted to these thoughts and feelings. He said that he would dramatize it and proceeded to go to the couch, lie down prone on the couch, and embrace the pillow. He said that in this way he tried to get next to me. Then pointing to his chest as though I were part of his clothing, he put his chest up against the mattress of the couch and said that in this way he protects me and attempts to shield me. He then began to talk about his father and how he told his father that he was despicable. I attempted to bring some of these features together in terms of his anger and destructiveness toward his father and toward me. Soon after this, he began to cry and seemed unable to talk about his feelings toward me. He said it felt as though he were in front of a professor who says, "Yes, you do know the answer!" and yet the student is unable to give the answer. I concluded there was something that he knew he should tell me yet he was unable to. On leaving that session, he reminded himself of what day it was and commented, "Yes, it is Tuesday. I will see you tomorrow. Yes, I do miss you."

In an appointment almost three years after starting treatment, the patient described an experience that occurred at the time that his brother demanded that he leave the house and no longer live with him. Just after this the patient heard a voice that told him to go to an ice-cream parlor and do "terrible sexual things" to children. In describing it, the patient seemed much more willing to accept this as an experience of his, and did not speak of it as though it had been induced or had been done to him by some trick. He agreed, when I reflected how this must have been very difficult and very troubling to him. I thought that he was much more accepting of this kind of phenomenon within himself.

This patient became an outpatient four years after admission to the present treatment program. Except for a brief readmission, he remained an outpatient until treatment was discontinued when I left the hospital. The patient lived in several rooming houses and a halfway house. In many ways, he used the hospital in a manner that is now designated as "day patient." While living out, he went shopping, visited museums in an appropriate way, but also spent considerable time at the hospital talking to nurses, the clinical administrator, and various recreational people.

After becoming an outpatient, he began to give me more gifts. While some of the gift-giving seemed to express his feelings of affection, it also appeared to have a hostile component connected with it. For example, he would place a chocolate bar on the seat of my car in ninety-degree weather. At other times, he would place flowers in the car or he would tuck a twig under the windshield wiper. On a rainy day, this meant that I had to remove the twig in order to have the windshield wiper work effectively.

His life outside the hospital had an important reality confrontation aspect to it. There were certain experiences that assisted him in reality appraisal. For example, it had been mentioned that he had rather grandiose notions about ecumenical movements and bringing various religious groups together. On one occasion he attended the local church with his landlady. During the service, he watched what was going on and witnessed the baptism that had taken place. Afterwards, he commented, "The singing was wonderful but I'll *never* be able to change these people!" He thought that it was just impossible to do anything with them. In another situation related to his imperviousness to people's comments about his appearance, he was walking near the White House when he was confronted by two panhandlers who asked him for money. He reached into his pocket and finally came up with a fifty-cent piece, saying, "This is all I have. You two will have to split this." They stepped back, took a look at him, and said, "Well, fella, you're worse off than we are!" and returned the coin to him. On another occasion, reality came home to him at an employment agency when the woman told him that the first thing he would have to do was buy a white shirt, get a suit, and get a haircut before applying for a job.

While telling about his visit to a Japanese restaurant where he had drunk some saki, he spoke of his frequent visits there and said very poignantly, "You know, I've gotten to know those people. I have been there before. I am actually getting friends in town. I could send Christmas cards."

His attitude toward psychiatry and toward psychotherapy changed. When the patient described in Chapter VIII angrily stormed out of his hour before it was over and headed out toward the ballfield, this patient intercepted him. He asked, "Are you sure you told him everything? Why don't you go back there and really tell him what's on your mind? Go on back in!" With that, the other patient returned to continue his session.

He remained an outpatient for the terminal nine months of the present therapy. The brief readmission occurred when we became concerned about the possibility of his suicide. This was in the context of my approaching departure from the staff and his increased amount of depression and grief, culminating in a note to an FBI agent, saying he had to "get out of these places or commit suicide." An additional contribution to his instability was the troubled relationship with his landlady during that period. Upon my departure, he continued treatment with a new staff member.

DISCUSSION

SPLITS WITHIN THE TREATMENT TEAM

From the beginning, this patient looked upon the therapist as a predominantly "good" figure and the rest of the people in his environment as "bad." He tended to isolate himself from almost the entire staff with the exception of his ambivalently close relationship to the therapist. At first the ambivalence was not prominent, since the angry feelings came out in an episodic, dissociated way. In fact, it was characteristic of him that he seemed unable to hold mixed feelings for a sustained period of time toward any one person. This one-sidedness made it very difficult for the hall administrator and the nursing, recreational, and occupational therapy staff. If they attempted to force contact by keeping him on the ward, he seemed so miserable and resented it so much that it was difficult to maintain this position. If he was allowed to go off, he would get away from people, isolate himself, and give the personnel the feeling that they were rather futile in their efforts to influence him. We decided at that point that we would not push him, since his relationship to his therapist seemed solid enough. When he approached some children at a playground and the police were notified, there was considerable concern about him. For a while he was not allowed to leave the hospital unaccompanied. This, of course, forced contact and interaction with the ward staff, but there was no great change in his behavior. Most of the interaction was of a negative type in which he would complain and resist the approaches of the personnel. He looked upon his hall administrator as a person who opposed his leaving and therefore as a mean person. Once, when the administrator tried to explain why he had taken a certain position, the patient started to cry. Many of his letters were rambling and confused, and could not be sent through the mail to those other than his family. He had many odd requests and insisted on wearing certain clothing and a certain type of white sneakers. As with many of his ideas about society, his preference for turtle-neck shirts was years ahead of the times. His possible contacts with children gave the staff considerable concern, and he was also found peeping in the student nurses' residence. He flatly denied this and insisted that he had not done it, although it was quite clear that he was the person. We felt that, in general, his degree of self-sufficiency was a problem because he could isolate himself and be easily overlooked. If he had been less self-sufficient, he might then have been drawn into interaction with others.

With this patient it was relatively easy for the therapist and the remainder of the personnel to stay in contact with one another so that the split, as seen by the patient, did not become an actual split within the staff. There are patients, however, who seem to express their internal pathology through a division within the staff. Such patients seem to project their good and bad figures from the past onto the present environment. The staff who are the "favored ones" begin to feel that they have a special ability to understand the patient and those who are considered the "bad" figures will resent their fellow workers in the opposite camp. Harold Searles has pointed out how, with patients of this type, splits within the staff are to be expected.[1] He believed that the patient's ability to work out these internal oppositions would gradually lead to a unity within the staff. This approach is opposed to emphasizing an enforced "consistency" within the staff that would ignore the more subtle aspects of the reflection of the patient's pathology. The important thing is the maintaining of communication within the organization rather than trying to prescribe attitudes that will be identical. Sometimes these inconsistencies are a reflection of the parental inconsistencies, and, consequently, of the patient's own internalized inconsistencies. The patient seeks relief from the internalized inconsistencies by externalizing them onto the personnel and thereby ridding himself of the conflicts. This probably was most clearly described by the patient when he was able to recognize the "civil war" that was going on within him. Such splits were also reflective of this patient's view of his parents as being opposites; the father as the rigid, cold businessman and the mother as the loving, tender, Mediterranean type.

Stanton and Schwartz placed considerable emphasis on the covert disagreements occurring within the staff.[2] They saw the patient's symptom as being reflective of such covert disagreements. Consequently, when the disagreements were brought out into the open, the symptom often disappeared. We have found that sometimes the mere scheduling of a conference about a patient who seems to be creating considerable difficulty leads to a decrease in the symptom before the actual conference can take place. What probably happens in such instances is that the scheduling of the conference is likely to bring any covert disagreements out into the open. It is this recognition rather than the resolution of differences that leads to a decreased tension in the patient.

The problem involves the early recognition that something going on with the patient may be because of a covert disagreement. The therapist is at a particular disadvantage in this regard when he has a senior position within the hospital staff hierarchy. Lower echelon physicians and nurses are reluctant to express themselves about any differences that they might have with a senior doctor. This leads to a delay in the resolution of any split, and, more importantly, a delay in the recognition of the split. This is one of the "hazards" of a senior staff member treating patients, although we strongly advocate such a participant role by the entire senior staff.

Sometimes this patient manifested these oppositional tendencies by dealing with the same doctor in two opposite ways. For instance, when he met his hall administrator on the grounds, he talked in a friendly and charming manner. If he met him in his administrative capacity, he would regard him as a fool and a villain, and would not want to have anything to do with him. When seen by this same doctor in group therapy, the patient at first would not come into the room. He would sit in a chair just outside the door and call in various insulting remarks. He would speak of the administrator as a "fool" and a "slum boy," and would refer to the other patients in the group as "indolent bums." Little by little, he gradually came into the room, and over a period of a couple of months, he moved his chair from outside the doorway into the periphery of the room, and finally into the room where he took over the group. He would castigate each patient in turn, saying one was feebleminded and another one was to be exterminated. Immediately following the episode, he would wait by the car of the same doctor and want to be friends with him. If he was given a ride in the car, he would make complimentary remarks about it, and speak of his enjoyment of the ride. He became more and more friendly with this doctor, would tease him, and made him a present of one of the bowls he had created in occupational therapy.

The latter point incidentally raises a question about what to do concerning gifts offered by patients and perhaps even more frequently by their relatives. Generally, it is our position not to accept any expensive gifts from either party. If it is a small gift and especially if it is something made by the patient, it can be a very meaningful acceptance of the patient and a boost to his self-esteem for the staff to accept the gift with thanks. Actually, patients have very little opportunity to reciprocate with expressions of gratitude. While it is true the personnel, including the therapists, are being employed by the hospital and the patients contribute either through fees or through tax support of the institution, it makes it a more personal expression of thanks if they are able to make a gift of some small item that they themselves have created. If such a gift is included in the decorations of the doctor's office, the patient can leave with a feeling of considerable pride.

THE PARANOID MECHANISM

Freud, in his discussion of the Schreber autobiography, brought forth a formula for the explanation of paranoia that has remained the most frequent explanation in psychiatry for this phenomenon.[3] It was his thesis that the paranoid patient is unable to accept his own homo-sexuality, and, instead of being able to say, "I love him," he turns this into its opposite by saying "I do not love him, I hate him." Finding this unacceptable, he projects it onto the other person and says "He hates me." It is rather unusual for a paranoid patient to so openly acknowledge his homosexuality or at least his homoerotic feelings toward the therapist. This patient showed a peculiar mixture of paranoia in addition to the desire for physical intimacy. The poly-morphous character of his sexuality was contained in the denied perverse sexual content that was exemplified by his dreams. Toward the latter part of the course of treatment, the patient no longer vehemently denied these perverse aspects but acknowledged them more and admitted their presence in his earlier life. An example of this was when he told of a time that his brother asked that he leave the house and no longer live with him. The patient then heard a voice that told him to go to an ice-cream parlor and do "terrible sexual things" to children. In this instance he accepted this as part of him-self much more willingly, rather than as something induced from the outside. It is certainly characteristic of paranoid patients to use denial with projection to the outside as exemplified in Freud's formula.

An additional aspect of paranoia is the grandiosity that accompanies it. Such a patient sees himself as the most persecuted figure or as being special in some other particular way. It is rather important to make a distinction between paranoid symptoms and a diagnosis of paranoid schizophrenia. Many schizophrenics experience paranoid ideation without having fixed delusional formation with some degree of organization to the delusions. Dr. Dexter Bullard has pointed out

that the patient with a fixed paranoid delusion, such as with a paranoid schizophrenic, will find these delusions quite compatible and acceptable. The paranoid symptom by contrast, would be considered a
disturbing or frightening experience by another patient who was
not a paranoid schizophrenic.

There are some important techniques in dealing with such paranoid
delusions. Dr. Maxwell Boverman has pointed out the importance of
not going along with paranoid delusions by means of silence.[4] If the
delusion is not questioned or challenged in some way, the other person may be unwittingly giving tacit agreement to the delusion. This
approach can be compared to the more traditional recommendation
that one avoid using logic to argue a patient out of his delusion. The
caution being expressed in the latter approach is that delusions are not
amenable to factual argument or logic, and therefore this should not be
attempted. Boverman is not speaking against this approach. Rather,
he indicates that one should not really stand by idly as the patient
expresses his delusion, even though he would not want to try to alter
the delusion by lengthy logical explanations. For example, in the first
encounter with this patient, the therapist made it quite clear that the
patient's misunderstanding about not being near Baltimore was due
to the location of the airport handling his flight destination and *not*
any attempt on anyone's part to purposely mislead him. Another approach we have found is to state simply, "I do not agree with you."
To have said nothing would give tacit approval to the patient's
paranoid misinterpretation.

Another technique that we have found useful in dealing with the
patient's projection begins by accepting the projected part. For example, when this patient accused the therapist of being a coward, the
therapist was able to acknowledge that certainly it is not possible to
face everything bravely at all times. The therapist did not try to point
up that he must really be talking about himself and has to project it
onto others nor did he defend himself by saying how bravely he was
able to face up to him and his accusations. Instead, he tried to see
if he could find this experience within himself and somehow acknowledge it to the patient. Similarly, if a patient accuses the doctor of
being angry, one could simply acknowledge that this is a possibility.
First of all, these patients with their uncanny perceptiveness might be
correct that the doctor is angry at that moment, although he might not
realize it. Even if this were not so, the patient could surely see that
the doctor does experience anger at times. The importance of this

step is for the patient to see that the doctor or other staff member can accept such feelings and then for the patient to be able to identify with the doctor. Eventually, if he can identify with the other person, he will accept such feelings within himself and no longer have to deny and project them. The same would apply to members of the nursing staff. A relatively new member of the staff who is feeling inadequate anyway, can be made quite defensive by having a patient refer to him as an "idiot who poses as an aide." It is important that the staff member understand that the patient is projecting some of his feelings about himself. In this way the staff member can accept his behavior without feeling the need to retaliate.

Incidentally, one must be careful upon first hearing what is an "apparent" paranoid delusion and not take for granted that it is delusional. Occasionally, what had been thought of as a delusion turns out to be a reality. Although it initially sounded like a delusion of grandiosity, this patient was actually part of a study of gifted children. At times, patients have confessed to crimes they have actually committed, but these were presented in a way that misled people to think they were masochistically confessing to "delusions."

This patient's action of seeking physical contact was unusual for a paranoid patient. Often, such contact is terribly threatening until the patient has an awareness of his denied need for intimacy and dependency gratification. It did seem that this patient's separation anxiety exceeded his fear of intimacy. Upon experiencing some distance from his therapist, when the latter said he did not understand him, the patient felt he must embrace the therapist. When the patient was threatened by angry feelings toward his therapist, he would have to come over and touch him in order to reestablish the contact. For the patient, the physical contact was a more primitive continuity that most people experience in an abstract form. As this patient indicated, the therapist's strength did not go out from the office to him when he was in the store involved in the shopping debacle.

It is important to be alert to signs of improvement in these patients. Generally, one can regard it as a substantial gain when the patient shifts from a paranoid, schizoid position to a depressive position. According to Fairbairn's[5] theory, following that of Melanie Klein,[6] the person moves from a preambivalent position, where he must keep the good and bad people as separate objects, to an ambivalent attitude in which he can feel both good and bad attitudes toward the same object. When the patient moves up to ambivalence, he is capable of being depressed. Certainly, depression in a paranoid patient is not a reason to prescribe antidepressant medications, electroshock, or other attempts to terminate the depression. Most importantly, it indicates that the patient has a sufficiently organized ego to experience depression rather than deny, become fragmented, confused, or in a paranoid way project onto others. Another important indicator of change is the acceptance of aspects that were formerly projected. When the therapist talked with him about his contempt of others, the patient spoke of contempt for himself, "Not my life but of myself." Similarly, his acknowledgment of his own sexual inclinations toward children as being part of himself rather than coming from some outside influence was another indicator of change. In speaking of further acknowledgments along the line of sexual thoughts, he said, "we all have the devil in us." He spoke of himself as feeling both male and female, "I have breasts and they have milk in them, too." The change when he saw the therapist as a composite of several people rather than several separate people was an important indicator.

One important way to facilitate changes in their early stages is to prepare personnel for change in the patient. For example, the patient may be moving toward an increased expression of his anger, his depression, or increased activity. Sometimes these changes can be alarming to personnel who have developed certain stereotyped expectations from the patient. If they can understand the beneficial aspects of what appears to be troublesome behavior, they are more likely to welcome the change in their patients. Preparation for changes in the patient is also important to the patient's relatives. They will then welcome the new developments that otherwise might be greeted with alarm.

BENEVOLENT PARANOID DELUSIONS

Occasionally, we encounter a patient, who, in contrast to the patient reported here, is not suspicious and distrustful but has a delusional system characterized by the environment's benevolent attitude toward him. Such a patient has marked ideas of reference, but the content is one that emphasizes how everything is being done to be of assistance to him. Often, he believes the entire hospital and all the people in it will have been specially placed there for his benefit. Even the doctor's shortcomings, such as forgetting things or arriving late for appointments, are all "explained" as attempts to help the patient in some way. The self-centeredness and grandiosity in such patients is obvious. The main difference seems to be the absence of the projection of hate.

We have not had the opportunity to study these patients in treatment for a sufficiently long period of time to come to any certainty about the mechanisms involved. We have, however, some speculations about the dynamics involved. First of all, these patients seem to be so threatened by the possible malignant features in their object world that they must endow them with "good" qualities and thereby make up for a lack of object constancy. We have thought of this process as being parallel to that of the manic-depressive patient in the manic phase where the depression must be totally denied. To continue the analogy, the paranoid patient would have to deny the "negative" aspects of the object. Similarly, a sign of improvement in such a patient would be the development of hateful projections onto objects just as the sign of improvement in the manic-depressive would be the appearance of some depression within awareness.

PATIENT'S FEELING OF HELPLESSNESS

This patient rather eloquently described his feelings of helplessness when he compared himself to an infant. When he advocated that the therapist be controlled by the American Medical Association, he sought reassurance that there would be control over the object toward whom he felt considerable fear.

Patients will often attempt to deny feelings of helplessness because they have considerable conflict over seeking assistance or they have considerable despair over the possibility of deriving help. As one can imagine, this conflict about helplessness can be manifested in many ways. Sometimes patients will miss their appointments because the therapist schedules them at his convenience. The patient feels at the beck and call of the doctor and is unable to do anything about this. Especially if the doctor is rescheduling an appointment, the patient does not want to feel that he is passively acquiescing. Dr. Fromm-Reichmann advised that if one has the option in rescheduling, the appointment should be scheduled earlier than the original appointment rather than later. Patients are able to accept the former more readily. This, of course, applies only to the patient with the marginal ego rather than to the neurotic patient.

Another manifestation of the patient's feeling of helplessness is his attempt to bind or control the therapist in various ways. In the hospital, this sometimes comes about by trying to obtain a promise that the therapist will not act on certain information disclosed by the patient. The therapist feels that if he "betrays" the patient's "confidence," the patient will never tell him anything in therapy again. In a similar way, patients will try to extract a promise from the nurse that she will not chart what they are going to tell her. Rather than view such behavior as a conscious "manipulation" on the part of the patient, it might best be thought of as a way of maintaining some control and thus avoiding the feeling of helplessness. The many ways in which patients convey that they do not "need" the therapist can be a manifestation of conflict over helplessness. This conflict usually manifests itself as an active approach to something that they fear might happen to them passively. For instance, when the therapist is about to leave for a holiday or vacation, the patient may cancel the preceding appointment, attempt to move out of the hospital or go on vacation before the therapist.

This patient showed many reactions that were prompted by his separation anxiety. Already mentioned were his wanting to embrace the therapist when the latter said that he did not understand him, and his indication that the therapist's strength did not go beyond the sessions. Additional examples were his wish that the therapist not take his eyes off of him and his use of a blanket for security.

Since anger is a more acceptable feeling in our culture than helplessness, it is often used to mask feelings of helplessness. There can be something ominous and frightening about the intensity of anger that can be viewed in the eyes of a paranoid patient. This patient was a rather large man, which compounded the discomfort in the presence of his anger. We have felt no less uncomfortable in the presence of paranoid patients who were physically smaller. The misguided notion that members of the staff sometimes have that they must not let the patient know they are afraid does a disservice to both. It deprives the patient of honest feedback, and usually results in minimizing the contact that staff has with the patient, which permits the patient to perpetuate his isolation. Such isolation increases the feelings of helplessness. Other patients, similarly, find themselves frightened of these paranoid patients. In our culture it is often difficult for men—patients and nursing personnel—to acknowledge that they are afraid. Ward meetings, sometimes initially without the paranoid patient present, can be used to bring this fear into the open for discussion. The support the group can give one another helps to reduce the intensity of the fear. We also feel that an open acknowledgment to the patient of the frightening feelings he engenders can be useful. It clears the air for both parties. If the contact with the nurse is important enough to the patient, he may be able to handle his helplessness in some other way. If the patient remains angry after this type of confrontation, the staff member may at that moment have to back away to an appropriate distance.

There are many things inherent in hospital life that both foster the patient's helplessness and counteract it. The nursing approach must be careful not to promote helplessness. Even the extremely helpless, confused patient has to have whatever degree of autonomy that he can muster acknowledged and supported. One does this frequently with very small children. For instance, in giving a youngster a bath, the mother might prepare the tub and even put the soap on the washcloth but then encourage the child to use the washcloth. Patients who require considerable physical care in a general hospital are asked to assist to the extent that they are able even if this assistance is only slight. There are many opportunities in every hospital to promote self-help in the patient. The hospital work program is an important force in counteracting the patient's feelings of helplessness and inactivity. Occupational therapy is an important outlet for a patient's creativity and accomplishment. This patient's making of the artistic bowls for the Japanese party was a valuable contribution.

TRANQUILIZERS

The timing of the use of tranquilizers is an important consideration. Generally, we attempt all nonpharmacological aspects of the treatment program before we utilize tranquilizers. If, after extensive approach with other methods, we find that the patient is harming himself and becoming physically exhausted through his disturbance, in addition to making life impossible for other patients or the personnel on the ward, we then administer tranquilizing medications. The personnel's feeling of getting beyond endurance is an important consideration for everyone in the hospital. It has been noted at times that when tranquilizers are ordered after the nurses "have had it," the patient sometimes improves before the first dose is given. It appears that the proposed relief being within sight is enough to ease the tension of the personnel and reflects itself in some change by the patient.

We were interested in approaching this patient by giving the minimum amount of tranquilizers to produce change rather than the

maximum dose that could be tolerated. Following the recommendations of Dr. Berl Mendel, we generally feel that the minimum amount
that can produce some reorganization is not likely to bring about
blunting of affects that large doses seem to produce. With this patient,
the changes were clearly documented and reflected themselves in the
ability of the patient to communicate more coherently and to organize
his train of thought. Even when he was distracted, he first noticed his
distraction and then went back and picked up the point. He rarely did
this prior to receiving tranquilizers. A change in the content of his
written notes is apparent as given in the case presentation. The change
reflected in the psychological tests was accelerated with the addition
of the tranquilizers.

CHANGES IN THE THERAPIST'S VIEW
OF THE PATIENT

A review of the therapist's feelings about the patient during the
period of over four years of working with him reflected a considerable
change. Initially, this patient was thought of as part of a research
project in which the therapist was given a dictaphone with an un-
limited number of discs to describe notes on the sessions with the
patient. Here was a hopeless person who seemed to have a fascinating
research potential.

When the therapist became more emotionally involved, he forgot
about the research, almost stopped dictating notes for a while, and
found himself responding to him much more as a person. The therapist
had much more empathy about his situation, the starkness of his life,
and the lack of people in it who were interested in him.

The initial "research" attitude corresponded to Searles' initial "out-
of-contact" phase.[7] The second, "involved" phase was equivalent to
his "symbiotic" phase. Gradually the treatment moved on to his phase
of "resolution of the symbiosis." During this period, while continuing
to be empathic the therapist became more aware of the extent to
which the patient himself brought on much of his plight. The patient
was viewed as continuing a variety of mechanisms to keep people
away from him. The therapist began to point out *how* he was doing
this in his current interactions rather than focusing on *why* (historically-
genetically) this all came about. As the differentiation process proceeded, the therapist stopped being "permissive" and imposed some
strict limits on the barrage of talk, the amount of body contact that the
patient desired, and was generally more disengaged from the patient.

THEORETICAL CONCEPTUALIZATION
OF CHANGE IN THE PATIENT

Edith Jacobson's concepts of "self-representation" and "object-representation" are useful in thinking about this patient.[8] Her concepts would have parallels in Sullivan's terminology of the "good" and "bad" *mother* being equivalent to object-representations and the "good" and "bad" *me* being equivalent to self-representations in the early part of a child's experience.[9] Jacobson thought that in schizophrenia the self-representations and object-representations tended to be rather blurred and became fused and confused in contrast to the normal healthy person where there was greater stability and consequently, separation of object and self-representations.[10] Within the normal person, they may be subject to change and reevaluation but would not undergo the considerable distortion that occurs in the schizophrenic. With this patient, we thought that his psychopathology was mainly concerned with the defense mechanisms of denial and projection, particularly of his anger and violence. This man seemed to have very little concept of his violence and destructiveness, and mostly projected these onto others. He then felt terribly threatened by these objects now distorted by violence and anger. The task here was to get him to accept some of this within himself so that he could tolerate awareness of his own violence, his destructiveness, and his anger. This would have priority over trying to ascertain the historical genetic roots of the violent identifications with his father, for example.

The patient related an incident in which the church sexton had apparently seduced him when he was a youngster. At that time, the sexton threatened him with sending him to Alcatraz if he ever told on him. The patient thought of this as a very bad act and was very wrought up about this man and often referred to it. He would then often complain about men whom he said had some sexual interest in children. At the same time, it was reported while he was hospitalized that he had invited a child from the playground to take a walk with him in the woods or have some candy with him. As outlined in the case presentation, after the patient was on tranquilizing medication, he described how, after a disagreement with his brother, he had heard a voice that told him to go to the ice-cream parlor and have sex with children. In this instance, he was half-way admitting that this was something within himself. Although it was experienced as a voice from outside of himself, he was at least bringing it closer to acknowledgment that this was within him. About six months following his description of this incident, he presented additional history. He described a time when he actually did lure a juvenile into his car for sexual purposes and how ashamed he felt about this. Clearly, this was admitting this aspect of himself. A similar shift in the projective mechanism occurred in his homosexual wishes. He had complained that men would scratch themselves in their genital region as a come-on and invitation to him. He thought of this as a "smutty gesture" and he became very angry at men who would do this. At the same time, he himself was walking around wearing tight trousers which revealed the outline of his genitals. Sometime later, he said that the therapist would look at his crotch but would never put his hand down there nor did the therapist embrace him. He felt disappointed that he and the doctor could not have this kind of sexual contact. Here, again, was a clear acknowledgment of such desires on his part.

From the standpoint of Jacobson's theory of self-representations and object-representations, it is important to see that denial and the projective mechanisms facilitate fusion and instability of the self and object representations.[11] On the other hand, integration of these split-off aspects of the self facilitates more stable self-representations and differentiation from the object-representations. Such stability of object-representations contribute directly to the sense of object constancy which this patient lacked when he said, "Dr. Schulz, do you think your strength goes out to me when I'm out there? It does not!"

POSTSCRIPT

During the four years following the previously reported account of treatment, the patient has continued with the same therapist. He has lived out of the hospital and, on one occasion, made an unsuccessful attempt to seek his release through legal channels. He continues to be a deeply psychotic man, and, from present appearances, there is very little indication of any potential rehabilitation.

NOTES

1. Harold Searles, "Integration and Differentiation in Schizophrenia; An Over-all View" (1959), in *Collected Papers on Schizophrenia and Related Subjects* (London: Hogarth Press, 1965), pp. 329–338.

2. Alfred Stanton and Morris Schwartz, *The Mental Hospital* (New York: Basic Books, 1954), p. 345.

3. Sigmund Freud, "Psycho-analytic Notes upon an Autobiographical Account of a Case of Paranoia (Dementia Paranoides)" (1911), *Collected Papers* (London: Hogarth Press, 1925), III, 448f.

4. Maxwell Boverman, "Some Notes on the Psychotherapy of Delusional Patients," *Psychiatry*, XVI (1953), 139–151.

5. W. Ronald D. Fairbairn, "A Revised Psychopathology of the Psychoses and Psychoneuroses" (1941), in *Psychoanalytic Studies of the Personality* (London: Tavistock Publications, 1952), pp. 49–58.

6. Melanie Klein, "A Contribution to the Psychogenesis of Manic-Depressive States" (1934), in *Contributions to Psycho-analysis* (London: Hogarth Press, 1950), pp. 308f.

7. Harold F. Searles, "Phases of Patient-Therapist Interaction in the Psychotherapy of Chronic Schizophrenia," *British Journal of Medical Psychology*, XXXIV (1961), 170ff.

8. Edith Jacobson, "Contribution to the Metapsychology of Psychotic Identifications," *Journal of the American Psychoanalytic Association*, II (1954), 241.

9. Harry Stack Sullivan, *Conceptions of Modern Psychiatry* (Washington, D.C.: William Alanson White Foundation, 1940), p. 38.

10. Jacobson, *op. cit.*, p. 255

11. *Ibid.*, p. 241.

CHAPTER VI

Rapid Remission in a Schizophrenic Adolescent[1]

CASE PRESENTATION

I was called to see this eighteen-year-old youth on Sunday because he had been admitted to the hospital two days previously and was persistently requesting a doctor. When I arrived at the nurse's office, she told me that the patient had been scrubbing the walls of his room.

The patient was a fairly tall, medium-weight adolescent with a very short crew cut. He spoke with pressure, and it was immediately apparent that he was distressed, frightened, confused, and burdened by guilt. He recognized his confusion and his memory difficulty. He was not sure what school he had been attending. I later learned that he thought that I was a former teacher who was scheduled to visit him that afternoon. A paranoid orientation was apparent in his questions about people listening in, altering his books, talking about him, and locking the doors. However, he was uncertain about the validity of these paranoid explanations. Such uncertainty was a hopeful note. He described his thoughts as flooding in on him so that he was unable to read. There were hallucinations of voices telling him things that had happened in his past—forgotten memories, and statements he had made. He was particularly preoccupied with changing his handedness because he thought he had the sexes inverted by being interested in men rather than women. Nocturnal emissions also bothered him. He showed me a note telling of his wish at age five to marry his mother if his father died. Upon questioning, he gave general information about his family, which consisted of his mother, father, and two sisters who were several years his senior. Both sisters were married and lived away from home.

After forty minutes elapsed in this initial interview, I asked him if he had any questions about me or the hospital. He surprised me by asking, "Yes, Sir. Who am I?" I told him we would be trying to find out who he was. He asked, "How?" I said that I guessed he was uncertain about himself and all of these thoughts and feelings. We would talk together about these things and try to understand what had happened to him. He was agreeable to this but wanted to leave as soon as possible, by fall at the latest, in order to attend college in another city.

In the second and third interviews the patient was able to provide more history, including the onset of the present illness. Three weeks before his admission he had a week-long recurrence of chronic bronchitis. At the end of that week, his father had to leave the country on business, and, as was his custom, he told the boy to look after his mother. During the second week prior to his hospitalization, the patient, who was an excellent student, fell behind in preparation for an oral report. On the following Saturday, one week before admission, he began to feel bothered but didn't know what it was about. On Sunday he made an appointment with his headmaster but could tell him nothing. The headmaster contacted the patient's mother and suggested that he see a psychiatrist. His mother wanted him to be seen by his allergist because he had been taking antibiotics for bronchitis all winter. The allergist suggested an internist with a background in psychiatry. The internist, Dr. X, saw the patient Sunday evening, one week before our initial interview, and suggested he read, relax, and watch television. The patient was unable to read, disliked television, and couldn't relax. On Monday he remained away from school and saw Dr. X. Upon the latter's advice he went to a movie that evening. The movie, entitled "My Uncle," was a Jacques Tati comedy that involved a little boy. The patient did not think the film funny and found himself identifying with the little boy who was lonely. He thought that in some way the movie made reference to him. Upon leaving the movie, he thought that he saw someone familiar walking ahead so he caught up with this person and found it was Dr. X, who was out taking a walk. This seemed to the patient to be more than mere coincidence.

The next day he felt quite depressed. That evening when his mother was in the garden, he went to her, and, sensing something was wrong, she asked if he wanted to "blow up" at her. He felt like doing just that but couldn't. He then thought of a scene in George Bernard Shaw's *Antony and Cleopatra* in which a soldier kills a woman at the altar. He became very frightened and thought that he might do this to his mother. He told her he needed a psychiatrist. She called Dr. X who had him admitted to the psychiatric unit of a general hospital, where he received tranquilizers. His grossly psychotic state did not improve, and three days later he was transferred to this treatment program. While he was in the previous hospital, a maintenance man removed the filter from the air conditioner and tapped the dust into a wastebasket. The patient thought this was an attempt to stir up pollen and aggravate his allergic bronchitis. His attempt to scrub the walls soon after his admission was an effort to remove pollen and dust that he felt threatened him. In a similar way, upon his admission he believed that he'd been doped and this undoubtedly was connected with tranquilizers. Subsequently I learned from his comments about his books being altered that he actually did have a prayer book that was altered in the process of being rebound. Some of the pages had been put in upside down and others were left out.

The week following his admission, during which the patient was off all tranquilizers, he cleared rapidly. When he appeared for his appointment, he looked almost like a different person and was obviously improved. He had gone on a beach picnic with his unit and had enjoyed himself. He announced that he was back to his old self again, felt as well as he ever had, and thought that the hospital was a wonderful place. However, he did not want to stay here and especially wanted to go on to his college.

Psychological tests were performed as soon as the patient was able to participate in the testing.

PSYCHOLOGICAL REPORT

The patient was seen in my office one week after his admission to this hospital, and a day or two after his sudden clinical improvement. He was pleasant, talked readily about himself, and approached the tests with energy and confidence.

Wechsler Adult Intelligence Scale

The patient functions in the very superior range. He is keenly motivated to do brilliantly, and he obviously has benefited from an excellent classical education and a rich cultural environment. His talents are better developed in bookish areas than in grasp of everyday events (for instance, when asked Washington's birthday, he blandly says "don't know").

His performance shows some obvious ego weakness and disturbance at present. Obsessiveness, impulsive errors (sometimes retracted), and small defects in logical thinking and judgment appear whenever questions relate in some way to authority, morality, anger, or sex. A not quite buried preoccupation with amputation and self-destruction is hinted at. The greatest failure occurred when the patient was unable to put together a simple puzzle of a hand, despite recognizing what it was and trying to use one of his own hands as a model; afterwards, he decided that he had been using the "wrong one" (handedness having been a delusional symbol for him).

	I.Q.		Weighted Score
Full Scale	131	Information	15
Verbal Scale	134	Comprehension	15
Performance Scale	122	Arithmetic	12
		Similarities	16
		Digit Span	16
		Vocabulary	18
		Digit Symbol	10
		Picture Completion	13
		Block Design	17
		Picture Arrangement	16
		Object Assembly	10

Projective Techniques
(RORSCHACH, FIGURE DRAWINGS)

The tests are consistent with the clinical picture of an acute schizophrenic episode in partial remission.

The Rorschach reflects youthful energy, impulsivity, much open anger, heavy use of denial and intellectualization, and still quite shaky ego controls.

The long-term personality pattern appears to be more hysterical than schizoid. Morality, gentlemanliness, and aesthetic appreciation are the touchstones. Women are seen as seductive. Male sexuality is associated with cruelty and pain, though he sees himself clearly enough as a man.

Paranoid elements are apparently concerned with something else than anger. Anger itself comes out in fairly "healthy" head-on clashes, although this is the only kind of relationship he sees between people. But there is also in the Rorschach the eeriness of things silently watching or looming over the patient, Dracula, an empty executioner's hood, etc.

The patient is not clear about what comes from him and what comes from outside. He may leap to an unwarranted conclusion, or unnecessarily deprecate an inference quite adequately supported by external data. He can recognize the inadequacy or oddity of an idea, without recognizing that he is responsible for it and can do something to improve it. He has trouble abstracting single elements from a total context and dealing simply with them, nor does he organize creatively at a level commensurate with his intellectual ability.

With so much explosive potential and such a narrow range of feeling and action acceptable to him, the patient obviously needs continuing psychotherapy to avoid future psychotic episodes. There is no indication that a college environment per se will be more stressful for him than any other outpatient environment he might be in, however.

PROGNOSIS:

Good.

Additional biographical background was contributed by both the patient and his mother. His parents were socially and economically from the upper class. His father, who had a brilliant college record, became a successful executive in a large organization. Because of the international scope of his work, it was necessary for the family to make frequent moves to foreign countries. One of the patient's predominant memories is of packing crates. His father would often precede the rest of the family to a new assignment. This, together with the sisters being older and attending boarding schools, meant that the patient spent a great deal of his early life with his mother. She was a person who was always interested in her husband's career and did a great deal to adjust herself to the inevitable disruptions in the family's life. For example, when the patient became psychotic, she did not contact her husband, who was out of the country at the time, because it would interfere with his work. One of the sisters had a nervous breakdown during college but went on to complete college while in psychotherapy.

His schooling in the early years was frequently interrupted by the geographical shifts. He had suffered from a chronic, recurring, allergic bronchitis. Consequently, there were brief changes in location within a particular geographical assignment in an attempt to obtain a more suitable climate for him. In the fourth grade he entered a private, church-affiliated school. He remained in this school until the onset of his psychosis at the end of the twelfth grade—except for the seventh grade, which he spent in a foreign school. One prominent disagreement occurred when his father attempted to persuade the patient to change to his own prep school and then go on to his college.

In his contacts with other children, the patient always tended to avoid fights. At times he would become furious and lose control, which usually stopped the other person's teasing and picking on him. When the patient went to summer camp, his counselor told his parents that he got along better with adults than with boys his own age. He developed some friendships with the boys at his school. When at age sixteen, the patient began to consider a career as a minister, he initiated a practice of going to daily, early morning chapel with some of these friends.

His sexual life was limited to masturbation and fantasies. When he was invited to participate in homosexual play by another boy, the patient refused. When he was about eleven or twelve years old, he had intense heterosexual fantasies, but decided these were bad and put them out of his mind. This was followed by nocturnal emissions. He had done some dating, but never developed an attachment to any particular girl. He was interested in astronomy, but was bothered about his frequent tendency to use his telescope to look into the windows of girls in order to observe them undressing.

He enjoyed swimming but was not much interested in athletics. Scholastically he was always at the top of his class and showed a wide range of interests and curiosity about his studies.

His interest in religion far exceeded that of others in the family. At school he had many discussions about religion with his teachers and classmates. He participated in church services and confession. During recent months he began to question whether he was a genuinely religious person or whether he was attending church because he liked his friends who attended. He recently became concerned that he was losing his friendship with a classmate who was becoming closer to another classmate.

The therapy lasted for three-and-one-half months. He was seen four hours weekly and had a three-week vacation in the middle of this period. At the end he left for college with a plan for continuing therapy in the new location.

Following the acute psychotic phase he wished to leave but expressed a willingness to continue therapy if we recommended it. He made it clear that psychotherapy would not be the real answer to his problems. He felt he must return to the discipline that he had allowed to slip during the past year, that is, daily meditation, confession, and attention to his studies. He was of the opinion that such a breakdown would never happen again because he was now familiar with the warning signals and would be able to go off for a rest.

I took the position that it would be advisable for him to become better acquainted with some of the factors operating within him. I used as an example the anger that he had, earlier in the hour, linked with his mother. He replied that he "plugs it all in" and gestured toward his chest. He thought he should learn to release his anger through physical activities such as sports.

During an hour when we were discussing his wish to attend his class graduation and then go on to his job as a counselor in a summer camp, it turned out that he was concerned that if he left the hospital, he would have to return to live with his parents for the summer. This led us into a discussion of two previous near-psychotic, but clinically unrecognized episodes that he associated with visits to his parents. The first of these occurred one-and-one-half years previously when he visited his parents during Easter vacation. One night he found himself sleepwalking to the end of the hall with the idea that there was a girl waiting for him. As he was about to turn the handle of the door he awakened and became frightened of his behavior.

The second incident occurred less than a year ago, when, upon returning to his parents from summer camp, he stopped off for a visit at a monastery. While staying there, he had an attack of bronchitis, was depressed for a few days, and felt quite strange. Incidentally in this session, I learned that when he was introduced in a social group, he would try not to let people know his name because they would then immediately recognize his father, who had the same name, and the patient could not be sure he was being accepted for himself.

During our seventh session he related a dream he had had the previous night. In this dream he was watching a play being put on for him. Then someone turned on a record player very loudly. He became furious and was about to smash it when he was awakened by an aide's knocking on his door. His associations brought forth a description of two fellow patients who attempted to entertain him when he was first admitted and also an episode of his hospital roommate's playing the record player loudly. This led to a discussion about his anger, his repression of it, and his difficulty with it. During this same session, he spoke of not wanting to get to know me well or to become friendly with me. He had felt this way toward his teachers and the school chaplain. He said he was afraid he would take over the other person's ways and thereby lose something of himself.

At the initial staff conference, two weeks after the patient's admission, we decided to recommend a choice between his continuing therapy here, while going to one of the local universities, or transferring to a new therapist near the college that he had already selected. He chose the latter, but his immediate response to the recommendation was an expression of concern about therapy becoming too influential in his life.

About four weeks after beginning therapy, he became an out-patient. This meant that he returned to his parents' home to live, but spent several hours each day at the hospital. He participated in the ward meetings and the work program, and had his individual therapy sessions.

At this time there was a change in his position about treatment, which up until then had been largely one of a denial of his need for therapy. As far as I could determine, this change was ushered in by a dream in which the patient was building a castle on a table. He had no support except from one man, and the castle failed. Then, still during the dream, he was sitting on a bed. A girl and a man were in the next room. The man said something about it being easy to have her. The patient became rather indignant that this other person spoke of her in this way. Then to his surprise, he found himself having inter-course with her, and awakened.

In his associations to the castle he spoke of *Joan of Arc,* by George Bernard Shaw. He greatly admired Joan and her ability to be almost superhuman. He spoke of his fantasies of wanting to be superhuman. He recalled that there was a pennant flying from the castle, which was the same color as the *summa cum laude* hood he received at gradua-tion. He thought the sexual part came from a book he was reading. He was impressed that he was indignant about intercourse and yet participating in it. I suggested that the castle crumbling away may have represented his school coming to an end for him. He disagreed saying he looked forward to school ending. I pointed out how he could have contrasting feelings about it just as he did in the second part of the dream. As though he had discovered something, he re-plied, "Oh! Ambivalence!"

During the next hour he said that he noticed a change in himself and was concerned that he was becoming depressed. "Things are pushing in on me," he said, and described this as being the opposite of feeling "able." This began after his father returned from abroad and just after the aforementioned hour when he talked with a female patient and discovered that they had known each other in Europe. It disturbed him when she described her difficulties in school and her subsequent two years at the hospital. He was afraid this could happen to him. He became further depressed upon talking to a male patient who had psychotherapy while going to the college the patient had decided upon and then, following graduation, went into a "nose-dive" and was admitted to the hospital. These events were very important in his reappraisal of whether or not he was in need of therapy.

In a dream reported eleven weeks after beginning therapy, the patient awakened perspiring and tearful. In this dream he had an idiot brother who was reading from the Book of Psalms. His mother made fun of this brother and objected to his reading these psalms. The patient stuck up for him, protested, and said they would leave home together. His father was pleasant. In talking about the dream, the patient said it was his outburst against his mother that made him perspire. I ventured that the idiot brother was the helpless part of himself. He thought this might be so because his mother had once told him to stop reading the Psalms because they were "too depressing." We then talked about the onset of his psychosis, his feelings toward his mother, his not wanting to fight other children, and his more recent stand as a conscientious objector.

DISCUSSION

SPECIFIC PROBLEMS OF TREATMENT OF THE ACUTE PHASE

The manner in which a patient is hospitalized can make a considerable difference in the outcome of the course of treatment. This patient's hospitalization was delayed by the feeling of stigma attached to emotional illness and the discouragement that is implied with the diagnosis of a "nervous breakdown." Both the patient's mother and the physician collaborated in postponing his hospitalization in their effort to ascribe the symptoms to a somatic disorder. Sometimes patients are sent to clinics for a physical checkup in the hope that a psychiatric referral will be made and thereby the patient will be "eased into" psychiatric treatment by someone other than the patient's doctor or the family. While it is essential that somatic pathology not be overlooked, it is equally essential that the emotional origin be acknowledged and frankly presented to the patient and the family.

Referring physicians and families often ask advice about how to hospitalize the patient. Of course, one must work within the legal confines relevant to the particular jurisdiction in which one practices. Sometimes trickery is used to bring about an admission, and this deplorable practice almost always causes a difficult initial period of hospitalization. All sorts of devices are used. One prospective patient was told that they were stopping by the hospital to obtain a record.

On another occasion a husband persuaded his wife to join the "real estate salesman" for a drive to the suburbs to look at a new home. The hospital was in the suburbs. Even physicians will engage in deception to some extent by assuring the patient that he will be there only for a "checkup" or for a "two-week stay," and that the hospital is like a resort or a "country club." By contrast, a frank statement to the patient as to the assessment of his incapacity, together with his need for hospitalization and treatment, is more often greeted with relief rather than opposition. A frequent practice some years ago was the use of heavy sedation in order to bring about the transfer. The patient arrived in a pharmacologically induced confused state, and this generally worked to his disadvantage by fostering confusion that may have already been present as a result of ego disorganization. A new patient who is agitating to be released from the hospital and confused about where he is, has sometimes been calmed by being taken on a tour of the hospital and the grounds and being informed as fully as possible about what was going on and what is to be expected.

With the present-day emphasis on trying to keep the patient in the community rather than removing him through institutionalization, one almost gets the impression that hospitalization itself is a bad thing and is to be avoided if at all possible. Certainly there are many marginal situations in which it is advantageous to the patient to have him continue to maintain his role as a wage earner or housewife, with an emphasis on expectation of performance. This will often prevent regression and assist in maintaining the stability of the family. On the other hand, when patients clearly are unable to be maintained on the outside, hospitalization can be extremely beneficial. Such removal of the patient from the family may not only be beneficial to the patient but spares the family considerable anxiety as well. Day hospitals are a useful addition in dealing with patients who need only partial hospitalization. Certainly, suicidal, homicidal, or other self-destructive behavior must be interferred with. We know of no clear-cut way of establishing guidelines in the marginal situations.

For the newly admitted patient, the initial reception at the hospital is probably as important a time as any comparable span throughout the hospital stay. We think of the treatment as beginning with the initial contact with the patient. This phase can be therapeutic or antitherapeutic. It can be disruptive, confusing, with intensification of anxiety, or it might be reassuring, clarifying, and educational in its impact. It is our practice to arrange for the admitting doctor to be the doctor who is assigned to the patient for treatment. This prevents the patient from having to make a change to someone other than the admitting physician. It also eliminates the evaluation period, practiced in some hospitals, after which time a decision is made as to whether treatment will be begun or the patient will be referred elsewhere. Similarly, the process of history taking and assessment of the patient is placed in the context of treatment as an effort to obtain as much understanding about the patient as possible. All of this is in contrast to traditional somatic medical procedures in which the emphasis is on a preliminary period of evaluation and diagnosis—with treatment considered to be secondary to the initial workup of the patient. When many different disciplines are involved in the treatment of a patient, the initial orientation of the patient to the treatment program can become hopelessly splintered. This can only serve to compound the confusion in an already confused patient. It is very important that simple explanations of the various aspects of the program be given and that some clear-cut responsibility be established. Too often the nurse assumes the therapist has explained his function *vis-a-vis* the hall administrator; the occupational therapist thinks that the hall administrator has explained the function of occupational therapy, and no one has explained anything.

We make it a practice to involve other patients in the orientation of new admissions, feeling that, from their own experience, they know better than we what some of the immediate concerns of a newly admitted patient are. Our patient government has prepared a booklet of information for new patients. When the admission is planned in advance, this booklet is sent to the patient prior to his admission. Its value is questionable for the extremely confused patient, but other patients have found it very helpful.

There are many practices involving the newly admitted patient that make a significant difference. Traditional procedures of giving the patient an admission bath and placing him in a hospital gown, while all of his belongings are being inventoried and marked, fosters a deprivation of the familiar things that might affect his precarious identity at that moment.

However, we have questioned some of the more modern practices and their effects on patients. For instance, there have been many changes to make hospitals less traditional and less "medical" in ap-pearance. If the nurse does not wear a uniform, a confused patient may have some difficulty distinguishing the person to whom he should turn for help. Of course, there are other ways to clearly identify such people for the patient. One acute young schizophrenic patient was admitted to a modern hospital that had no locked unit, the nurses were not in uniform, and he felt that he did not really know what was expected of him. The admission took place on a weekend, which added to the confusion. Finally, he decided to get on the elevator. Since no one stopped him, he thought that he really was not expected to be there. He hailed a cab and went home. The problem is to provide a setting that has structure and clearly delineated communication to the patient without being rigid and dehumanizing.

IDENTITY DIFFUSION IN ACUTE SCHIZOPHRENIA

The concept of identity diffusion developed by Erikson is extremely useful in conceptualizing the experience of the acute schizophrenic.[2] This patient's question, "Who am I?" was an eloquent description of a sense of loss of identity. When a person's identity is jolted to psychotic proportions, the repercussions involve many aspects of ego functioning. Such ego disturbances affecting perception, memory, foresight, and repression were prominent in this young man.

Of the term "identity diffusion," Erikson says the following in a footnote to his paper on "The Problem of Ego Identity": "In identity diffusion, however, a split of self-images is suggested, a loss of centrality, a sense of dispersion and confusion, and a fear of dissolution."[3]

There were several examples of this patient's unstable identity, both before and during his therapy. His desire to avoid having people know his name when he was introduced was a reflection of his uncertainty of being recognized for himself—apart from his father. He also showed tendencies to identify himself with others—sometimes in a conflicting way. For example, he identified with the superman concept and wondered how he could accomplish the most for the billions of people in the world. On the other hand, he had fantasies of being born a Negro boy so that he would not have had so many expectations placed on him. In addition, he thought that any achievements he may make as a Negro boy would be more valid because he had been given so many advantages in his present life and therefore could never feel certain about his accomplishments. Still other examples involving a precarious sense of identity were his readiness to identify with the patients who became sick during college and his wish to avoid emotional attachment to his teachers, chaplain, or therapist because he would not know which were his thoughts and which were theirs.

We have speculated about some of the factors leading up to his identity crisis. Certainly there is evidence that the frequent moves of this family during his formative years brought about an instability within the family as well as an instability of the relationship of the family to the community. His mother was under considerable stress during his early years and while the specific effects of such stress are unknown to us, we can assume that they were detrimental to the mother-child relationship. The transference caution about attachment to his therapist would point to the likelihood of a lack of basic trust in his relationship with his mother. Also, his father's long periods of absence meant that the patient was placed in closer contact with his mother, thereby increasing his Oedipal problems. She, in turn, may have looked to him for fulfillment of some of her own needs, which would ordinarily have been gratified by his father.

According to the patient, his relationship with his father was less difficult than with his mother. Perhaps it was simply easier to avoid his father because of the latter's absence. This avoidance meant that he never came to grips with competitive feelings toward his father. In addition, he showed difficulty with masculine identification and primarily evolved a negative identity in relation to his father. That is, he wanted to be as different from him as possible. He chose a different school and a different career. He avoided athletics and the country club social life, which his father enjoyed.

This patient's childhood was one of considerable loneliness. In addition to the disruptions in the continuity of his life, the frequent international geographical moves exposed him to the results of the destructiveness and violence of war. He was very much affected by the sight of dead children in the streets in the Orient and of sunken ships that he had seen in some of the harbors he visited during his travels. Some of the early indications of his problems about aggressiveness and anger have already been mentioned.

With this background, he began his first continuous schooling in the fourth grade. This private school became a source of permanence and continuity for him. His schooling became an anchor in his identity formation. His excellent intelligence, together with his politeness, pleasantness, and cooperativeness, brought him success. His school life was an outer shell of apparent adjustment built on a foundation of an unstable and faulty ego synthesis.

Many things helped keep this apparent adjustment going. The chronic bronchitis largely removed him from athletics and the chance for competition in sports. It was also used to remove himself from classes and the family at certain times of stress. His interest in religion brought him into closer contact with some of his teachers and a few of his fellow students. When he contemplated a celibate life in a monastery, where, to quote him, "The brothers live like one, big happy family," he disposed of at least three large problems. Such a monastic affiliation would eliminate conflicts over anger, heterosexual intimacy, and loneliness. He had achieved an equilibrium in which, on the surface, he appeared to be a friendly, bright, and energetic student but, at the same time, a person who had dissociated areas having to do with competition, anger, and intimacy.

It is our impression that several factors combined to bring about his psychosis at this particular time. Among these factors, are the following, listed in the order of their occurrence: (1) a growing doubt about his religious participation; (2) the increased pressure of his sexual drives in adolescence; (3) the threatened loss of his student friend; (4) the approaching graduation and separation from his school; (5) falling behind in the preparation of his studies; (6) his father's departure, which put the patient in a closer position with his mother; and (7) his lack of an adequate enough relationship with someone that would have allowed him to communicate some of these troubles to the other person.

PROBLEMS INVOLVING TREATMENT AFTER THE ACUTE PHASE

This patient reacted poorly to the use of tranquilizers, and, in fact, cleared up when they were discontinued. This, of course, may have been just coincidental, since there were many other variables introduced at that point, including the patient's transfer to another hospital. Certainly the usual experience is that acute psychotic states can be terminated, at least in their grosser manifestations, by the use of tranquilizing drugs. The frequency of this occurrence poses the question of what to do about the patient at this point. Even before the days of tranquilizers, remission of acute symptoms raised the same question. Twenty years ago, the advice was to allow the patient to "recover by repression" and do nothing to stir up any conflicts. "Let sleeping dogs lie" was the guiding philosophy. Patients seemed quite content with this approach since they often felt embarrassment, shame, and a certain awkwardness about what they could remember during the psychotic period. They were too ready to go along with the doctor's recommendation of not getting back into an intense degree of anxiety again. This patient seemed to be perfectly willing to leave the hospital and resume his religious practices since he felt that he had to make a choice between religion and psychiatry. He thought that psychotherapy would not be an answer and might make him too dependent on the psychiatrist.

It is our belief that an attempt should be made to help the patient understand the nature of his psychotic experience, why it occurred when it did, and what the major conflicts are that leave him unable to cope with his anxiety except by psychotic regression. It is conceded that not all patients are psychologically minded enough to embark on such a program but, given a situation where the patient has the treatment available to him by someone who is skilled in the work with these patients (or an unskilled person who has a skilled supervisor), we feel that a serious attempt should be made to do psychotherapy. It, of course, would be fine if we had statistics that would back this up but unfortunately there are too few instances where such psychotherapy is carried out other than on a most superficial basis. The volume of cases to compare with suitable controls is too small, but such research is highly indicated. We do not think that patients who are in remission should continue on tranquilizers such as a diabetic might continue on insulin, unless, of course, tranquilizers are necessary to control psychotic disorganization. The long-range effects of tranquilizers are still unknown. Circumstances certainly must enter into any consideration of plans for such patients, but we recommend the optimal approach, knowing full well that in any particular case one might have to settle for less.

ADOLESCENTS AND PSYCHOTIC DISORGANIZATION

It is often difficult to know at any cross-sectional period of observation of an adolescent whether this person is undergoing an acute adjustment reaction or a more severe psychotic disorganization. Hindsight is much more accurate in these situations. Even fairly normal adolescents under stressful situations can show some of the symptomatology of a psychosis. Depression, elation, emotional instability, paranoid projection, and denial can be quite alarming but turn out to be self-limiting. We are seeing an increasing number of adolescents seeking hospitalization as a result of crises that occur during their high school and college years. This may be a reflection of the increasing number of adolescents in our society. A probable additional factor is that these young people are now coming to hospitals rather than finding a moratorium through a job, military service, or an assignment at sea. Most of these patients are not psychotic in the sense that they show a thinking disorder but, rather, manifest their difficulties in behavioral patterns, with participation in the use of marijuana, LSD, narcotics, barbiturates, and other antisocial behavior. These patients present an entirely different problem in hospital treatment from that of the adolescent who is more regressed, confused, hallucinated, paranoid, and so forth. We will focus on these differences in the final chapter on the antisocial patient.

Sullivan stressed the importance of conflicts around intimacy for the adolescent and young adult.[4] He looked upon these patients as having had some difficulty in their earlier development, especially in their pre-adolescent era when they failed to form a trusting relationship with someone of the same sex. As the result of a failure to negotiate these previous eras successfully, the adolescent experiences considerable conflict when propelled by pubertal sexual development into intimacy with another human being.

FAMILY OF THE ADOLESCENT

Our approach to visitors for the patient is a flexible one. In general, we encourage relatives and friends to visit the patient from the beginning of the hospitalization. We feel that this is essential to keep the patient's life outside the hospital in focus and to reinforce the expectation that he will be returning to this life. There are, of course, situations when permitting visitors is contraindicated. A patient, who is so disorganized that one cannot be certain how much awareness he would have of the presence of visitors, might himself later be embarrassed that certain friends or relatives have seen him in this disorganized state. Visits at these times can be quite disturbing to visitors also. In addition, there are occasions when the patient may specifically request not to be visited by certain people. We honor these requests.

When, for the above reasons, the relative may not see the patient, we continue to encourage them to visit the hospital. They have the opportunity to talk with the social worker, the patient's therapist, and nursing personnel. In this manner they can establish a positive relationship with the staff who cares for their relative. At this time, the patient may, to everyone's surprise, be able to have a satisfactory visit.

From the time this young man reintegrated, visiting with his mother and calling her on the telephone was encouraged. His mother initially felt some reticence about having him contact his close friends. She felt that she did not want them to know he was in a mental hospital. In her discussions with the social worker it became clear that she was concerned about how this knowledge might affect her husband's position, and also about her son's illness as a reflection of her failure as a mother. The social worker was able to help her put both of these concerns in a more realistic perspective. When she realized that it was in her son's best interest that he maintain his contacts in the community, she withdrew her objections to his contacting his friends.

The family is almost always a necessary participant in the treatment of the adolescent. We find ourselves regularly assigning a social worker to see the parents of these patients. The way in which the adolescent and his parents can irritate each other points to a high priority of social workers' and other staff's time to help ease these crises. Recently we have utilized a family therapy diagnostic conference with such patients to very great advantage. Early during the course of the treatment, an interview is scheduled that includes the patient, whatever immediate family he has available, the patient's doctor, and the family therapy interviewer. An hour-and-a-half conference devoted to this, with fifty minutes of this time set aside for a one-way mirror interview by the aforementioned participants, has given us an early delineation of the predominant patterns of family communication. We are thereby alerted to an understanding of subsequent interventions on the part of the family or provocations on the part of the patient or family. We have not had enough experience to come to a conclusion about continuing family therapy sessions over a long period of time. Certainly, as far as the productivity derived from the time involved, the one-session family interview with the adolescent has been extremely worthwhile. With this particular patient, one can see how the mother's invitation to "blow up" at her had threatened his controls to an even greater extent. By contrast, his immediate removal from the family situation, together with the structured program of the hospital, tended to reinstitute the patient's controls over rage and anger.

POSTSCRIPT

After his release from the hospital, this patient went to college in another city and continued his psychotherapy as a private outpatient. He completed college and married. Four years after discharge the patient was hospitalized elsewhere. We have had no further information.

NOTES

1. An abbreviated report of this case was given in an unpublished paper: Clarence G. Schulz, "Identity Diffusion in a Schizophrenic Adolescent," at Chestnut Lodge Symposium, 1959.
2. Erik Erikson, "The Problem of Ego Identity," *Journal of the American Psychoanalytic Association,* IV (1956), 77–102.
3. *Ibid.,* republished in *Psychological Issues,* I, No. 1 (1959), with footnote added, 122f.
4. Harry Stack Sullivan, *Conceptions of Modern Psychiatry* (Washington, D.C.: The William Alanson White Foundation, 1940), pp. 28–34.

CHAPTER VII

Initiating Treatment with a Mute, Withdrawn Patient

CASE PRESENTATION

This single young man in his mid-twenties was admitted for the present treatment program in a catatonic stupor. Two years previously, while in college, he had had feelings of "tension" and concern about his feeling of sexual attraction toward other men. In graduate school, he consulted a psychiatrist and complained of sexual tension. He had also begun to think that there were things that emanated from other people that influenced him, and, in turn, things that came from him had an adverse effect on others. As an example, if his little nephew, when sitting on his lap, would cry or become distressed, he felt something extrasensory was being communicated to the child. He made several visits for consultations to various psychiatrists, including Wilhelm Reich. On one occasion, upon returning from a consultation, he began to pray in public in a railroad station. He was then taken to a psychiatrist and hospitalized. There followed a series of hospitalizations for supportive care and evaluation. He was finally hospitalized at a sanitarium that had open ward facilities. Initially, it was decided not to undertake intensive psychotherapy with him because of the potentiality for regression and a possible explosive outburst. However, during the course of the evaluation, he reacted favorably to psychotherapy. The idea of transferring him to a closed facility was abandoned.

The catatonic episode that necessitated his transfer to the present treatment program occurred in the context of his having become engaged to a female patient while hospitalized. The patient, his girl friend, and his mother arranged to meet in another city. After meeting the girl, his mother disagreed with his choice and discouraged him from continuing the relationship. In response to this, the patient stopped eating and became withdrawn and mute. He took the train back to the sanitarium by himself, failed to get off the train in time, and got off instead at the station in the town where his therapist lived. He walked back to the sanitarium and arrived there in the middle of the night. His therapist was called. The patient, who was very disturbed, asked for a cigarette and then asked the therapist to kiss him. The therapist kissed him on the hand. The patient took the cigarette and burned the spot where the therapist had kissed him. He spoke of being afraid of becoming dependent on the therapist. Since he continued to refuse to eat, it was necessary to tube feed him and give him intravenous fluids until he could be transferred.

A brief summary of the patient's history reveals that he was the younger of two children. He had a very close relationship with his father, in which they played tennis and enjoyed doing things together. The patient's mother felt that this relationship was too close and she vaguely hinted that there was something unhealthy about it. She repeatedly emphasized her concern about his being too close to other people. During her pregnancy with the patient, there was a physical complication that made it necessary for her to remain in bed following his delivery. Consequently, she found a nursemaid who took care of the infant. When the patient was about six months of age, his mother decided that he and this nursemaid were becoming too close, and she discharged the nurse. The patient was always compliant, very gentlemanly, and known for his sense of fairness, politeness, and agreeableness. His sister, by contrast, was more rebellious and caused the family much more overt difficulty in her early years. She was five years older than the patient and always seemed independent of the family. This was especially true when she began having girl friends of her own. When the rest of the family wanted to go to their farm for the weekend, the patient's sister would remain in the city. During those years, she did not pay sufficient attention to her appearance, overate, and provoked considerable disagreement within the family about this.

The patient's relationship with his mother was one of polite consideration. They had no open arguments until he was grown. In addition to the nursemaid and the patient's father, the mother disapproved of the patient's closeness with any of his girl friends. This theme was later to continue in the relationship to his therapist when he began to work well in treatment. His mother suddenly began to suggest that someone else could be friendly with the patient, play the piano with him, or in other ways break up what she considered to be an excessively close relationship.

The patient seemed to get along well academically in school and was regarded by adults as a charming, lively person. In his college years, he failed two courses. One was a course in harmony, which he selected upon his mother's recommendation because of her interest in music. However, he did not have the background that he needed as prerequisites to pass this course. The other was a science course in which he refused to bring his laboratory work up to date because he felt that it was silly. He remained out of college for a year and worked as a lab assistant in a research project on hypertension. At this time his father had a stroke and was hospitalized in the same hospital in which the patient was participating in the research program. The timing of this stroke was dramatic in that it followed an argument at the breakfast table between the patient and his father. The father remained a semi-invalid from that time until his death two years later. After his father had been ill for a time, the patient began to display a considerable amount of anger and impatience with his father's helplessness.

The patient's sexual history reflected a pattern of considerable sensitivity and tenderness toward other boys but an abhorrence of homosexual participation when he received frequent overtures from other young men. In college and again in graduate school, there were attempts at heterosexual intercourse. In each of these, he was impotent and unable to achieve an orgasm. Each experience ended quite unsatisfactorily.

The patient contrasted himself with his sister in a number of ways. While she was overeating he was undereating, and his parents would often encourage him to finish his food. He said that he had difficulty in learning to read, whereas his sister, by contrast, was quite good at reading. Similarly, he seemed unable to remember facts, while she had a good memory. As mentioned before, he was always much better behaved and more polite than his sister. He disliked fighting with other children when he was in kindergarten. Although he took part in competitive athletics, he never liked the idea of fighting.

During his father's illness, the patient would make unfavorable remarks about his father's being incapacitated and useless. Similarly, he felt very encouraged about any improvement in his father's condition. Following this period of interruption in his college work, he returned to college, graduated, and went on to graduate school.

The patient's father died while the patient was hospitalized in the open hospital. This was approximately five months prior to the onset of his stupor. His mother indicated that he failed to accept the reality of his father's death until two weeks before the onset of his stupor when the patient and his mother had to transact certain business regarding the father's estate. It was also noted that shortly before the onset of the stupor, he broke the engagement with his fiancée and just prior to the onset, he had told his doctor that he did not want to become dependent on him.

During the first nineteen months of the present hospitalization, the patient worked with a woman therapist. He was a tall, thin young man who was lying in bed looking at the ceiling, quite catatonic, and saying nothing. He had been incontinent of feces, was not eating, and required tube feeding. To that therapist, he seemed like a big guy who was acting like a little boy. In reviewing the first interview, she described how, in the absence of any conversation from him, she spoke aloud about how he might have felt some despair since he had been in several hospitals prior to this. She indicated that she was interested in working with him but that he did not need to feel under any pressure. She pointed out that there probably would be periods in which he would not talk but that she would sit with him. When he had things that bothered him, she would like him to talk about them if he could. In that hour, she also indicated that possibly his incontinence was a way of telling people that he needed help and that there were nurses around to be of help and make him as comfortable as possible when he was unable to help himself.

At the time of her second interview with him, about the fourth day following his admission, he suddenly had a grand mal seizure as she came through the door onto the hall for their appointment. A work-up for epilepsy was instituted immediately, and his first conversation with her was on the subject of his convulsion. He said, "I just resent having to take pills. I feel as though I ought not to have to." He seemed to resent the fact that there might be anything wrong with him. She brought up the possibility that, in addition to epilepsy, he had an emotional difficulty in living but he would not discuss this. When he did speak, he intellectualized on a very high plane, discussing cybernetics and neurophysiology concerned with communication, the thalamus, the mid-brain, and so on.

One day, when his therapist came into the room, he was on the floor nude, crawling on his hands and knees. He had piled up his books on the floor and was using his nose to push them out into the hall like a dog. She commented, "You feel like hell and I just feel a great deal of compassion for you in this situation." He returned from the hallway, got into bed and spoke of cybernetics and what makes the brain tick. Another concern that he expressed during these early periods was, "I thought I was sick because I was homosexual."

Psychological tests were performed shortly after admission. These test results were compared with the findings at the previous hospital.

PSYCHOLOGICAL TESTS

The patient was seen in my office about two weeks after admission to the hospital. He was very quiet, seemed rather preoccupied, but did everything that was asked of him without protest.

The Wechsler-Bellevue Intelligence Scale was not administered since this had been done within the past year. At that time the patient's score (I.Q. 121) placed him in the superior range of intelligence.

Rorschach Test

The test seems to be that of a paranoid schizophrenic who is at present overtly psychotic. He seems to be quite confused and in poor touch with reality.

He is a person of very good intelligence and imagination, but is at present unable to integrate his intellectual functioning in an effective manner.

The evidence of perseverative thinking, the tendency to automatic phrases, the inability to shift his form of thinking, are all suggestive of an organic defect.

The patient is apparently experiencing his relationships with others primarily as an unresolved struggle. There seems to be a connection between this and his orally determined needs. It is as if he were making enormous, greedy demands upon people that he cannot get satisfied. The overt expressions of this may be hostile or grotesque since the whole process occurs in a psychotic form and with a great deal of confusion and dissociation.

Prognosis: If it were not for the possible organic component, the patient would probably have a favorable prognosis. This is based on the liveliness of feeling and imagination and the need for human contact, which is so close to the surface even in his present psychotic state.

Wechsler Memory Scale Form I

The patient shows very extreme impairment of memory on this scale. The extent of this can be measured to some extent by comparing the Memory Quotient of 73, which he obtained with his Intelligence Quotient of 121.

The impairment is shown in all the types of memory tested on this scale although in "Visual Reproduction" (memory for designs) and repeating digits forward the patient did make approximately an average score. Since he is a person of superior abilities, however, even an average score represents some impairment.

Although it is possible that this poor performance is simply a function of psychosis, and in particular of an inability to concentrate and attend, at the same time an organic component in the memory defect must also be considered possible and even probable.

Four Pictures Test

The patient was unable to "tell a story" about the pictures, but remained "stuck" in his own experience. The degree of "concreteness" exhibited, the inability to shift from the immediate, and the inability to integrate the separate items into a meaningful whole is suggestive of an organic defect as well as of autistic preoccupation.

Drawings

The patient's drawing shows rather marked regression of forms to a primitive level. His verbalizations show the same quality described above.

Summary: The evidence of the psychological tests points to a probable though not certain organic factor in a paranoid schizophrenic patient. It is impossible to state with certainty whether certain trends in the test performance are schizophrenic or organic in origin, but the evidence for organicity seems to pile up rather heavily especially in view of the patient's originally high level of endowment.

Comparison of Rorschach Tests

In comparing the Rorschach Test previously administered to this patient with the one administered approximately ten months later, a number of differences emerge. The differences all point in the direction of a significant change for the worse in the patient's intellectual and emotional organization. These changes would be consistent with the development of an organic involvement but they might also occur in a patient who had simply become more withdrawn, more autistically preoccupied, or, in a word, more psychotic.

More specifically, the patient seems to be less productive, slower, and less communicative. He is less able or less willing to put his thoughts and impressions into understandable words. His whole inner life seems to have become more stereotyped, constricted, and impoverished. He is less emotionally responisve to what goes on outside him and less creative and original in his imagination.

He is also more vague and confused in his way of perceiving the outside world. Further, there is a perseverative trend in the second test, not so clearly present in the first, which, more than anything else, suggests an organic component.

His therapist attempted to relate to the "primitive, infantile, regressed, frightened little boy" aspect of him while, at the same time, listening to his intellectual formulations. She also attempted to respond to him physically. When he was untidy with his feces, she would attempt to clean him up. One day, she arrived when he was frozen in a catatonic position, holding a large lump of feces behind himself. On seeing this, she said, "Gee, you look uncomfortable. Give it to me." She held out her hand but he did not release it. She then indicated that she would take it, whereupon she unfolded his fingers, removed it, obtained a towel, wiped off his hand, and told him that he could sit down. He then returned to bed.

Because the therapy seemed to be at an impasse, a change in assignment of therapists was made. Prior to this, I had known the patient because I had tube fed him several times. While being tube fed, he would work out in his head some of the physics problems for the aides who were going to school at the same time that they were working. My first interview with him took place nineteen months following his admission. I met him in his room and, in response to my statement that I assumed that he knew about my assignment as his therapist, he grunted a "Yes." I was not very eager to work with him when we started out but accepted the assignment. When I saw him he was in bed, usually covered with a sheet. Sometimes he had his head out, sometimes not. He was a tall, thin man, carelessly dressed and withdrawn. I reviewed what I had known of him and some of the brief things of his history. I also told him what I had observed of him in my contacts when I had to tube feed him. I spoke of being impressed at the way he worked out the physics problems in his head. He replied, "a little bit." My questions about what he thought his problems were or how he felt about a change in doctors brought no response. When I tried to find out how he became ill, I had little success. He did say that he had been at graduate school and spoke of his interest in his major, mathematical biology, and also that he had a side interest in gerontology. When I learned that he and I had come from the same geographical area, we had a relatively lively discussion about where he lived, where he went to school, and something about his father's illness and death. This discussion was remarkable by its contrast with his usual mute, withdrawn state.

The next day I saw him in his room where he was lying on his bed quite withdrawn, coughing and blowing his nose. When I asked about the latter, he told me of his sinus trouble. He then talked about his previous illnesses and medical attention. I learned that his tonsil-lectomy had been performed by an otolaryngologist who was a class-mate of my father at medical school. From there, we went on to talk about early glimpses of his illness, which he described as "tension states." In addition to speaking about his present illness, he referred to experiences in high school where he felt "stupid in a different way" while in his studies there. He then began to fill in some details about his family background.

In the succeeding hour, I learned more about his tension states and his "fear of failure." He frequently qualified things with the statement, "I don't know exactly." It was as if he couldn't be sure of a lot of what I wanted him to talk about because he didn't know "exactly." When I asked, "Well, whoever thought you should be exact in your talking?" he thought of his father. He thought this had been present since he was five years old. He also told me that he thought his mother was a perfectionist, and then we talked about his eating problems. He referred to his visit to the city just prior to the onset of his stupor. He remembered how he felt like vomiting and then the first thing he knew they were feeding him intravenously. Additionally, one of the things he mentioned at that time was the problem of con-trolling his violence. He said that he felt that he might explode. When he spoke of his "fear of failure," I remembered that he said that he wanted to go to medical school but felt that he might fail. Because of this fear he shifted away from the premedical course of study. I speculated aloud that he might feel that he failed in therapy with three previous therapists and therefore he might be afraid that he would fail with me. He did not confirm this conjecture on my part.

In the fourth appointment, I inquired about his requiring me to take the initiative each time. He said that he had none. I wanted to find out what had silenced him. In a logical, almost debating style, he asked me about "repression" and forgetting "unpleasant" things. He thought that this was really the best way to handle such unpleasantries. He inquired about the effect of strychnine on a frog's inhibitions and how this might affect a human being. I thought that the patient was frightened lest his inhibitions be removed and he would be unable to repress and forget.

After the first two weeks of this initial fairly good contact, he seemed more withdrawn. He had been eating his meals for several days but after he skipped his breakfast, I inquired about his fasting. He said that he was determined not to eat. After saying that, he quickly changed "determined" to a milder word. After a few silent hours, he asked, "Is disagreement necessary?" He went on to explain that he thought that disagreement should be avoided if at all possible. He spoke of how he had reacted to his sister's disagreements with the rest of the family and that all of this was very upsetting to him.

Our subsequent meetings continued to center around his feeding problems, which I brought up for discussion. At the beginning of this particular session, the patient was making a belt as an occupational therapy project while sitting on the hospital porch. The size of the belt brought up a discussion of his small waistline. He said that his feeding problems started with the weekend previously described and that it was ushered in with a spell of vomiting. At that point, he blocked and would not pursue what was going on. When I inquired about this, he merely said that he didn't know "exactly." I brought up my information that he had had feeding problems since childhood and I had understood that especially around ages five to ten, at supper-time, his parents would make him stay at the table until he had finished eating. During this discussion, when mentioning the problem of controlling his violence, he said that he could either repress it or explode. He felt regretful after his explosions and spoke of these as being very angry feelings toward his parents. He began to fill in details of what he had learned about being sickly as a child. His mother was sick while she was pregnant with him. He said that following his birth he had been underweight and almost died while in the hospital. After a few months, he became overweight. He also spoke about the disagreements between his sister and his parents. They argued about her becoming overweight at age ten while he at age five was eating too little. He mentioned other opposites between himself and his sister. He was better behaved and she was more precocious.

I was impressed that this patient was holding back a large amount of hostile feeling. He saw his parents as making demands of perfection and exactness on him. It was almost as though anything outside of precision would result in catastrophe. He observed that when I would ask him a question, possibly fifty different answers might flood his mind at once. The one out of the fifty that he might select seemed crucial to him. As a result, it was impossible to pick any one of them and he would remain quiet rather than make a mistake. Once, he spoke of some problems concerning sex and asked if I thought he should buy a certain book on sex. I treated this in a matter-of-fact way and suggested that if he wanted to buy the book, why didn't he just send for it. He also described his failures in his heterosexual attempts prior to his breakdown.

A few months after my treatment with him began, his mother visited the patient. When he entered the room where she had placed presents on the table, he kicked over the table and sent the presents flying. At the end of this visit, his mother commented that in a way she liked this visit because she felt more in contact with him compared to her visit eight months previously. During that visit she felt that things were rather superficial. On this visit, he had questioned her, "Do you really want to help?"

When I attempted to see him in my office, he angrily kicked the wastebasket across the room. Following this, I resumed seeing him in his room on the closed hall. A couple of months later, he asked, "Couldn't I see you at your office?" I reminded him of the previous incident and he replied, "Well, I don't think you have anything to worry about." He again began to see me in my office. At that time, he was talking about how he wanted to go home. He felt that psychoanalysis was wrong and that Freud was an atheist. He spoke of feeling criticized in various ways. He felt that when I spoke of him as being withdrawn, he had to "turn off" his ears. What he heard was something like "You shouldn't be doing this, you should be doing differently." I found that if I spoke to him about his feelings of failure or disappointment rather than withdrawal, he would be more likely to discuss it.

The following is a sample of the content of the appointments during this period. He would say, "Supposing I asked you to answer a question of blah, blah, blah?" I told him that I didn't understand. He said, "Well, it ought to be self-evident what I mean." I told him that it really wasn't self-evident. We continued in this vein and he indicated that he wanted to leave the hospital. I took the attitude that I felt it was possible for him to leave and to go home but I didn't think he should go home. I thought he needed to be in a hospital. He began to badger other people, other members of the personnel, with this. He would say, "You've got a chip on your shoulder. This person didn't do right. The other person didn't do right." I felt somewhat relieved since he was attacking others, I did not feel it so personally. I told him, "Well, you have these feelings about everybody here at this time and I think if you went to another hospital you'd have the same feelings toward them."

He made a fairly steady and relatively rapid improvement. Four months after beginning treatment with me, he had ground permission and moved to an open unit. He remained there except for a brief episode three months later when his mother visited on his birthday. Within two hours after her visit, he was back on the closed hall in a cold wet sheet pack. While in the pack, he told the aide, "I want to see my doctor—I mean my mother." When I went up to see him, he very belligerently said, "I don't want to see you." I replied firmly, "Well, I want to see you." He responded meekly, "Oh, that's different." I sat down and we talked. When I tried to connect his disturbance with his mother's visit, he said, "Oh, you and your Oedipus complex." After she left, he was soon able to return to the open unit. There, he was much more openly angry with me because he felt that I was criticizing him. He said, "Why don't you speak clearly?" and "None of this is logical." "Why don't you speak the truth? The truth is simple and you ought to be able to speak it out." It seemed to me that his lashing out at me was an attempt to get some feeling of separation and distance from me. I thought that he had anxiety about being close to me and in some way felt that his own boundaries were so indistinct that he might be engulfed. When I operated from this position, I soon stopped arguing defensively about how logical I was being and also stopped trying to enunciate more clearly. Instead, I sat back and felt that at that moment the patient needed to blast forth. I would just wait and see what happened. Actually, I was not able to do this consistently and I often found myself being drawn into what was a whirlpool of confusion and argument in which he would say something and I would respond and then he would take issue with that. This would go back and forth until I had the feeling that our interchange was like a car stuck in the mud, spinning its wheels, grinding down to the axle, and getting nowhere.

About five months along in the treatment, the patient's mother consulted with an internationally famous psychiatrist about her son's case. As a result of his asking, "Is Frieda in on the case?" I had a consultation with Dr. Fromm-Reichmann. She told me, "Don't be so easy with him. He knows that he has to talk about these things and so do you." This gave me encouragement to be more forward with him, but his response to this was to feel that I was like "steel." He felt that I was a precision machine and was smacking into things, and sometimes it felt like he was being hit over the head with a sledgehammer.

He became quite open in verbally attacking me but never directly physically attacked me. He would make noise, jump up and down on the floor, and take his shoe off and bang it on the floor to emphasize a point. Much of the content had to do with his opinion that I was inconsiderate, was not trying, did not listen to him, changed the subject, and the intonation of my voice indicated that I did not listen to him. He improved temporarily after each blast. One evening following a particularly big blowup, he went to a ballet performance in the city. This was his first visit out in a long time.

In a session typical of this period, he began by saying that if I knew more about him, that if I had more information, I would not have taken the approach to him that I have. I said practically nothing the entire hour and he talked on. He said that he may be wrong about some of these things and if he is that that needn't affect me. If what he says doesn't really apply, then it won't make any difference to me and he'll forget it too. It was as though he were saying if the shoe fits then wear it. He said, "You're the doctor," but thought that he had to be the "doctor's doctor" and felt that we—the hospital, psychoanalysis, and myself—placed emphasis on what the patient could do. "So and so did this today" and that was completely missing the point. He said, "It isn't so important that I be cured; it is whether I am a better person at the end of it." He said that when he hits the window (and then demonstrating) "sure, that's noise. You might call it that but that's no noise at all. It's the noise you make, the violence you do to me that really counts. The other just goes out into thin air." Then continuing, "It's your intentions that count above all else. If you have the wrong intentions in the first place, nothing will help." He said that he felt that he was the victim of the past cruelty that was done to me, that I did not practice what I preached, and that it was insidious. On one occasion, he said that I do violence to him and then "come up with something as sweet as daisies." He complained that by my questions in a half-an-hour from now or next week, I will show that I haven't listened to him, so that I don't care about him. "This hospital misses the boat on so many things. You would think they would spread sick people out rather than put them together. Also, they have locked doors and all that stuff and all that sort of stuff and that isn't the important thing." He also thought I was not logical and that, in a debate, he could prove his sanity more than I could.

Some of this seemed to apply, but a lot of it sounded very much like what his mother was saying to him. As I looked through some of her correspondence with the hospital, there was a similarity in her complaints about the hospital and his complaints about me. It was his feeling that I should be able to take criticism. I told him that criticism was pretty hard to take sometimes. There were times when he told me to get out, but I did not obey his request. In reference to his "intellectualizing," I told him that I thought that it was only natural that we would expect him to look at things intellectually because of his brilliance. He said, "Well, you know if you have a canary and you let him out in the woods all at once, he is not going to survive." I thought that that statement described his situation with his feelings of dependency and his fears.

During the early stages, his negativism and uncertainty were baffling to the nurses. When they wanted to take him on a picnic, it seemed that he wanted to go but just as he was ready to leave and was going out the door he would stop, turn around and return. "No, I don't want to go. Just leave me here." The nurse would talk to him, and other patients would ask him to go since they were interested. They wanted him to but he would not. Also during that time, he would play games and work puzzles. He particularly enjoyed teaching games of bridge or chess to the new student nurses. When he received a game of Scrabble as a present from his mother, he enjoyed showing this to the nurses and enlisting their participation in the game.

The clinical administrator was experiencing a great deal of pressure from the patient's mother. After the patient had completed some long-postponed dental work, his mother sounded rather disappointed that this had all been completed. It was as though she wanted to push him further to have something else done. Each thing that she complained about would be answered and she would push further to find other things to be done or to complain about. When he wrote home for the first time in the year-and-a-half following the onset of his catatonic stupor, she did not respond with any enthusiasm about the fact that he had written. Instead she responded to his complaints about "psychoanalysis" and asked whether we might be able to have a minister see him.

Nine months after starting with him, and just before he was arranging to take his first vacation in about three years at the family summer place in another state, I attempted to discuss the possibilities of certain problems about meeting relatives and getting back into the "swing of things socially." I was actively pushing this when the patient rose from his chair, went to the window, and said calmly, "I wish you would realize how important it is for me to be able to criticize you."

It seemed like a revelation to me to recognize that actually the patient was quite socially adept. It was a needless concern on my part. Much more to the point was his ability to raise hell with me and have us both survive it. He went on the vacation and at first it went well. By prior arrangement, he was not supposed to see his mother, but somehow she arranged to see him on this visit. He became mute while returning to the hospital.

Following this, the patient seemed to be doing much better. He was eating well and taking at least two well-balanced meals a day. If he did not take adequate nourishment at mealtime, he would always come to the nursing office where he could obtain something from the refrigerator. He entered into games on the ward, especially when there were student nurses on duty since he seemed to derive pleasure from teaching them new games. It was noted that, on the days that he did not have his individual therapy session, he seemed to be more upset. On those days, one of the personnel usually tried to stay with him most of the time and this helped considerably. Generally, his upsets were brief and the frequency of the storms decreased.

During the ensuing months, the patient varied between eating fairly well in the dining room and having trays on the ward. There was a marked increase in his general activity. For a while, he had been going into the adjacent fenced yard behind the building where he resided. Gradually he began to go to activities in other buildings. Often, he would appear interested in these activities and express a desire to go but, when he was ready to participate, he would suddenly balk and remain on the ward. The personnel took up this problem in their psychodrama session and came to the conclusion that, if they were indifferent to him at this crucial moment, they were more likely to encourage him to participate. They tried this consistently and found that he responded much better. He began to expand the scope of his activities. He went into town to obtain a haircut and have his shoes repaired. On his own volition he decided to go for a ride with a group of patients and an aide, and enjoyed this. He selected a project at the occupational therapy shop, which he worked on at the shop and brought to his room to continue working.

His appearance improved. He wore sports clothes for the most part and maintained a neat appearance. He spent his time going out walking by himself, reading in his room, playing the piano, or going to church. He seemed to enjoy receiving letters from his friends, but his mother's letters upset him. He also enjoyed visits from his minister.

He began to stress the point that he wanted to do things that were useful, not just to be doing things. He said that he wouldn't want to weave a belt or do any kind of occupational therapy work just to be busy. He wanted to do something that would count. Consistent with this interest, he helped construct a building to house a canteen, which was to be run by the patients on the hospital grounds.

At about this time one of the occupational therapy workers met me in the hall one day and said "My gosh, what are you doing with ———— (patient's name)? He is just working all over the place. He's a changed person!" I responded to this query by feeling quite uneasy and wondered what I was doing. He was now wearing clothes, working, and participating in things. I had mixed feelings about the changes that were going on in the patient. In talking this over with a colleague, we came to the conclusion that it was something that a parent might experience with an adolescent who is suddenly growing up and making changes. The parent then wonders whether the youngster is ready for this.

During the sessions he made it difficult for us to pursue anything that might be regarded as his "problem." As long as we would talk about making a bow and arrow, making a model motorboat, or the weather, mathematics, or similar topics, it was all right. If I wanted to take up anything with him that looked like it might be a problem to him, he wanted nothing to do with it. This was an obstacle to me all the way along. He was very touchy when I attempted to discuss an emotion-laden topic. He would reply, "Well, if you're going to talk that way, then I'm going to leave," and he would walk out of the session. There were many hours from which he walked out. I would usually follow, stay perhaps twenty to fifty feet away from him, and gradually get a little closer. Sometimes we would sit on a bench or take a walk, but usually there was nothing more that would transpire in the conversation during this time except that he would shout at me and say he wanted nothing to do with me. I might end by saying, "Well, I'll see you Thursday," and he would reply, "OK, I'll see you." I gradually became reconciled to my inability to explore his pathology when he felt so upset.

I found that it was very difficult to take up certain topics with him because I felt that I had to be very delicate. I finally brought this out into the open with him, saying, "It is almost as if you have your problems locked up in a vault and that these are jewels which you cherish. Neither you nor I must get to these." He smiled at this, and that seemed to break the ice. I felt more courageous in taking up these things with him. It was noteworthy that the more the patient was able to angrily attack me verbally during the hour the more he was able to participate in activities, both within the hospital and without. He claimed that if his criticisms about me did not apply, then I really shouldn't be bothered by them. He made the observation, "If you need someone, the first thing you know they are forcing you to do things." Also, "I am beginning to hate the guts of those who try to run me."

In a typical hour of this period, the patient talked at length on the theme of religion, saying among other things that psychoanalysts were atheists. He carried on full-blast. At the first opportunity, I said something along the line of, "I don't agree. (The Medical Director) is a Methodist from way back. Where did you get this idea from?" Then, I continued, "You know, I wonder if this problem about religion isn't really one more of your own rather than that analysts are atheists. I think almost every college kid gets to wondering about these things and I wonder if you haven't." The patient grunted and said, "Maybe so." Also, in that same session, he said, "Well, there are some things that I just haven't been able to tell you. I don't know whether I'll ever be able to tell you." I said, "Well, I guess you'll get around to it sometime." It was raining and I offered to take him back to his building in my car. He accepted and then said, "Time, time, time, it's taking so much time." I replied, "Sure it does. We'll get there." Then, as I dropped him off, he said, "Well, it has been somewhat of a useful morning."

In a session just before he was to go on vacation during the summer, he criticized me severely, and this culminated in his stomping out of the appointment. I followed him outside into the nearby orchard. For a while we were both standing out in the hot sun, and he said something about my being so superior and that I seemed to have to act superior. I took this to mean that he felt inferior and that perhaps he was uneasy about going on vacation. I did not say anything to him about this, but, instead, I reassured him with, "I think you will do all right on this vacation." He said, "Oh, do you think so? Let's go back in the shade." We walked over into the shade, and the mood seemed more relaxed.

He did go on vacation but we received scant information of what went on between his mother and him. After his return, he seemed quite active and was busy with many things. He went shopping, bought a camera, took pictures, and typed for the hospital newspaper. He also signed up for a course in the local high school, was active in a play, went out with friends, and participated more with people. He remained reluctant about my attempts to explore anything in the way of his problems. When I asked about the vacation, he spent a good part of the time on various details but, when I asked about how things went with his mother, he said, "Well, it all went well until the last day and she seemed to be peeved with me about something." Any attempt to draw him out on this for elaboration was futile.

A few months later, his mother visited and they took a trip together to visit friends. This visit went extremely well, and his mother commented that this was the best she had seen him since he had become sick. When they visited Mount Vernon, the patient bought a three-cornered hat, a ukulele, and some presents for his nephews. He put on the hat and played the ukulele while his mother and their friends sang. Finally, his friend said, "My God, I can't stand that ukulele any longer. Why don't you stop it?" and he did without any feeling of disappointment. After they returned, I saw his mother and she related a story that I was able to take up with the patient in our next appointment. During their vacation two months earlier he persuaded her to play golf. She had been complaining of chronic back pain and the patient began by getting her to do some putting. Then he said, "Why don't you try some iron shots?" She did, and when this worked well, he said, "Well, Mother, I don't think it would hurt if you tried a wood shot." The first thing they knew, they were playing golf and having a good time. They then came across a bird that had fallen out of its nest. The patient wanted to take this bird home and care for it. His mother said, "Oh no, if you take it home it will die. The mother bird probably knows where it is and will come along and take care of it." She emphasized that he just couldn't get that bird out of his mind. "It just ruined our day." The longer he talked about it, the more of a menace the bird became. It spoiled the entire day, and the patient started home holding his head down.

After his mother's visit and their trip to Mount Vernon, through a combination of circumstances with his being away from the hospital and my missing some hours and then his becoming physically ill with a cold, there was a week's interruption in our sessions. He did not come to the office so I went to see him. The minute I stepped through the doorway, he was ranting and raving and throwing things around.

He said that he didn't see how I got through medical school or how I even got through the first grade. He said that I didn't know anything, and if that's the way I was going to treat him, he doesn't want anything to do with me, he doesn't want to see me any more, and he wants to leave the hospital. I replied, "Well, I don't get this. What's it all about?" but he continued in this vein. I sat down, and he went out. I awaited his return, meanwhile looking at one of his magazines. When he came back in he said, "Get your hands off my magazine." I put the magazine down and sat there for a while. He went out again and watched television. I waited until the end of the hour and said, "I'll be over again tomorrow." He said, "Oh, OK." On the next day, I didn't have a chance to go over to see him because he was at my office ahead of time. I said, "Well, I sure was bewildered about what was going on yesterday." He replied, "Oh, I was in a mood. I didn't feel very good." I said, "I gathered that but what was it all about?" He answered, "Well, I didn't like what was going on." He seemed unable to tell me anything beyond that. I took up the story that his mother related about the bird and told him that I thought this would make a problem for him in his feelings of tenderness toward people and that it seemed to me that his mother disapproved of such tenderness. I further conjectured that, when we got to feeling close to one another, there might be a similar disapproval of what he might feel. He listened to this and grunted his approval. Being encouraged by this, I added that this was similar to her feeling that the relationship between his father and himself was one of unhealthy closeness. He replied, "Well, she said something about that again this weekend." That was a very rare confirmatory response from him. I felt encouraged about this, and, as I wrote it up in my notes, I expressed an enthusiasm as though we had discovered this for the first time. In reviewing my notes in an overall sequence, I found that I had taken this up at least five times and yet I felt that this came through as though it were the first time I was describing it.

These first two years contrast to the second two years of treatment. During the first two-year period, the patient showed a remarkable transition from a withdrawn, mute, catatonic state to one of social participation, verbalization in his appointments, and expression of his anger, but a thoroughly marked reluctance to explore psychological problems and conflicts. In reviewing the record by hindsight, it seems that one of the outstanding themes running through this period was his emphasis on becoming an outpatient. He frequently stressed that he wanted to live more independently and to move out of the hospital. In retrospect, I wonder if the entire course of treatment might have gone differently had he been given more encouragement to pursue his request at the time.

Since this presentation focuses on the initiation of treatment, we will quickly summarize the course of the second two years. We saw a recurrent increase of anxiety while the patient was in contact with his mother. At Christmas he visited home, and, while there, he stopped eating. Upon his return, he appeared to have lost weight, was slumped over, and his responses were brief. A few weeks later on the first of February, he walked about twenty miles into the city after having told himself that he would not be at the hospital on that particular date. After becoming quite exhausted, he returned to the hospital on his own. There were additional episodes in which he became much more disturbed and regressed. On one occasion, the patient threw away his books and brought out more psychotic thought content involving "telepathy" and "telebody." The latter he explained as a transmission of body impulses from one person to another. All of this happened just prior to a proposed vacation trip home at the time of his birthday. He did not make the trip as originally planned but after postponing it for a week, he was able to depart. Upon returning, his behavior was variable. At times, he would be active and eating and at other times withdrawn. His verbal level in the sessions after his return was much below that of the period prior to his trip. Of the visit, his mother reported that she had talked with him at some length about his becoming more active and eating more. During the first part of the visit, he cooperated to the extent of drinking protein supplements that his mother prepared. On the last two days of the visit, he became irritable and stopped eating almost completely. Upon the patient's return, he was withdrawn, rather uncommunicative, and unwilling to leave his room and did not take any of the regular meals in the dining room. The administrator and nursing staff approached him by conveying their concern about him but, at the same time, trying not to do anything that he might regard as pressure. Within about a week, there was a rather dramatic change, at which time he came out of his room, was more cheerful, and spoke spontaneously. He ate ravenously and continued with a good appetite, after which he made plans to go out and play golf.

A month later, he visited another patient on the disturbed ward where he had formerly resided. He then voluntarily had himself transferred to the disturbed ward, where he remained for almost the entire period of the remainder of his hospitalization. Subsequently, when his mother visited, he became withdrawn and inactive. There was one brief period during which he was tube fed. This ushered in a long period during which he spent a great deal of his time in bed. Sometimes he was silent, sometimes angrily critical, but, for the most part, quite withdrawn. His mother brought in two prominent consultants to review the situation, and, when they recommended that the program with the present therapist be continued, she overruled the recommendations and had him transferred to another hospital.

DISCUSSION

SPECIAL FEATURES OF THE WITHDRAWN CATATONIC PATIENT

Preventing malnourishment is an important aspect of the total physical care of the catatonic patient. Dr. William Elgin, who has been following the character of patients admitted to The Sheppard and Enoch Pratt Hospital over a period of almost the last forty years, has observed that there are fewer feeding problems among patients admitted in recent years, although these continue to occur occasionally. While one might first think that the use of tranquilizing medications is the explanation for the decrease in frequency of feeding problems, this is not necessarily the cause of the change. One would have to consider the possibility that changes have occurred in the manner in which the present day staff relate to patients. In the past, the nurse's principal interactions with patients revolved around their being kept clean, and their eating and sleeping an adequate amount. As the nurse's role has expanded to include many other channels of interaction, both nurse and patient have had to rely less on these basic functions for involvement with each other. Could it be that at the time the present generation of patients were children the parents were no longer placing so much emphasis around eating, with rigid schedules for infants, instructions to masticate the food thoroughly before swallowing it, and to eat a balanced diet every day, which would include all the necessary vitamins, minerals, and calories? While all of this is in the realm of conjecture, it illustrates the wide range of variables that must be included in trying to assess any particular change in the nature of symptoms of patients in any particular era.

Although tranquilizers may be of assistance with these patients, we wish to reemphasize that there are certain patients who cannot be given tranquilizers. Some have an allergic reaction to a wide range of medications. Others have an idiosyncratic reaction reflecting itself in a dangerous drop in the white blood-cell count, while still others show hypotensive effects that are prominent enough to require discontinuation of the drug. All of this is mentioned by way of emphasizing the importance of nursing procedures to cope with problems in preventing malnourishment in these patients. Before summarizing particular problems and their procedures, we would first like to review some reasons why patients fail to eat properly.

First of all, there is the fairly common experience of the patient having a delusion that the food is poisoned. This reflects his general distrust of the environment and is probably specifically symbolic of the "bad" mother or "bad" breast. In Melanie Klein's scheme of psychopathology, this would be a reflection of the infant's projected "bad self" onto the mother.[1] Certainly it would belong to that very early phase where there is a split between the good and bad object. However, there are other reasons for patients' failure to ingest the proper amount of food. For instance, some patients are quite concerned about overeating. Even though this may be very difficult for the personnel to grasp, as they notice how little the patient actually eats, the patient has a completely unrealistic impression that if he eats a little bit this may give way to consuming large quantities, which then becomes related to the concern about overeating, overactivity, and loss of control. Still other patients have delusions about eating people in their food. One patient with whom we were acquainted would not eat any food that could not be peeled or was clearly discernible as to its origin. For instance, this patient would not eat a stew for fear that some human being would be cut up in the food and she would be ingesting a person. These patients are struggling with cannibalistic desires and concerns about destructive impulses. Here again we see the concrete expression of concern over fusion of self (body ego) and object. Similarly, such concerns about destruction can cause a patient to attempt to weaken himself by failing to take in adequate amounts of food. The defense against aggression is carried out by means of malnourishment and the consequent physical limitation of aggression. Such a defensive posture goes along with the catatonic's immobility as a defense against aggressive striking out. This was very prominent in the patient described in this case presentation.

A rather unusual instance is illustrated by a case mentioned by John Whitehorn in a paper describing a patient at the Phipps Psychiatric Clinic.[2] This case poignantly illustrates the pitfall in jumping to conclusions about a patient's psychopathology. Dr. Whitehorn described how one day when he was making rounds he encountered a patient who was not eating. When he inquired of the patient the reason, she suggested that he sample the food. He ate a little bit of it and, as a result, the patient began eating. A week or so later, when Dr. Whitehorn was again making rounds, he was told the patient had continued to eat after he had sampled the food. Dr. Whitehorn became curious and inquired of the patient what her thinking was behind this change in her behavior. The patient replied by saying that she was from New England and she wondered whether the people in Baltimore used their right hand or their left hand in taking the food to their mouth with a fork. She was so careful to conform to the social mores of her group that she was reluctant to eat until she had seen the proper way demonstrated by the doctor.

A particular variant of the feeding problem is the so-called "anorexia nervosa" patient, who does not clearly fall into any of the traditional nosologic categories but is often diagnosed as a schizophrenic reaction. These patients will show, among other things, induced vomiting, marked swings in weight, with alternate gorging and starvation. Such patients may include swallowing foreign objects as part of the clinical picture. They are almost always female. They appear to be younger than their chronological age and will frequently have amenorrhea as part of the symptomatology. The self-concept of these patients is sometimes reflected through their drawings of self-portraits which indicate that they are huge—like a large "glob" ballooning out into an inhuman, unfemalelike, large circle or sphere. We cannot go into this intriguing problem at any length here but we do observe that, in our experience with a few such cases treated by colleagues, the picture is not at all as hopeless as it might appear early in the course of illness.

In a modern treatment program in which patients are expected to care for themselves, including eating in a cafeteria and using the water fountain, the acutely disorganized schizophrenic patient can quickly become dehydrated and malnourished unless the nursing staff is particularly alert. We know we may have to bring the nourishment to the withdrawn, catatonic patient, but we may not be as aware that a confused patient (similar to patient in Chapter III) who has opened the hall refrigerator six times has really not taken anything out of it.

It is important to try to find a balance that maintains appropriate concern for a patient's nutritional intake, without this becoming the main focus of interaction between the nursing personnel and patient. The stereotyped feeding problem seems to be a product of the latter. Inadequate eating and staff concern about it perpetuate each other.

Our approach generally to patients who do not eat adequately is to first try to provide nourishment in a variety of ways, the goal being to sustain life, not to enforce proper eating habits, and then try to minimize the intensity of the concern of personnel. We have simple nourishment available—milk, fruit juice, peanut butter, bread—so the patient can be given them at any time he seems receptive. An adult, free of physical disease, can be sustained for some time on such a diet.

Another method is to provide foods the patient has requested or has agreed he will eat, whenever this is possible. Recently we had a patient who stated he would eat fish, rice, and tea. By using canned tuna and instant rice, the dietary department was able to provide this menu three times a day without any inconvenience to anyone.

There are, of course, occasions when the standard nursing measures, such as spoon feeding, high caloric liquids, frequent small feedings, and any ingenious measures we may try, do not succeed in maintaining the patient's nutrition. It then becomes necessary to tube feed the patient. In this situation we should not let ourselves get in the habit of thinking of the patient as needing to be tube fed. We feel that the gavage tube should be inserted and removed each time the patient is tube fed. To leave the tube in place communicates to the patient that we expect to have to continue tube feeding him. Leaving a gavage tube in place in a psychiatric patient is more dangerous than in the case of a comatose physically ill patient. There is always the possibility that the patient may either pull the tube out or swallow it. If the patient is moving about at all, it is very easy for the tube to become dislodged. The tube also mechanically interferes with eating, which we should be encouraging. Moreover, tube feedings must be spaced to allow the patient to develop some feeling of hunger.

Staff members who do not wish to spend the additional time inserting the tube each feeding may argue that repeated insertion and removal of the tube is uncomfortable for the patient and irritating to the mucous membranes. To make tube feeding a pleasant, comfortable experience for the patient should not be the object.

While discussing the patient who is threatened with malnourishment, it seems appropriate to mention the patient who is overweight and some observations we have heard from patients about this symptom. Some "narcissistic" patients have seen their obesity as a type of body "insulation," which preserves an inner core of themselves as being separate and impervious from the outside. Obesity can also be a defense against the fear of sexuality. A person thereby spares herself any concern about sexual interaction and at the same time removes herself from sexual competition. Here again, narcissistic aspirations can be clearly preserved and remain untouched since the person never openly enters the field of competition, which would test her desirability. A particular problem about patients who enter treatment because of obesity centers around the fear that if superfluous weight is discarded, they will no longer have reason to continue treatment. Such dependent patients maintain their symptom as their "ticket" into treatment until they are reassured that there are other problems to be resolved while the dependency itself is being dealt with.

There are some severe secondary consequences of physical inactivity with chronic catatonic patients. Most of these complications can be prevented by an active aggressive type of physical nursing care, together with encouraging participation in other activities. We have seen patients develop severe muscular atrophy due to decreased activity. This has even gone to the point of their developing contractures in the Achilles' tendon from lying in bed. Unless activity and physiotherapy are instituted, such patients may later require corrective surgery. Other patients have developed decubitus ulcers because of lying in their urine with pressure to the skin areas while on rubber covered mattresses. These occurrences are much less frequent than they were in hospitals a generation ago, but they still occasionally occur. Another particular area for the inactive patient has to do with oral hygiene. Nursing care is especially important to prevent mouth infections and dental caries, but, perhaps most importantly, it gives the nurse a way of relating to the patient with physical care. We wish to emphasize that all of these physical measures can become vehicles for establishing relationships, developing trust, and encouraging physical gestural interaction in place of verbal communication. We have found that these patients respond best to simple physical activity, such as going for a walk, using hydrotherapy, especially the use of a swimming pool or dancing with a circle group.[3] Frequently, very excited or withdrawn patients will respond with an amazing amount of participation in a swimming pool.

The mute patient is sometimes a particular object of frustration to the personnel. Staff members vary a great deal in their comfort with interacting on a purely gestural as opposed to a verbal level. Such patients are frequently plagued with an already low self-esteem and when the staff insists that they respond verbally, the situation is aggravated by their inability to comply. Our experience over the years leads us to feel that such patients, being treated by individual psychotherapy, are apt to experience a great deal of pressure from the psychotherapist, particularly if the therapist is having the case supervised. Supervision in itself centers largely around the verbal transactions between patient and doctor, and the treating doctor is sometimes under a needless burden to present "material" in a situation where the patient is unable to furnish it. This situation can often be relieved if the treating doctor can select another patient to discuss in supervision and give only occasional periodic reports to his supervisor about the progress of his mute patient. The response of the doctor to pressures to have the patient talk or to obtain information from him can, of course, be varied. We have sometimes seen ECT used with a favorable symptomatic response. Similarly, amytal interviews can be attempted to "get the patient talking." These approaches are successful in counteracting the muteness, but they illustrate a different philosophical approach than we are advocating. Such measures attempt to cut through the defense rather than try to establish a relationship that overcomes the need for the defense. We would consider it more important to provide a situation in which the patient is able to talk rather than to reach the content being concealed behind the lack of talk. The parallel here might be thought of in connection with the place of hypnosis in the treatment of neurotics. While hypnosis may get to the conflicts within a shorter period of time, one is not thereby dealing with the defenses that facilitate the neurotic repression.

Patients are mute for a variety of reasons, including their concern that words might "kill." Here again, we see a variation of the fear of the destructiveness in the patient. The patient in this particular case was so flooded with a variety of thoughts that he was unable to select the most appropriate one, especially since he felt he had to be "exact." When a patient is mute because of concern that he will say the wrong thing, it can be useful to observe that others in the environment say or do the wrong thing and survive. Late one evening this patient was helping the nurse by washing the dishes that had been used for evening nourishment. He was making a lot of noise in the process and the nurse cautioned him about this. He ignored her and continued to rattle the dishes until another patient who was trying to sleep complained. He then became quite irritated and began making statements to the effect that he was misunderstood and that no one had any consideration for him. As he started to walk out of the kitchen the nurse asked him to take his bedtime anticonvulsive drug. He said, "I don't need it, it doesn't do any good, I need to get out of here," and stormed into the Television Room. A few minutes later, the nurse approached him in front of the television set, as a program was ending, and said, "I realize I picked a bad time to ask you to take your medicine. Will you take it now?" He followed the nurse to the nurses' station and took his medication. This approach was certainly preferable to an automatic response of the nurse requesting an order from the doctor for an injectable medication. Still other patients are concerned that their words will be recorded, used against them, and spread out on television or in some other public display. This is a reflection of the patient's egocentricity, megalomania, exhibitionism, and distrust. The patient in Chapter II expressed his concerns about this in the first interview.

The staff can facilitate patients' communication through speech in several ways. First, the lack of pressure, combined with an essential quality of respect for the patient, can provide an atmosphere of trust that facilitates verbal communication. Communication through a gestural response will often come earlier than verbal speech. One patient who was mute for an extended period of time remained inactive and covered with a sheet during her psychotherapy sessions. A new therapist assigned to the case initiated a chain of developments leading to full verbal interaction. He asked her to at least roll over in the bed where her face would reveal some response to his occasional verbal comments. When he suggested this during the second session with her, she at first did not respond but as he was concluding the session and saying goodbye she rolled over, exposing her face. Certainly, in our general social interaction many gestures such as offering food, drinks, and cigarettes facilitate a type of responsiveness "that breaks the ice" more easily than speech. Again, these patients can respond through physical movement, such as dance, much more easily than any kind of verbal responsiveness. When asking questions of such patients, the probability of obtaining a response is much greater if the question is easily answerable. This is true in any kind of psychotherapy but particularly appropriate to this type of patient. A patient who has a phobia about heights, for example, can more easily indicate *when* this started than *why* it started. In the case presented in this chapter, the similarity in geographical background formed a bridge that made it easier for the patient to answer questions. Similarly a Yes or No answer is more easily given than one with a more complex sentence structure. This contrasts to psychotherapy with the patient who has become more verbal. There, one might be careful to phrase the question in such a way that it required more than a Yes or No answer to encourage the patient to enlarge the discussion. We have also found it useful to have the staff person make occasional comments in the form of a soliloquy with the patient. This can be done without the expectation that the patient will talk but one can express one's speculations as to why it is important to the patient not to talk. It is also a way of conveying information to the patient as one carries out various activities and procedures with him.

In addition to the physical inactivity and relative muteness, we have been impressed by indecision in so many of these withdrawn catatonic patients. Here again, we encounter the problem about making choices because of the concern that any decision might be catastrophic or destructive. It is particularly contraindicated to offer these patients a large number of choices of activity. To approach such a patient with a "smorgasbord" of options, such as "Would you like to go for a walk? Can I read to you? Would you like to rake leaves or go to the Occupational Therapy Shop?" is almost guaranteed to fail. By contrast, one aide initiated a successful response from a patient by leading him to the floor polisher that he himself was pushing and said, "Here, help me do this."

Nursing personnel have a tendency to react to the withdrawn patient's helplessness by doing everything for him. Initially this may be necessary, but if it continues for any length of time, the staff may become quite frustrated by the patient's lack of response. This can result in the decision to "really push" the patient. This approach is also destined to failure. What we try to do is to start with a relatively simple expectation of the patient, as in the example of the floor-polisher. As the patient meets one expectation, we have another in mind until he reaches the level of full social participation on the hall.

Having a schedule of activities each day in which all patients are expected to participate facilitates the involvement of the withdrawn patient. If it is part of the daily routine that patients make their own beds, the nursing staff seems to be more relaxed about encouraging the patients to do this, and consequently the response is better. It is more difficult to push a withdrawn patient into activities that have significance primarily for him—for example, going to the Sundry Shop to purchase his own toilet articles. This can often be accomplished if it is done in a way that simultaneously permits some dependency gratification. A patient may be able to purchase his own toilet articles after a nurse has helped him prepare a list. A distinction needs to be made between pushing a patient to do things for himself and coercion. If a patient feels he is being coerced into something to meet the staff's need to feel they are making progress, he will surely balk.

There is a frequent tendency to think of patients as being incapable of entering into a decision, especially when they show such blatant evidence of indecisiveness. It is well to remember how important it is to try to include the patient in decisions concerning changes in the treatment program, transfers to other hospitals, or financial matters. All too frequently staff and relatives alike will think it better to "spare the patient" the burden and make decisions for him. Even though the patient may be unable to give a clear-cut answer to the staff and/or relatives, in the long run it is most useful to take the trouble to explain the situation to the patient and at least allow the opportunity for participation in an active decision-making process.

These severely ill patients show considerable anxiety over change. For many of them it means the relinquishment of patterns to which they have become quite accustomed and around which much of their complete identity as a patient crystallizes. Similarly, the staff has some problem in accepting change, as was evidenced by the reaction of the therapist toward change in this patient. There is an opposite problem of anxiety over slowness of change. Some of the most difficult decisions in psychiatric consultations center around the recommendation as to whether the slow-moving program should be allowed to continue its course or whether more active, "radical" intervention should be made. Several of the patients described in this book have had prolonged periods where the change was immeasurably slow. Such periods are not necessarily an indication of an ineffective treatment program or the lack of a patient's response to the treatment. We consider this a very important reason why staff members—as well as the patient's relatives—have outside interests to avoid putting undue pressure on the patient. Such outside interests for the psychotherapist might range anywhere from having a private practice to various hobbies, family interest, or scholastic pursuits. Sometimes these patients respond remarkably when people do not "try harder."

Isolation from others is a frequent problem with the withdrawn patient. Sometimes within the hospital program these patients achieve considerable freedom, which takes them out of activities and leads them to a rather isolated existence. At one point this patient's ground permission was cancelled because he was using it to isolate himself. Such self-isolation can be detrimental to the total treatment program, and, as long as the patient does not "get into trouble," the disadvantages to the patient might be overlooked. Fear of the patient is another factor that leads to the staff's collaboration in such self-isolation. The patient is then seen as someone who shouldn't be tampered with lest he become explosive and uncontrollable. The opposite concern that if the patient's pattern of withdrawal is interfered with, he might "collapse" is probably more frequent. From such a vantage point, the patient is viewed as "fragile," and any approach by the staff to change the pattern of withdrawal is apt to lead to concerns about regressive disorganization, return to tube feedings, and the seclusion room. Harold Searles has accurately put this concern in perspective by speaking of these patients as "durably fragile."

CATATONIC EXCITEMENT

Catatonic excitement appears to be the other half of the mute withdrawn behavior that is somewhat parallel behaviorally to the manic excitement of the manic-depressive patient. With the catatonic whose anger is directed toward others, there are periods of explosiveness that sometimes alternate with paralyzed inactivity because of fear of aggression. One such patient later reported that he had been concerned that he was going to have a heart attack and had to be absolutely motionless. In the management of these patients, we have continued to rely on the use of cold wet sheet packs and the use of the seclusion room. We regret that hydrotherapy has to a considerable extent passed from the scene as part of the armamentarium in coping with the catatonic excitement. New residents and nursing personnel often regard the cold wet sheet pack as a form of punishment that they hate to "inflict" on the patient. However, it becomes a very useful sedative and restraining influence. Once established as a procedure, patients will often request its use. It becomes very valuable when the individual therapist feels physically threatened in the presence of a patient. As Dr. Fromm-Reichmann emphasized, the doctor can then concentrate on helping the patient rather than be preoccupied with fear of attack from the patient.[4] It would be interesting to speculate on the relationship between the effectiveness of the cold wet sheet pack and the swaddling of infants.

The seclusion room decreases the amount of stimuli for the patient and prevents him from harming himself and those around him, and from destroying property. It is possible for someone to be safely with the patient most of the time. We feel that while the reduction of stimuli is useful, the complete lack of human contact is not. The nursing personnel assigned to the patient visit him frequently and sit with him for periods of time. We do not have "disturbed wards" as such, but have seclusion rooms available on all the admission halls. That it is beneficial to the disturbed patient to be in an environment that includes better integrated patients was validated by the reduction in seclusion hours reported by the hospital following the discontinuance of the "disturbed" halls. The monthly average of seclusion room time for the entire hospital is less than one-tenth of what it was when we had "disturbed" halls. The opportunity to interact with other less-disturbed people in a more civilized atmosphere conveys to the patient the expectation that the disturbed behavior will cease. The expectation of the group can influence the patient to use what functioning ego he has to control his behavior. We use hall meetings to discuss the problem when other patients want to be "rid of" the disturbed patient. The hall group can then come to see how they can all work together to help the patient become a part of their group.

It sometimes becomes difficult to decide when to utilize tranquilizers with such patients. Certainly tranquilizing medications are often quite effective in terminating the disturbed state, or at least to attenuate the degree of disturbance. Our approach is to utilize tranquilizers when the patient seems not to respond to the other treatment measures or when he is physically a danger to himself, approaching exhaustion or self-destruction. It is the chronically disturbed patient who shouts night after night, keeping the other patients awake, or the one who repeatedly attacks personnel and in other ways presents major problems in management who will receive tranquilizers. In such cases, the tranquilizers appear to be more effective if given parenterally as an initial large dose. We have also, on rare occasions, used electroshock treatment with such patients. This may be performed on fewer than one out of three hundred patients in a year. Occasionally, we encounter a patient, usually a man, who is terribly assaultive or self-destructive, who does not respond at all to tranquilizing medications or who for some reason cannot be given tranquilizing medication. With one young man who had already broken his hand and was repeatedly breaking the cast by hitting his fist against the wall, we utilized electroshock and terminated the disturbance after tranquilizers had failed. Our reluctance to use shock more frequently to change such behavior stems from our concern that the resultant temporary memory loss makes it very difficult for us to enter into a productive psychotherapeutic relationship. There have been instances reported when a patient's prolonged catatonic excitement has resulted in death.[5] By contrast, prior to the use of tranquilizing medications, we had noticed numerous instances at a large state hospital, where the presence of physical illness led to a termination of an acute catatonic excitement. Such patients suffering from an intercurrent infection, fracture, or nitrogen imbalance would be sent to the medical and surgical unit where they would be treated for their physical illness and concomitantly show a marked favorable change in their catatonic reaction. It could not be known for certain but there were speculations that this involved some kind of endocrinological stress reaction, a response to nursing care for the physical illness, or a combination of both.

There are probably many patient-to-patient interactions that go by unnoticed and therefore are underemphasized in an account such as described in these case presentations. We remember one patient who became assaultively disturbed in the dining room and started to attack another patient. A third patient, who seemed to be rather disorganized and at the time totally mute, busily scribbled "Third Floor" on a piece of paper, the message being that he would be transferred to the third floor, which at that time was the disturbed hall. He shoved this piece of paper in front of the patient who was about to take a swing at his opponent and the message brought forth an immediate relaxation and a cessation of activity. By contrast, it was noted that the patient referred to in this chapter was never told off by other patients during his tantrums, although his behavior warranted it. In our current approach, we place much more emphasis on encouraging patients to confront one another about their behavior, complaints, and commendations. This, of course, is very much the basis of any therapeutic community approach.

The very severe management problem of the self-destructive patient stands out in contrast to those patients whose anger is outwardly directed. Self-destructive patients will burn or cut themselves, bang their heads, attempt castration, enucleation of one or both eyes, or suicide. It is a frequent practice to "special" such patients in an effort to combat their self-destructiveness. While this often is successful, it is a two-edged proposition in that patients get the message that if they are self-destructive, they can then receive special care. We have completely abandoned "specialling" in the traditional sense that one member of the nursing staff will be assigned to stay with a patient for an entire shift. During periods of crisis we may feel that for a few days a patient should not be left alone. We then place heavy emphasis on keeping the patient involved in whatever activities are available on the hall. A member of the nursing staff may be assigned to constant observation of the patient while he is participating in activities. This is not always the same person for an entire shift and is usually not formalized in terms of a patient being told he is being "specialled." Having a "special" can serve the function of isolating the patient from his peer group. We also feel that the use of the seclusion room is contraindicated with self-destructive patients. Such patients in isolation cannot be well-observed. They also can relieve the monotony of isolation by self-injury.

We are reminded here of a marked contrast of interaction that these disturbed patients have with nonclinical employees such as porters, carpenters, plumbers, or dietary help. It is amazing how patients will somehow treat a nonclinical person as being "off-limits" without anything explicitly being stated to them by the clinical personnel. Plumbers can have wrenches and carpenters can use ladders, but patients never seem to do anything but walk around these objects to get to the nurses' scissors to cut themselves or to attack. Sometimes a particular porter who mops the hall can be more effective in having a patient return quietly to the seclusion room than an entire task force of nurses.

Finally, in discussing the catatonic patient, we wish to point up the use of denial and projection as a primitive defense mechanism with these patients. Certainly, these are prominent with all schizophrenic patients but it seemed to be especially prominent with the patient in this chapter. The projected aspects of the patient can sometimes be very difficult for the staff who become the target of such projection. This is especially true since the patient's sensitivity to a staff member may be quite accurate although the distortion as to the extent of the projected aspect is another matter. The staff person must be able to accept these dissociated aspects in order to allow the patient to integrate them. This was illustrated in Chapter V with the paranoid patient who accused the doctor of being "cowardly." With the angry catatonic, it is important that the staff person not react defensively and deny his own anger, but, instead, accept this, allow the patient to identify with him, and in turn accept his own projected anger. Certainly these patients are really quite capable of provoking anger in any staff member. The staff person should not attempt to deny the patient's anger or try to emphasize how essentially "sweet," "kind," or "good" the patient is.

PARTICULAR PROBLEMS IN THE PSYCHOTHERAPY OF THE SCHIZOPHRENIC PATIENT

We cannot discuss here the many technical details involved in the psychotherapy of these patients but we would like to comment on some broader issues. We recommend that the reader consider Frieda Fromm-Reichmann's *Principles of Intensive Psychotherapy*[6] and Lewis Hill's *Psychotherapeutic Intervention in Schizophrenia*[7] for a discussion of the many technical problems.

First there is the matter of the selection of the therapist. Kubie has questioned the assignment of inexperienced residents to the task of doing psychotherapy with psychotic patients.[8] Some training programs do not begin such an assignment until the second year of residency. One factor is the belief that treatment progresses so slowly that the beginning resident will become quite discouraged and will suffer a jolt to his self-esteem, which is already precarious. By contrast, we assign beginning residents the task of treating schizophrenic patients, but, at the same time, give them adequate supervision to ensure a learning experience. It is our impression that in any particular resident's caseload, a sufficient number of these patients moves along fast enough to prevent discouragement. On the other hand, the severe psychopathology can often call forth a countertransference reaction in the resident that is much more threatening to his professional and personal identity. Searles has given detailed examples of this reaction with even experienced therapists in his paper on the phases of treatment.[9] Experienced supervision on such cases can turn a chaotic situation into an immensely rewarding learning experience for the resident and a consequent benefit to the patient. The fact that the psychotherapist is only one member of the entire treatment team tends to offset the notion that such a patient might be "shortchanged" by the neophyte resident. In what we hope has been amply documented with examples in this book, the reader can readily see how many components there are to the treatment experience for any particular patient. We contrast this situation with the outpatient treatment arrangement in which much more of the leverage of treatment is dependent on the doctor and his relationship with the patient. This is in no way intended to minimize the importance of the psychotherapy component of the inpatient treatment complex.

An important aspect of the psychotherapy assignment in our treatment program is the opportunity for continuity in an extended relationship of treatment if necessary. In other residency programs in which the "block system" leads to the assignment of a doctor for blocks of time to inpatient programs, outpatient programs, neurology, and other aspects of training, there are frequent interruptions of treatment and resulting transfer to a new therapist because of the dictates of the schedule and calendar. For instance, a resident may begin treatment with a patient at the end of May to find that in July he must leave the inpatient service to fulfill his training in neurology or on a psychosomatic assignment. We have provided for an assignment to the inpatient service that can run the entire three years of training. Potentially it is possible that if the patient and therapist require this amount of time, the treatment can continue. Other residency assignments run concurrent to the inpatient experience. Some treatment programs rely heavily on the more experienced psychiatrist who comes in from his office to the hospital to carry out the individual treatment sessions. While this may be a satisfactory arrangement with some patients, we have found that opportunities for communication are usually inadequate. In general, we would prefer a more inexperienced therapist who is employed full-time on the hospital staff in order to coordinate his efforts with those of the total treatment impact toward a resolution of the patient's pathology.

There is room for much research on the selection of psychotherapists and the attempt to match the patient with the therapist. Our experience indicates that there are some doctors who seem to have a "knack" for working with these patients but, other than these empirical observations, we really have no way of formulating the important factors in the selection of a therapist. Even the gender of the therapist, often specified when requesting the assignment of a doctor, is selected without much solid theoretical basis. In the particular case cited in this chapter, the patient made a rather dramatic change with reassignment of the therapist. That this may have been related to the second therapist's being a man was brought out by Otto Will in the conference on this patient.[10] He speculated that the patient's grand mal seizure, occurring at the beginning of the second interview with the female therapist, reflected a massive anxiety reaction of a transference nature from the patient's mother. There are so many questions that we would like to be able to solve experimentally that, here again, we are reminded of the fact that it is difficult to find matching patients and then alter only one variable in order to compare treatment approaches. It is impossible to run the same patient through treatment twice and change only one variable on the second go-round.

Another broad issue concerning psychotherapy with schizophrenic patients is the value of psychotherapy during the regressed phase of the patient's illness. This has already been discussed to some extent in Chapter II. The reasons that some give for not including psychotherapy as part of the treatment program during this phase reflect the attitude that such psychotherapy is ineffective. The typical analogy is to liken psychotherapy during the regressed phase to the use of a garden hose on a burning building. It should be apparent from the treatment programs described in this book, and especially in this particular chapter, that the psychotherapist does make a difference in the regressed phase. From what we could tell about the patient in this particular chapter, the psychotherapist was the only new variable introduced in what had become a static situation. In the program of treatment we are recommending, the psychotherapist does not act alone but in conjunction with other members of the staff. Although the actual effect from the standpoint of "insight" might be minimal, he becomes a central figure in the formation of a relationship and often the person around whom the rest of the staff rallies in facilitating the patient's reintegration. Other positive features already mentioned in Chapter II deal with the use of the therapist's observations from the acute phase or the regressed phase and how these are later integrated into the patient's experience during the verbal period of treatment in subsequent phases. It is emphasized by Searles that the therapist participating during this period of treatment can work out the symbiotic phase and the period of differentiation that is an essential part of any permanent personality reorganization.[11]

When deciding on psychotherapy with any patient, a group of factors must be considered, as they relate to the schizophrenic patient. The patient's age has sometimes been thought to be a barrier, and this seems to have some correlation with the age of the person making the decision. Young residents are apt to view anyone over thirty or thirty-five as being too old for psychotherapy, and as the age of the therapist increases his upper limit for the patient moves up accordingly. When seen in this light, the older therapist often finds no limit at all as long as senile or organic changes do not interfere with the treatment process. In general one would be more optimistic about treating the younger patient, although certainly the older patient sometimes brings life experiences and accomplishments to the treatment situation that may lead to a shorter course of treatment. Another factor is the duration of illness. A follow-up study by one of the authors indicated a correlation between the outcome of treatment and the length of hospitalization prior to treatment.[12] Generally, those patients who had been hospitalized for a longer period of time are less likely to be able to function on their own in the future. When looking at any particular patient, there are a sufficient number of exceptions to make this generalization invalid. Fromm-Reichmann once commented, "Schizophrenics deteriorate when no one any longer cares." Intelligence is also a factor, especially when it drops below the average range. What is being referred to here is the native endowment or potential of the patient rather than his functioning intelligence. Patients may be functioning on a much lower level than their potential because of the degree of their psychotic disorganization. Many patients are capable of an average or even a superior performance. If the patient does not have at least an average potential, the insight-type of psychotherapy that we are advocating is unlikely to be successful. An important factor in evaluating any patient for treatment is the patient's pre-illness level of psychological development. Generally, those patients who have not progressed beyond very early levels of fixation have a poorer prognosis. A patient such as the one in Chapter II, who had accomplished a great deal in his life but whose regressive disorganization would lead one to feel rather pessimistic, made a dramatic improvement. Here a knowledge of normal development and theory of what is to be accomplished at various psychosexual and psychosocial stages is important in evaluating the history of any particular patient.

If a private facility is being considered for treatment, another important factor is the patient's ability to sustain the cost of treatment. One of the most difficult decisions to make is the estimate of the length of treatment and therefore the amount of necessary financial backing. Often relatives will willingly impoverish themselves in their efforts for a "therapeutic trial" to see if the patient can be helped. If, indeed, it is ascertained that the patient could be helped, the subsequent events are heartbreaking when there are no funds to support the treatment. If accurate estimates can be made in advance, the financial uncertainty should preclude embarking on such a program. However, we have at times seen financial shortage work to the advantage of the patient. Occasionally, patients who have made considerable progress will be assisted by the reality factor of a lack of funds, which pushes them toward greater self-reliance. Dependency factors and secondary gain in these cases collide with realistic necessity for competent performance. Geographical availability is another realistic factor in considering the recommendation for psychotherapy. Of course, as long as the patient is living in the hospital as an inpatient, this does not become a factor except as far as the relatives are concerned. Geographical remoteness is important if the patient is living at home and has no skilled psychotherapist within commuting distance. We have no solution to this problem except to remind the therapist that, even though visits by the patient may be infrequent, they sometimes make the difference between maintenance of the patient and total collapse. A final factor to be mentioned relates to the degree of pathology within the patient's family. This is often difficult to determine. During the crisis involving the admission to the hospital, the family can show rather severe degrees of anxiety, panic, confusion, and even paranoia. Sometimes such families improve considerably when the patient settles down and begins to improve, such as the mother described in Chapter II. The situation is especially fortunate if the parents are able to develop some independent interest such as that of the father described in Chapter III. The mother of the patient in the present chapter seemed unable to allow individuation to take place. She repeatedly made suggestions, such as a letter requesting a minister, or her continued interest in the patient's dental work. These concerns of hers were relevant, but the problem was her intrusive manner. We certainly would not consider the degree of pathology in the family as a contraindication to treatment but, rather, would be alerted to make particular efforts toward helping the patient's family. Simply trying to make them stay away often boomerangs.

The next particular problem in psychotherapy of the schizophrenic patient upon which we wish to focus is the narcissistic countertransference. Some of the therapist's subjective feelings experienced in the treatment of the patients described in this book reflect primitive kinds of experience that one has when he becomes truly involved with such patients. This applies to any member of the staff and not only to the psychotherapist, although he is more apt to experience the primitive nature of these feelings because of the more intense relationship. One brief example of another therapist's symbiotic relatedness to his patient was illustrated by his reviewing his notes during supervision. He came to one quotation where he was absolutely unable to ascertain whether he or the patient had spoken the particular sentence. Robert A. Cohen commented that he thought that inexperienced therapists probably did better with the very sick patients since they were working something out in themselves in the process of treating the patient. After one had been through this process a few times, one was no longer interested in repeating it, and, therefore, had somewhat less enthusiasm for treating such severely ill patients. Certainly it has been our experience that the emotions that accompany the involvement with these patients add a great deal to one's own personal analysis. Searles, in a paper entitled "Concerning the Development of an Identity" developed the concept of a therapist's awareness of his own reaction as being particularly useful in the treatment of the patient.

And I felt, still further, that it is most essential for us as analysts not to endeavor to hide from our patient such feelings of personal loss. My belief is that any human being, whether healthy young child or adult patient, can progress from one developmental phase to the next only if he finds the sense of loss which this change, this step in maturational "progress," entails is shared by the parent or analyst. Thus, I think of an analyst as not simply helping a patient to progress through various developmental states, but as going through, himself, in a very real sense, these developmental stages with the patient, sharing with the latter the feelings not only of fulfillment but of loss which have to be faced and integrated in order that the next stage of maturation and of interpersonal relatedness can be established. In a paper in 1961 concerning schizophrenic communication I described, for example, the sense of loss felt by both patient and analyst when, after many months of predominantly non-verbal relatedness, they became able to communicate with one another, increasingly reliably, in words—leaving behind their mutually-cherished, more predominantly symbiotic, non-verbal relatedness.[13]

I believe that the more successfully the infant and young child in-

ternalizes as the foundation of his personal identity a symbiotic relationship with a predominantly loving mother, the more accessible is his
symbiotic level of existence, in all its infinite richness, to the more structured aspects of his identity which develop—which develop not primarily as imposed restraints upon him, but as structures that facilitate the
release of his energies and capacities in creative relatedness with the
outer world. Such a symbiosis-based identity serves as one's most sensitive and reliable organ for perceiving the world, not merely by mirroring
a world set at some distance, but through processes of introjection-and-
projection, literally sampling, literally mingling with—in manageable
increments—the world through which, moment by changing moment, one
moves.[14]

A special quality in the therapy with psychotics is the likelihood of
a wider range of feeling responses and fantasies on the part of the
therapist. This phenomenon seems to be correlated with the more
primitive types of thought and feeling going on within the psychotic
patient. Feelings of anger, helplessness, omnipotence, and uncertainty
of identity are frequent experiences of the inner world of the psychotic
and borderline patient. These aspects of the patient's life can remain
hidden, and, as Searles has pointed out, they are often, in the interactions with the therapist, most clearly manifested by corresponding
inner experiences of the therapist.[15] Such reactions are a part of the
relationship and can be potentially useful. They are not necessarily
signs of an insufficient personal analysis nor an indication for a change
in assignment of the therapist. Rather, the countertransference reactions serve as a way of "smoking out" these hidden aspects in the
patient. In our experience, the patient's narcissistic aspects are especially the ones that the patient will attempt to wall off and keep
secret, and in these ways preserve some of the most cherished beliefs
about himself. If and when they can be brought out into the treatment
situation, they may shrink through the light of realistic appraisal.

We would like to express some warnings concerning this technical
approach. First of all, we think that such an approach could degenerate into "wild analysis" particularly with the inexperienced therapist
and/or the one who has relatively little knowledge about himself. One
would have to be very careful about assuming that whatever impression one is experiencing at the moment had actual validity as far as
the patient was concerned. There is the possibility, and indeed the
likelihood, that the therapist is actually tuned in on his own "station"
rather than that of the patient. If, however, a therapist, for example,
had repeatedly noticed that he tended to reject the patient when there

were strong dependency demands covertly expressed by the patient and that this was a particular phenomenon the analyst had experienced many times in the past, it would seem to increase the probability of the accuracy of such an assumption of dependency demands going on currently with this patient.

Our final emphasis on psychotherapy relates to what we speak of as a "forging" of the therapist. Again, these remarks apply to other members of the staff as well. The therapist who is deeply involved in this symbiotic relatedness and moves on to various aspects of differentiation, integration, and autonomy, which we have referred to in a variety of ways, comes through the experience as a different person. To recapitulate, we would point out that the therapist experiences a threat of loss of his own identity, both professional and personal, and shares in the patient's helplessness and grief. These encounters will shake his psychological foundations, yet there is no cause for alarm or need to avoid the experience if adequate supervision is available. One can learn about human beings from one's patients in ways that are not available in books. The latter can only generally point the way toward understanding what one is experiencing and particularly to point out that such experiences are not unique.

THE USE OF CLINICAL PASTORAL COUNSELING IN A HOSPITAL PROGRAM

This patient's interest in a religious affiliation, and especially his concern about a possible antithesis between religion and psychoanalysis, points up the role of the hospital chaplain in the treatment program. It might have been very useful for this patient to have met with a clinically trained chaplain to discuss what he thought was an irreconcilable conflict between religion and psychiatry.

One young schizophrenic girl we treated in the period immediately following her admission spent all her waking hours reading her prayer book. No amount of encouragement could interest her in anything else. Because religion and religious practices seemed to play such a large part of her life, a clinically trained chaplain was included in the planning of her treatment. At a staff conference the decision was made to keep her prayer book in the nurses' station and to let the patient have it an hour in the morning and an hour in the evening. When the chaplain explained the decision to her, she accepted it.

Later on, when she had ground permission, she developed the habit of "dropping by" the chaplain's office several times a day. Although his usual practice was to welcome all patients to his office, he told this patient quite firmly that she was not to come to his office without an appointment. This action coming from the chaplain had more meaning to the patient, than if she had been told by the ward staff to stop visiting the chaplain's office.

The Reverend Ernest E. Bruder, Protestant Chaplain at St. Elizabeths Hospital, Washington, D.C., has written extensively of the role of the mental hospital chaplain. We include the following quotation that seems particularly relevant.

> It might be helpful to list the major criteria I regard as basic to what could be a real "healing team." Briefly, they are four. Each member should have: 1. clinical knowledge and understanding of the goals, methods, assumptions, and beliefs of the others' professions; 2. An attitude of openness: responsiveness, listening to and inquiring from the other members and the patients—as colleagues—mutually concerned about deeply troubled persons; 3. the ability to engage in conversation with the other members as persons, not just to read papers at each other, in terminology and manner almost guaranteed to make communication impossible; 4. the ability to tolerate, at least in some measure, the painful anxiety aroused when team members do get close to each other about things that matter deeply.
>
> To have a real team, we must have *clinical*, and not just theoretical, knowledge about what the other helping professions are concerned with and are doing. At this point, I must confess that psychiatrists have shown little, if any, interest or initiative in seeking such knowledge. They have remained in rather splendid isolation when it comes to finding out what the intelligent, informed, and sensitive modern clergyman really thinks about his faith and practice. They have made little attempt to become acquainted with what the chaplain is about. It may be wise, at this point, to suggest that, as long as there are ministers in the hospital, in some measure psychiatrists owe it to their patients and their treatment programs to find out what the chaplains are doing and teaching. It could well be—and it has happened—that much of what a psychiatrist rather laboriously strove for during the treatment week was sabotaged in a fifteen-minute sermon by an anxious minister who was trying to help but had very little understanding of the dynamics of what he was involved in![16]

POSTSCRIPT

We learned indirectly that ten years following this patient's transfer to another hospital, he was working and living in an apartment. Sometime during the interim his mother died.

NOTES

1. Melanie Klein, "The Psycho-analytic Play Technique: Its History and Significance," in Melanie Klein, Paula Heimann, and Roger Money-Kryle (eds.) *New Directions in Psychoanalysis* (New York: Basic Books, Inc., 1955), pp. 17f.
2. John Whitehorn, unpublished paper.
3. Marian Chace, "Dance as an Adjunctive Therapy with Hospitalized Patients," *Bulletin of the Menninger Clinic*, No. 6 (November 1953), pp. 219–225.
4. Frieda Fromm-Reichmann, "Basic Problems in the Psychotherapy of Schizophrenia," *Psychiatry*, XXI (1958), 6.
5. Marvin Adland, "Review Case Studies, Therapy and Interpretation of the Acute Exhaustive Psychoses," *Psychiatric Quarterly*, XXI (1947), 38ff.
6. Frieda Fromm-Reichmann, *Principles of Intensive Psychotherapy* (Chicago: University of Chicago Press, 1950).
7. Lewis B. Hill, *Psychotherapeutic Intervention in Schizophrenia* (Chicago: University of Chicago Press, 1955).
8. Lawrence S. Kubie, "Reflections on Training," *The Psychoanalytic Forum*, IV, No. 4 (1966), 97.
9. Harold F. Searles, "Phases of Patient-Therapist Interaction in the Psychotherapy of Schizophrenia," *British Journal of Medical Psychology*, XXXIV (1961), 169ff.
10. Otto A. Will, Jr., Staff Conference, May 13, 1953.
11. Searles, *op. cit.*, pp. 182–186.
12. Clarence G. Schulz, "A Follow-up Report on Admissions to Chestnut Lodge, 1948–1958," *Psychiatric Quarterly*, Vol. XXXVII (April 1963).
13. Harold F. Searles, "Concerning the Development of an Identity," *The Psychoanalytic Review*, LIII, No. 4 (Winter 1966–1967), 513. Reprinted from *The Psychoanalytic Review* through the courtesy of the editors and the publisher, National Psychological Association for Psychoanalysis, New York.
14. *Ibid.*, p. 529.
15. *Ibid.*
16. Ernest E. Bruder, "The Myth of the Healing Team," *Journal of Religion and Health*, II, No. 1 (1962), 63.

CHAPTER VIII

Antisocial Behavior Masking an Underlying Borderline Schizophrenic Disorder

CASE PRESENTATION

This final case differs from those of the preceding chapters. This young man was referred for treatment because of his antisocial impulsivity rather than his psychotic disorganization. This difference requires a different treatment approach.

The treatment of this case covers a period of four years. The patient, eighteen years of age and single, was admitted to the hospital as a transfer from jail. On admission he was a clean-cut-looking young man who was polite and well-mannered, and who showed no obvious emotional difficulty. There was nothing unusual in the mental status examination except that the patient had very little ability to locate any experience of anxiety within himself other than a vague feeling of "restlessness." At such times he noticed that he did not think as well as when he wasn't restless.

He was the second of four children from an upper class, socially prominent, but emotionally chaotic family. The patient's father was an outstanding athlete and student when he was in school. He completed college, and, after one year of successful employment away from his home town, returned to his wife's family business, which demanded very little in the way of his time or effort. The patient's mother, now dead, was also from a wealthy family but, in addition, had a prominent ancestry to which she often referred in order to derogate the father's relatively less distinguished background. The patient had only vague memories about his mother. His prominent thoughts were of her derogatory attitude toward the father, her spending long periods of time in her bedroom, and her interest in poetry. The patient was raised for the most part by a nurse employed full-time by the family. His father was away in service during most of the first three years of the patient's life, and upon his return from service, there ensued a long stretch of family bickering, drinking, and irresponsibility. The patient began to set small fires at about age five. At first, these fires were set around the yard, but gradually he began to set large fields afire. He never destroyed any structures nor were any people or animals ever hurt in these fires. This particular behavior continued up to the time of his admission and was well known in the community. Actually, very little was done about this. On one occasion, the fire chief gave him an individual lecture on the damage done by fires in the United States over a period of a year. For the most part the patient's propensity to set fires was treated as a joke among his boyhood friends. He was also the class clown, particularly when he was in the fifth grade. The patient did not do well in school until he was in a well-structured private boarding school in high school.

A typical day in the life of the family during the patient's junior high school years was as follows. The patient would awaken in the morning and be given breakfast by the family cook while his parents were sleeping off hangovers from the night before. He and the other children would then go off to school, and the parents would awaken around noon. In the midafternoon, they would begin to drink and would be fairly well intoxicated by the time the children returned from school. During the family's evening meal, there would be much fighting and criticism, especially by the mother toward the father. Frequently there would be occasions of a rather dramatic nature in which the father, in his drunken state, would choke on his food. Following dinner, the mother would return to her bedroom to continue drinking and the father would watch television—eventually passing out in front of the set. As the house began to become quiet in the early evening, the patient would sneak out for escapades in the neighborhood. He would indulge in taking things from people's food lockers in their garages, throwing stones at their windows to attract attention, and putting sand in automobile gas tanks. Occasionally he and his sister would steal bicycles and bring them home to take apart and reassemble into different bicycles. After such excursions, he would return home, go to bed, and then, sometime during the night, his parents would awaken and begin fighting. This awakened the rest of the family and frightened the patient. Eventually the parents quieted down; usually after drinking in order to sleep on through most of the next morning.

The patient had no close friends, although he did go on stealing excursions with other delinquents in the neighborhood. Following one of these, the police finally asked his father to remove the boy from the town. As a result, he entered high school in a boarding school. On a previous occasion, when the police intervened, his father asked the boy to keep a log of all his daily activities. The patient did this faithfully for about five days, but when his father never asked to see the log he discontinued keeping it and resumed his previous antisocial behavior.

While he was away in his second year of high school, the patient's mother accidentally set fire to the house when she was smoking in an intoxicated state in the living room. She died as a result of this fire. The patient was shocked for about the first day, but showed very little grief. He mainly remembered feeling thrilled that this made the headlines in the local papers. He also felt a vague sense of responsibility that, if he had been home, he might have saved her, since he had been interested in rescue work. He had cared for the family first-aid kits since he was a small boy and worked as a lifeguard during the summer while he was in high school.

During junior high school he had a successful paper route, and following completion of his schooling he spent six months in a service reserve unit in which he did quite well. After military service he enrolled for the spring term in an initial attempt at college. Since he did well scholastically at mid-term, his family purchased a car for him as a reward. He began to waste time and ride around in cars with a group, and as a result, his grades fell precipitously. There were some odd episodes during the latter half of that semester when he became drunk and ran back and forth in front of the fraternity house in his underwear. On another occasion, he went with a group of boys to a girls' dormitory for a panty raid. When the alert was sounded, everybody ran except the patient. He put his fist through the glass of the front door, where he stood until he was caught. He had no explanation for this behavior.

As a result of poor performance in college, the family did not permit him to accept a projected summer job as an ambulance driver but required him to remain at home with the family. Having no job lined up, he soon began to run around with another boy who was shoplifting and breaking and entering. He and the boy broke into several appliance stores. The patient began to consider this as his summer job. He would joke with his friends and speak of being on the night shift. Eventually he was caught, but through his family's intervention, the incident received no publicity, which was a disappointment to him. Arrangements were made to confine him to the family estate until he could be admitted to the hospital. Setting fire to a compost heap on the family property led to his being placed in jail until he could be transferred for admission.

Psychological tests were ordered after admission. These results were compared to reports from two years previously.

PSYCHOLOGICAL REPORT

The patient was seen in my office in two sessions during his first week at the hospital. His manner with me was stilted, with a lot of surface reactivity and eagerness to please.

Wechsler Adult Intelligence Scale

The patient functions in the bright normal range and has superior basic intelligence. There is no suggestion of schizophrenic thinking disorder.

The patient's concern about doing well is intense but self-defeating. He is decidedly poor at analytical thinking. He gets overwhelmed by complexity and seems to have no idea how to break it down into manageable parts.

The patient was tested two years ago. He does considerably better now in nonverbal problem-solving. This could reflect better management of anxiety now, or it could be due to his knowing a little bit more what to expect in the test situation.

	I.Q.		Weighted Score
Prorated Full Scale	119	Information	14
Verbal Scale	121	Comprehension	13
Prorated Performance Scale	113	Arithmetic	14
		Similarities	13
		Digit Span	14
		Vocabulary	11
		Digit Symbol	—
		Picture Completion	14
		Block Design	9
		Picture Arrangement	12
		Object Assembly	12

Projective Techniques
(RORSCHACH, FIGURE DRAWINGS, IFLUND SELECTIVE RECALL TEST)

The tests indicate some kind of personality disorder, the most salient feature of which is the avoidance of even mild anxiety as something exceptionally disruptive.

The Rorschach is constricted, unambitious, rather conventional. The patient seems simply to avoid thinking about something that would make him anxious, even when it is right in front of him. Generally he seems to experience feelings primarily in terms of bodily sensation.

The patient seems to be somewhat depressed, not schizoid at all, and socially fairly outgoing.

Although on the surface obsequious and painfully concerned about his social front, the patient seems to have a good deal of aggressivity and rebelliousness. Under some circumstances he may be quite attacking and argumentative.

Oral dependent and passive longings seem to be especially intense and impermissible. The patient shows a more or less usual adolescent concern about sexual identity. His concept of men and women is a rather undifferentiated one; both are passive-dependent children.

PROGNOSIS:

Good.

In psychotherapy, the history revealed a pattern of doing well in things and then failing. He also seemed to do well as long as he was living in a fairly well-regulated situation. Before coming to the hospital and while he was there, it was apparent that he was unable to delay his gratification. For instance, he would spend his money until it was gone unless external circumstances provided control. He immediately spent all of his first allowance on records. He remembered taking money from his mother's purse to buy candy. A rather striking aspect of his behavior was his tendency to resemble whatever situation he was in. While in the military, he was a typical good serviceman. In the hospital he often imitated the schizophrenic patients' speech. When one patient broke a window, he thought of breaking five windows, which he thought would bring him recognition. He reported achieving attention through difficulties in the earliest grades. Following the breaking and entering incident, he had hoped it would be spread all over the papers.

He avoided experiencing his feelings. Hence, he thought it strange when he began to notice feelings toward a student nurse whom he hardly knew. He would watch her carefully to see whether she would notice him or single him out in any way. If he experienced something that he took as a slight or rebuff on her part, he would have notions of taking her down a notch by "screwing her" or becoming a doctor and being superior to her. The personnel noted that frequently when he left from his psychotherapy appointment, he would act angry by imitating other patients who might be angry or cursing. He also avoided direct expressions of his feelings toward the charge nurse by attributing them to his therapist with the statement, "Dr. Schulz thinks you're sharp." He said that he often imitated those he admired. For example in college he walked with his toes turned in identical with the manner of a popular student. In service he had a "white-wall" haircut like the sergeant who looked "squared away." By contrast he was careful not to follow generally accepted fads if he could avoid them. When everyone was having his hair cut short he let his grow.

Quite early in his stay, he threw an ashtray at a window in the hospital living room, breaking the glass. Something inside him nagged him to do this. The aides rushed in and, seeing the glass on the floor, theorized that the object must have come from the outside. When they saw no one outside, they hurried past him to write the incident report without even questioning him. The patient, getting no response from them, went to his room and broke two windows. When the nurse discovered this and came to him, he felt a sense of concern on her part. He wanted her to be nearby. This he described as not really a sexual feeling but more like wanting a mother. He had missed her over the weekend, yet was afraid to get too close to her because it would become "too personal." He continued, "It would have to be broken off and I would feel hurt." Early in psychotherapy, he had strong, positive feelings toward the therapist and tended to idealize him. He made many extreme statements about the therapist's sincerity, his ability, and how generally well off the hospital would be if everyone else were this exceptional.

Six weeks after beginning treatment, at the time that the student nurse was leaving her affiliation, strong depressive feelings came out in the patient. Because his sadness was so intense that he was unable to stand it, he started to laugh in the very same way another deeply psychotic patient laughed. Several evenings later he was lying on his bed listening to a recording of Mozart and reading a doctor's autobiographical experiences. The doctor described how his wife had died following surgery for removal of a kidney stone. The patient then thought of the student nurse dying and fantasied himself at her bedside. He cried and said aloud, "Oh my God, No!" From other associations it was clear that these feelings of sadness were related to delayed grief about his mother. He had occasional isolated negative thoughts and fantasies about the therapist. More and more, the patient began to experience prominent affects, which were really quite unusual for him.

Largely because of the questioning in the therapy, he began to notice certain relationships between events. Prior to this, he had always attributed the situation to a "run of bad luck" or "someone just had it in" for him. Now, he began to see what part he might play in the chain of events.

He became the manager of the patients' work program, in which he performed competently—but only for a brief period. Conflict over doing well became prominent. He began one psychotherapy session with the comment, "I don't know what the hell is wrong. Everything has been going well lately." He became concerned about whether it would last or not. If he felt well now, attended school successfully, and got out of the hospital he might not really get to the things that bothered him. Consequently, he anticipated further trouble later on. These apprehensions about success were followed by thoughts of severe self-criticism. In comparing himself to my other patients, he said of the patient described in Chapter IV, "She may be aiming it in the wrong direction sometimes but at least she isn't running away like a coward." He ran away from the hospital but returned on his own. As a result, he wanted to resign as manager of the work program because he thought the patients and personnel would no longer have confidence in him. He became upset at a hospital party, and was returned to the ward where he got into a fight with a male aide. He was placed in a pack, where he voiced much anger and resentment. The alternation between doing well and doing poorly continued throughout his treatment.

Evidence of his malevolent transformation appeared two-and-a-half months after beginning treatment when he started to have negative feelings toward the charge nurse whenever he began to feel close to her. He found that he pushed away people toward whom he wanted to feel close. He recalled his experiences with the only girl to whom he felt close in high school. She lived near the boarding school and invited him to a party at her house. Together with several other couples they began to neck. He enjoyed this but "felt funny about it." The next day they were together at another girl's house listening to records.

She obviously wanted to continue the relationship, but he avoided her and as a consequence that ended their relationship.

Four months after starting treatment, the self-derogatory feelings became quite prominent. These attitudes revealed what a severe super-ego was operating in this young man. He would comment on the contrast between the way he thought about some of the things he had done and the way I talked about them in the therapy. He spoke of himself as a "sneak," a "rat" who wants "attention," and a "bum," who came to the hospital to "beat the rap" in order to avoid prison.

Five months after beginning treatment, we began to see some of the cruelty, hatred, and anger within him. An example of this occurred when he purchased a pet parakeet very cheaply at a Washington's Birthday sale. The parakeet did not respond to his attempts to have it climb out on his finger from the cage. Finally, in impulsive irritation he grabbed the parakeet and plunged it into a basin of water. He pulled it out and revived it. The process was repeated until the parakeet finally died. On examining the bird, he noticed that the bird was blind in the eye on which he was approaching him with his finger. Therefore, the bird could not have seen what he wanted. This was the reason he obtained the bird so inexpensively. The patient felt terribly guilty about this and thought of cutting his wrists. He then remembered that he had an appointment and could talk to me about it.

On a later occasion, while living as an outpatient he had another parakeet, which he named "Clarence." He gave this bird ether and set up a recovery room outside of the cage to revive the bird. In a similar repetition of anesthetizing and reviving the bird, he finally caused its death. Discussion of this brought forth an entire range of thoughts and feelings. He spoke of the loneliness as an outpatient as well as his complaint about my unresponsiveness, "You are like a damn blank wall." He desperately wanted me to react. He thought he sometimes had to try to play the part of the good boy to compete with my other patients and attract my attention. He spoke about how I must hate him because of these birds. His associations revealed how his mother liked birds and studied them. I asked, "Maybe she would not have wanted you to do this?" He replied, "God, she would have hated it." In addition to the transference aspects, the experience of the loss of his mother and his attempt to master traumata were repeated in these instances. These were also related to experiences in which his father would be involved in very hazardous activities such as operating a chain saw while intoxicated, driving the car while intoxicated, and otherwise endangering himself and his family.

On some occasions he showed identification both with the rescuer and the person being rescued. He would have fantasies of wanting to awaken in a surgical recovery room where he was the patient and everyone around him was giving him intravenous injections and applying emergency measures. He also had fantasies of resurrection where he would be close to death and be revived, or the reverse would occur where he would save other people. He thought that he would someday see his mother alive on the street. This theme was repeated in his attachments to student nurses. When one relationship would be broken off, he would always believe that somehow they would become reunited. One recurrent fantasy was that someday he would be a doctor manning a giant information control center. There would be incoming calls asking his advice. People's lives would depend upon his immediate decision. He would have to supply the answer and be 100 per cent correct. The theme of "all or nothing" seemed to be very prominent. In his approach to schoolwork, when he began taking classes, he would have to "know the material cold" or he would not want to take an examination. He could not be satisfied to have covered part of it in preparation and get the best grade he could, but would rather skip an examination and make a new beginning by studying for the one that was to follow. He would rather drop the course and get a fresh start the next semester.

A repeat of the psychological tests was performed to assess change in the patient.

COMPARISON OF RORSCHACHS

According to these tests, the patient in ten months of treatment has become more emotionally responsive, more elastically controlled, and considerably freer and more comfortable with his own thoughts.

The threat of explosive acting-out seems to have disappeared. Also, the patient no longer slavishly tries to do what the other person wants. In fact, he may rather insist on doing things in an opposite way.

The patient is more sensitive to nuances now and is less inclined to preoccupy himself just with his own body sensations. He still is adept at avoiding large, potentially unpleasant facts. The patient seems simply to ignore the most obvious feature in the forefront of a situation, as if it were instead merely an unimportant background. He makes little effort to tie things together; in fact, he may try carefully to keep them separate. Not all of this is acceptable to him now, however; he seems to be rather astonished at his tendency to go blank, in effect, in the face of threat.

In general, the patient feels much less threatened, either by his own impulses or by other people. He no longer visualizes people as clutching and devouring him. Not that he feels exactly warmly towards them yet. His general approach seems to be one of slight scorn, amusement, and detachment; people are unattractive or mean in his eyes, but, he now seems to feel, he can keep from getting caught up with them if he chooses.

He reacted quite clearly to separations occasioned by weekends, holidays, and vacations on my part. The following example reflects his newly developed way of thinking about his situation. Before the Labor Day weekend he was referring to something that we might take up on Monday during the appointment. I reminded him that Monday was the Labor Day holiday and we wouldn't be meeting that day, but I would see him on Tuesday. I later learned that the only reaction he had to this information was something along the line of "Oh, doesn't the doctor have a good memory for details to be able to keep track of the fact that Monday is a holiday." In the evening following the previously described appointment, he ran away from the hospital. On Saturday he found himself walking around in the city, wandering rather aimlessly, and looking at shop windows. Occasionally, certain questions would come to him. He considered calling me to let me know that he was all right so that I wouldn't worry, but then he thought I would insist on his returning. He finally decided that he would just wait until the weekend was over. He would also think along the lines that "some doctors" and "some hospitals" work all day and on weekends and holidays. He would gradually take such a thought and do what he called a "translation," to see what this might mean in relation to his therapist. Following this, he began to have feelings of missing me and brought himself back to the hospital.

Apparently, any kind of neutral position or silence on my part would be upsetting to him. He almost constantly required some acknowledgment that I was hearing what he was saying or was at least in touch with him. He felt that this was missing in his family situation as exemplified by his father's asking him to keep a diary and then not looking at it. On one occasion I began to fall asleep during an hour. He discovered this and immediately got up to leave, muttering something about not wanting to disturb my rest. As I was apologizing, I physically prevented him from going, but at the same time I indicated that I thought his leaving was the way he responded to his father's falling asleep in front of the television set. My physically restraining him from leaving at that point had a profound impact upon him. It indicated my serious attitude toward the situation and my commitment toward his treatment.

There were numerous emotional involvements of this patient with other patients and student nurses. These came under scrutiny and discussion in treatment as soon as they were recognized. We saw how certain acting out was a way of avoiding coming to grips with feelings. For example, he was getting ready for a farewell dance given for a group of student nurses who were leaving the hospital. He had hoped to ask a particular student to write to him after she left, but he was only dimly aware of the anticipated feelings of rejection. Instead of going to the dance, he and another patient broke into one of the medicine cabinets, were discovered, and promptly restricted. It wasn't until after the entire subject was reviewed in its sequence that we could see how his acting out was a substitute for feelings and a way of avoiding the situation. Many times the acting out was seen as a communication for help. He literally turned in fire alarms, called the rescue squad, and in other ways signaled situations of distress before he might set a fire or cut himself. These were interspersed with more direct verbal communications in which he would say, "Look, I have to return to the hospital," while he was living as an outpatient. On one occasion, he actually set off a fire alarm and was on his way to the hospital grounds when he was met by aides who were searching for another patient who had run away. Not knowing what he had done they asked him to join in the search for the other patient. He finally told them that he was the one who needed to be found, that he had just turned in a fire alarm, was in trouble, and should be brought in.

We obtained a third set of psychological tests at this time.

COMPARISON OF RORSCHACHS

This is the third Rorschach the patient has taken since he began treatment here sixteen months ago. The latest test shows even greater gains than were seen six months ago (when the Rorschach was administered by another examiner).

Most striking is the patient's new effort to integrate feelings. This is scarcely a smooth or always successful effort, but the patient does stay with the emotion-arousing situation and tries to get some ideational mastery over it. He is able to gain some distance and independence without having to shut it out of his attention altogether.

The patient must be aware himself of more internal power and control. The alternatives of dangling helplessly at the end of a life-line or being at the mercy of powerless nose-dives and cosmic eruptions have disappeared from the Rorschach.

He now seems to be more aware of a need for affection and care from others, where formerly he expressed the need in blunt impersonal terms (food, for instance) or denied it altogether.

The patient still has a hair-trigger alarm system. The emotional impact of events still tends to be compellingly unpleasant and anxiety-provoking. In impersonal or solitary contexts, however, the patient is beginning to show a pleasant, passive kind of aesthetic emotional response.

The idea of a woman still tends to disorganize this patient, but he approaches the idea more often now. Probably this is not especially related to women as sex objects, though sexual anxiety the patient certainly has, now in much abated degree.

The present test suggests that the patient is not through with depression. He still tends to preoccupy himself with the vivid and to act as if the dark and murky, no matter how central and prominent, simply are not there. One may infer that he would rather grapple with angry feelings, despite their discomfort, than come to grips with some central, lonely misery and deprivation in his experience.

He made a series of attempts to live as an outpatient, to go to school, and to work. All of these were abruptly terminated by his failure to perform to 100 per cent perfection or by feelings of tremendous loneliness. However, he did very well while working for a number of weeks as a hospital orderly. During that period he was considered a reliable employee who was very much interested in his work.

He was able to describe how when he wanted to be close to someone he would actually see a perceptually distorted image of that other person. Sometimes in the appointment with me, my face would seem distorted. If he became interested in a particular girl, he might see her face become distorted. As a minor variation he might, instead, begin to find fault with the other person, such as not liking the clothes the person was wearing. At times, he would have rather prominently distorted fantasies, for instance, of a girl friend having a long penis with teeth in it. At other times, he would begin seeing people who seemed to have penises coming out from all parts of their bodies. It was in conjunction with this material that we learned that he had had a couple of actual experiences of seduction with his mother during periods of her intoxication. On one occasion, he was viewing her genitalia as she was sprawled out, and, on another occasion, she lay on top of him and he fondled her genitalia.

He no longer required external events to coerce him into some performance or accomplishment. For example, he formerly delayed study until he actually was forced by the pressure of a deadline. This shifted in the direction of his feeling more inner control. He described how this happened in connection with a history test in which he began to speak to himself in the third person. He told himself that he was a country with a government, that he had a constitution, and that he had to demonstrate that he was a country with integrity. This was about the time the Congo nations were gaining their independence and demonstrating they really weren't ready for it. He began to doubt whether he was ready and also felt this really was an essential accomplishment that he must learn.

I find it difficult to describe the many pathological interactions with other patients, the wide range of moods, and the frequent interventions required of the hospital personnel on behalf of this impulsive patient. Selected samples from his reported experiences are apt to convey a picture that is fragmented as well as understated. In an episode that occurred twenty months after his admission, the patient had been moved to the closed ward after he had run away through the window of the open unit. In this session he described his anger at the hall administrator who had prescribed packs as a way of trying to calm him. After he left the building via the window, he stretched himself out on the ground and began to think. He decided that life was worth living even though he was now alone. His current girl friend, another patient, had broken up with him and there was now a rift between us since he wasn't talking with me in his hours. He had thoughts of blood coming out of his body, felt sad and cried. As he lay on the ground he thought of Christ's suffering in crucifixion. When he voluntarily returned, he decided to go back to school and to stop harming himself.

On a summer excursion in which the patients went off for a two-week vacation with the personnel, the patient succeeded in seducing the charge nurse. This was his first successful sexual attempt. As a result of her participation the nurse was dismissed. He continued his relationship with her and her husband in ways that were reminiscent of his family relationships involving his mother and father. He reported a dream in which he was working as an orderly in a hospital. The nurse asked him to remain on to work an extra shift. He felt in conflict because he had another appointment—his hour. He interpreted this dream as representative of the struggle between his feelings for the nurse and for his therapist. It probably also represented his wish that she remain in the role of nurse, that is, helper and provider. Actually, she was at that time quite dependent on him because of her own emotional incapacitation. He was back in his childhood situation with a helpless mother and her equally ineffectual husband. Later acting out efforts to rescue her and to save her from her chaotic home life continued. Prior to this, he had had dreams in which he was rescuing the nurse from a fire in the hospital building where she worked. Similarly, in the transference, he wanted to help his therapist. This was very much part of a theme in which he had expressed his view that I seemed to be troubled and overworked and he wanted to be of some assistance to me. During this period he began to uncover additional memories of positive situations with his father. Following this episode with the nurse, his negative feelings became more prominent. There followed a long period during which he was angry toward everyone and especially critical of me. These transference feelings were connected with his father.

About two-and-one-half years after beginning treatment, he had again started school and was contemplating becoming an outpatient. However, he was emotionally quite labile and unable to maintain a stable adjustment as an outpatient. When readmitted, he described a pull in himself to be a baby, to give in and be taken care of. He was restricted after suddenly submitting his three-day notice to leave the hospital.

He ran away from the hospital and as in the past we attempted to persuade him to return. We considered it an important part of our approach to keep the initiative with the patient rather than force him to return to the hospital. When he didn't return, I offered to stop by and see him in his apartment but this, too, he refused. He cut himself with a razor blade and had to be brought in. He was brought to the disturbed hall where he struggled and fought. He said he "felt nothing" and his appearance was wooden. However, his actions showed attempts to cut himself, hang himself, and beat his body. He continued to make attempts to leave. He became quite disturbed, combative, and actively suicidal. He was on the disturbed hall, in seclusion, and was being given Compazine. He then experienced some hallucinatory phenomena of bugs crawling around him, which very much resembled a toxic psychosis. As a result, the doses of Compazine and cogentin, which he was receiving, were decreased and the hallucinosis disappeared. After a quick reorganization, he experienced strong feelings of depression, sadness, discouragement, and a sense of hopelessness that this was going to go on forever.

A further attempt to resume life as an outpatient was terminated by the patient's cutting his arms. When he was readmitted, he tried to go without sleep and little food in order to weaken himself and thereby control himself. His grief was intense.

In summary, the final year continued to be one of periods of successful completion of some college courses interspersed with marginal social adjustment, emotional instability, and rehospitalization. Treatment was terminated when I left the hospital and the patient continued with a new psychiatrist.

DISCUSSION

IMPULSIVITY AND ACTING OUT

Certain primitive behavioral patterns occur without involving higher centers of the nervous system. For example, the knee jerk reflex can occur as the end result of a discharge by a path that involves only the receptive system, the spinal cord, and the motor system without involving the higher centers of the brain. Similarly, early in infancy there are actions that do not involve thinking. Later on, as the infant develops, thought begins to appear. Presumably, thinking occurs with lack of satisfaction, when, for example, the infant is hungry and is not immediately fed. It might then "hallucinate" a breast in its effort to supply a substitute for what is missing. In this way, primitive thought begins to take place. Freud spoke of thought as "an experimental way of acting."[1] A person does not have to act on something to see the consequences but can think about it, anticipate the consequences, and then decide what course of action to take. With this growing complex function of thought, there must be a capacity to delay action in order to give thought an opportunity to take place. In other words, thought is interposed between stimulus (internal as well as external) and reaction to the stimulus. This is the development of secondary process thinking in the personality, which implies a capacity to delay. Such delaying functions are a part of the ego developed after the initial primary process type of thinking that implies immediate discharge.

Joseph Michaels in a paper on impulsivity described a continuum extending from one pole of immediate discharge of the impulse to the other pole of the spectrum where there would be "secondary acting out, i.e. reproducing the repressed in behavior."[2]

As with many patients who show antisocial behavior, this patient seemed to have an absence of felt anxiety. He described an occasional period of "restlessness." In contrast to the anxiety-ridden neurotic or schizophrenic patient, these patients do not complain of such symptoms. Instead, they are brought to treatment because of their behavior and its antisocial aspects. In this way, the patient and those treating him are deprived of an important indicator—anxiety—which must be released during the course of treatment.

The term "acting out" was originally employed to describe a representation by action on the part of a patient in treatment, who, instead of being able to think of his conflicts and remember, would express such conflicts in action. The term was particularly related to the transference aspect of the treatment situation. Since then, it has become broadened to include almost any behavior that is a manifestation of internal conflict and especially of antisocial behavior. In fact, the term often incorrectly has an epithetical connotation with negative judgmental aspects. A patient who misses his psychoanalytic hour because he has locked his keys in his car is "acting out" his ambivalence about the treatment, even though this has no direct antisocial consequences. Certainly, acting-out has its discharge aspects, whether these be hostile or libidinal, antisocial or "accidental."

Acting out also has its defensive aspects, particularly in the instance of action as a defense against affects. This patient's actions involved defenses against becoming aware of grief and the experience of loss of someone. For instance, by breaking into the medicine closet, he thereby avoided feelings of rejection by the student nurse at the dance. These feelings were only partially within his awareness. Much of his action toward the student nurses obscured the delayed grief that was connected with his mother. At the same time action was also an outlet for this grief in that he provoked a recurrent loss through his action. While on the topic of grief, it is important to remember Freud's observation that mourning is a normal process and is the working through of the feelings of loss toward another person.[3] This patient's self-destructive acting out and irresponsible behavior also constituted a link with his mother by identification. Giving up such behavior would mean giving up an unconscious tie wth his mother. In treatment, we noted that as the acting out became less effective as a defense, other affects such as depression, anger, and loneliness became prominent. Even this patient's sexual feelings were largely obscured by his antisocial behavior. Sexual feelings can be very much connected with intimacy, which this patient seemed to recoil from consistently. One example of this was the way in which he would become intoxicated at a party with the result that someone else would have to take his girl home. Within a hospital patients often use rule-breaking as a diversion to obscure affects. Such a patient then becomes involved

over the issue whether he has been unjustly charted for an infraction
of rules rather than notice feelings such as loneliness.

Acting out is an expression of conflict in place of thinking or
remembering. It is the specific re-creation of unconscious fantasy.
Jacob Arlow has written very illuminatingly about the role of fantasy
in symptom formation.[4] Attention to the patient's fantasy can be
especially useful in elucidating the transference aspects of the patient's
interaction with the therapist. For example, when this patient attempted to nearly kill the bird and revive it, we saw a repetition of
the feelings of hostility plus the rescue operation in connection
with his mother. He was surprised to recognize that naming the bird
"Clarence" had a specific transference connection. Another example of
the transference was this patient's experience of anxiety when the
therapist took a passive or remote position. This patient reacted to
this the same way he did to his father's disinterest and his mother's
remoteness. In this way, the patient would push things until he elicited
a response from the therapist. Here, again, such action might be
thought of as "attention getting," which it is, but not clearly on a
conscious level. Such desire for response is often largely unconsciously
determined by the lack of a necessary minimum of loving attention
from one's parents. When a patient's history is realistically traumatic
as it was with this patient, it is difficult to think of the patient's contribution to the problem. That is, there may be a tendency to shift
away from the intrapsychic pathology in an effort to sympathize with
the patient and to try to correct or make up for his unfortunate experiences.

Acting out is also to be regarded as a form of communication,
especially since it takes the place of remembering and verbal expression. Certainly with this patient the acting out was a communication
of distress in which he would send in fire alarms, call for the rescue
squad, cut himself, break windows, or in other ways indicate a message.

The acting out can serve as a differentiation from the therapist. I
think this would be especially likely with patients who tended toward
more schizophrenic experience of loss of identity with fusion of self
and object representations (as described in Chapter IV on the negativistic patient). Here, the acting out serves the patient's purpose of
clearly differentiating himself from that of the behavior of the therapist
and thereby establishes a sense of separateness for the patient.

Acting out is sometimes an effort to see if the patient is accepted by
the therapist in spite of his behavior. This is the old familiar concept

of "testing." There is the additional facet that if the patient is rejected, he can think of it as owing to his "bad behavior." Blaming his behavior may be preferable to looking at his self-impression that he is empty. Since the acting out does form a type of relatedness, and, at the same time, maintains a differentiation as described above, it can be a variety of negativism as described in Chapter IV.

TREATMENT APPROACH WITH THE ACTING OUT PATIENT

Even though we are contrasting the treatment approach of the antisocial patient with that of the schizophrenic patient, we wish to emphasize it is the patient who behaves antisocially and not the label that is being treated. An important goal in treating such patients is to bring about a transition from action to anxiety and thought. This requires development of an observing ego with the capacity to delay gratification. The single most important strategy involved in bringing about this goal is an external structure involving a schedule and limits. Such structure acts as an auxiliary ego until the patient develops his own internal controls. From the outset of his hospitalization, constructive use of his time was arranged. Within a few days he was assigned work with the grounds crew. He was expected to work from 9:00 A.M. until 4:00 P.M., unless he had specific appointments such as therapy sessions and ward meetings. Three months after admission, he had a job as an orderly at a near-by general hospital. At this point the psychiatric hospital became a "night hospital" for him. Incidentally his job as an orderly caused him to experience a conflict in identity. He would go from the position of being a helper to that of being a patient. This transition is also experienced by staff members when going from their own analytic appointments as patients to that of being helping ones.

This patient developed his growing sense of self-control when he compared himself to a government. To another patient it became apparent how important his schedule had been to him after his classes in the hospital school ended. He used alcohol illegally when he had no class to attend. Such antisocial behavior, which is an externalization of the conflict, must be converted to an internal conflict. The internal conflict is then dealt with through thought, postponement, and decision-making that includes assessment of reality and the consequences of the action.

We have noticed a problem in treating schizophrenic patients having a thought disorder or confusion in the same setting with patients who are antisocial with poor impulse control and who act out conflicts. At times, there seems to be an incompatibility in applying the same treatment program to these quite different personalities. For example, a rather timid, phobic, neurotic, or schizophrenic patient might be encouraged to become more involved with the opposite sex by attending hospital dances. However, the antisocial patient in the identical situation requires more limits on his behavior because he is apt to act destructively toward himself or the other person. One should recognize that there are certain dangers in accepting for treatment some patients with symptoms such as a history of setting fires, as was the case with this patient. In a physically and architecturally vulnerable hospital, this can be so anxiety-provoking as to eliminate the successful operation of the treatment team.

The staff's attitude toward these patients also poses the rather difficult philosophical problem of "illness" versus "responsibility." To what extent are the patients sick, and, therefore, not to be held responsible for their behavior? In a way, this sometimes becomes a dilemma in the staff's attitude toward any hospital patient. There are extreme views that range from considering the patient to be sick and irresponsible in all aspects of his behavior to that of considering the patient to be responsible for everything he says and does. We recommend meeting this problem by setting an outer limit that defines an area within which the patient can make choices. With some limited choices he can then develop an awareness about what he is doing. The patient is permitted to assume responsibility to the extent to which he demonstrates his capability. Such capability must be extended in time and must be something longer than momentary. The rapid fluctuation in the behavior of these patients, with their unpredictability, makes the limit setting quite difficult to judge. For instance, this patient at one moment demonstrated his highly disturbed behavior by rolling in the raspberry bushes and scratching himself. When he came in and received a little attention and response, he calmed down and was able to accept responsibility. On the other hand, as an outpatient, when it seemed that he could control himself and, as far as he knew, was able to manage for himself, he would immediately get into further extension of acting out. After he left the office, the limits were sometimes insufficient.

We have noticed a frequent reluctance on the part of the staff to intervene when they observe the early signs of the patient's inability to control himself. Sometimes the nurse will feel that the patient should be told "No" as a form of limit setting but will be unable to do so. She will then invite the patient's clinical administrator to tell the patient that he is canceling a proposed trip or activity. Personnel who have a need to be "liked" by patients are reluctant to intervene for fear that the patient will not like them. Personnel often have difficulty imposing limits, because it somehow is not compatible with the image of the nurse as a "giving" person.

One very troublesome aspect of setting limits is the question of punishment. For example, when this patient returned to the hospital after a drinking spree, he was placed on a locked ward with no permissions. This seemed a reasonable limit to set. The following day he was given medication to settle his stomach and headache. To have ignored his discomfort with an "he-brought-it-on-himself" attitude would have been clearly punitive. These patients tend to view any restriction as punitive. Whether it is or not, if the staff member involved feels anger toward the patient, the staff member will feel guilty as a result of his anger. If the patient shows no disturbance or extension of his "acting out" after the restrictions have been imposed, the staff member may feel guilty. At times, the personnel intuitively feel that a patient should be restricted, and yet they are afraid they will be unable to justify this when the patient calls upon them to explain their intervention. Rather than go through the awkwardness of being unable to give logical point-by-point explanations, the personnel will not intervene. The tendency of the patient to joke about or to engage in "kidding" about certain activities makes it difficult for the personnel to know when to set a limit. The patient who frequently jokes about running away but doesn't, lulls the personnel into a sense of security and passive withdrawal. This, in itself, is apt to stimulate the patient to press further in order to get a response that he will obtain by actually running away. We suggest that all such kidding be taken seriously in order for the patient to learn to pay attention to his own communications.

This patient illustrated numerous problems in the staff's reaction to him. The charge nurse's sexual involvement clearly ended her usefulness as a nurse for the patient. The therapist frequently became involved in "trusting" the patient when a more objective consideration of the patient's behavior would indicate that limits were required. The usefulness of the clinical administrator in decision-making is very important with such patients. Clearly, in such cases, "two heads are better than one." Splits often occur among staff members who are, at the same time, reacting to various aspects of the patient. Some of the staff will see the helplessness and dependency in the patient while others see the hostile, defensive acting-out aspects of the same behavior. During this patient's brief psychotic periods, the staff were able to respond to his physical needs and to offer ego-support. Most of the time he related to female personnel in a seductive manner. Those who were not drawn into a mutually seductive relationship were able to see the hostile, defensive aspects of his behavior. Toward these women and toward the male personnel in the milieu, he remained distant.

The clinical administrator sometimes needs to develop special ways of responding to such patients. This patient's clinical administrator observed that if he moved toward the patient, the patient bolted away; if he moved away from the patient, the patient came to him, and they thus became involved in a process of mutual rejection. It is sometimes difficult to be clear-cut and firm without being punitively sadistic, condescending, or even gleeful in setting limits. John Cameron, as a clinical administrator, found it useful to make a decision regarding a patient's particular request before seeing the patient. This was in contrast to his approach to the more schizophrenic patient in which he felt he could discuss it with the patient and arrive at a decision during the course of the discussion.

Sometimes the reality factors in the hospital setting will obscure the transference features. For instance, the fact that the hospital must provide people in authority to set limits makes it more difficult to see how the patient is involved in transference reactions to feelings about the parents' restrictiveness toward him. This, in itself, will often lead some administrators to try to act unlike the parents and guide their administration accordingly rather than relate their approach to the more immediate needs of the patient. When these patients, just as adolescents, push their rebellious approach to find out where the limit is, they do need some response from the personnel to help them define this. If everyone ignores the signals, the person stretching to find the limit may go too far.

With extremely self-destructive patients, who in reality have considerable responsibility for their own funds, it is sometimes necessary to institute legal steps to prevent impoverishment and self-destruction. The release of funds may have to be set up under the control of a voluntary trust whereby the patient, plus a responsible official, must both agree before funds may be disbursed. While this presents the danger of maintaining the patient's dependency, it is considered an "outer limit" within which the patient can make many autonomous decisions that do not involve potentially disastrous consequences.

It is important that the personnel learn to detect the early cues of the patient's lack of control and respond to these in order to meet the patient's needs. At first these will be expressed in action and only eventually, after going over the situations many times, will the patient learn to verbalize his needs and obtain satisfaction by reaching out appropriately. This patient was able to do this when he was able to tell the others that he was the one who needed the help. Just before this, he had sent in a fire alarm, which was a communication by way of action. Sometimes, these needs of the patient are experienced as burdensome by the staff and in such cases the staff might quite unwittingly ignore the need. Also, anger on the part of the staff can lead them to allow the patient to get into trouble even though this is done entirely unconsciously. The needs of the staff and the hospital as a whole must be given consideration. Indeed, sometimes these patients can become such a total burden that there is a question of how many patients of this type the hospital can handle at any one time.

PRIMITIVE SUPEREGO AND EGO IDEAL

The superego is concerned with internalized guidance for what one should or should not do; what is right and wrong. This patient's superego was very harsh in its judgment of his feelings, thoughts, and actions. He commented that during the sessions when the therapist echoed some of his attitudes about himself, they didn't seem as terrible as when he described them. Sometimes, such superego attitudes can be projected onto others. In such a situation, the person feels that others are judging him severely and disapproving of his thoughts and actions. These concepts are important in understanding Anna Freud's concept of "identification with the aggressor."[5] This was one of the ego defenses described in her book *The Ego and the Mechanisms of Defense*. In such a situation, the young child identifies with the hostile parent or parent-figure. At the family mealtime this patient would be scolded by his father. The patient, in turn—through "identification with the aggressor"—would scold his younger siblings. Thus the introjects were quite harsh.

The ego-ideal is concerned with those systems of values related to what one should aspire to do. Ordinarily it holds up as a model, achievements that one might never reach but toward which one could strive. Thereby the ego-ideal normally becomes a source of motivation in ego functioning. When the ego-ideal remains largely on the infantile or primitive level, it contains much that is characteristic of infantile thinking by way of being omnipotent, perfectionistic, and so extreme that one almost always feels a sense of failure in trying to bridge the gap. One's adequate performance seems quite inadequate when compared with the extremes of the primitive ego-ideal.

This patient had many perfectionistic demands characteristic of such a primitive ego-ideal. Before he could feel at all secure in taking a test, he had to know the entire material "cold." He could not be satisfied to take a test having covered only part of the material, writing as good a paper as he could, and telling himself that he would do better next time. Anything less than a perfect paper was unsatisfactory to him. He would then drop the course in order to obtain a clean slate and start over again the following semester. Or, if not that drastic, he might skip that examination and study for the next one the following week. Such patients characteristically idealize the therapist during the course of treatment. While this is perhaps a boost to the self-esteem of the therapist and other personnel, they should be careful to realize that this is an expression of a primitive residual in the patient's personality. Actually, the staff cannot live up to such idealized expectations and, therefore, disillusionment by the patient will eventually come. The reaction to this can be quite severe indeed, and the personnel have to understand how this operates. One sees a parallel situation in the child, for instance, who idealizes his father and thinks of him as the greatest athlete in the world or the smartest or richest person, and then, as reality moves in, the youngster becomes progressively disillusioned. This is a normal experience leading to more realistic identifications.

This patient's frequent repeated fresh starts to erase previous failures characterized his inability to pursue goals. Patients utilize various devices to spare themselves the experience of failure, and, at the same time, to preserve a primitive, narcissistic ego-ideal. For example, a patient might repeatedly handicap himself in some way, such as using defective athletic equipment in competition in sports. In this way if he does not win, he can always cushion the blow with the thought that he might have done better by using the proper equipment. He could even preserve the belief in his potentiality as an Olympic star as long as his performance is never subjected to a realistic appraisal. Some people avoid competition altogether in order to preserve such grandiose expectations. The light of reality is not given a chance to shine on such idealization and show it off in a realistic perspective.

The patient's self-esteem is also very much related to what other people think of his performance. If a youngster grows up feeling repeatedly disapproved of by his parents, a sense of inferiority is engendered. Similarly, if the child retains an unrealistic ego-ideal, the difference between his actual performance and the ideal expectation is so great he has a sense of low self-esteem. Such unrealistic ideals are maintained by the opposite kind of parent who thinks the child is always wonderful in whatever he or she does and, therefore, creates an expectation that special achievements are the only thing that are acceptable.

This patient had a strong fear of failure. One time when he was on his way to class, he had the thought that he would do well. This, in itself, generated a tremendous amount of pressure and he found himself turning the corner away from the route to class in order to visit with another patient and join in the latter's self-destructive way of life outside of the hospital.

These primitive distortions of the ego-ideal and superego become modified through experience with reality and mainly through identification with the therapist as well as other personnel and other patients. This patient told the group therapy meeting that his therapist was "an annex to my conscience." Sometimes, patients have the opportunity in the patient self-government program to identify with the administrative functions of the personnel in the hospital. This gives the patient an opportunity for realistic self-control and self-appraisal of his performance.

Jacobson has emphasized how activation of the superego can help maintain the object-image.[6] Sometimes, when the depressed patient withdraws interest in people outside of himself, he might attempt to reactivate the relationship with his parents by activating the disapproving parental figures inside himself (part of the superego). Through self-criticism, he relates himself to his past and to his parents. This temporarily relieves the loneliness, but at the price of (superego) disapproval of the self and the consequent low self-esteem.

Superego activities also tend to bring forth considerable feelings of guilt, which can be relieved through self-punishment. In this way, the superego disapproval can be assuaged if the patient cuts himself, fails, or in some other way handicaps himself.

SCHIZOPHRENIC ASPECTS WITH THIS PATIENT

While this patient did not receive a label of "schizophrenic reaction" since his behavior was predominantly an antisocial pattern, there were evidences of schizophrenic thinking and transient psychotic disorganization at times when the antisocial behavior failed as a defense. In this way, the antisocial behavior masked an underlying psychotic regressive disorganization that was transient. "Narcissistic character disorder in a borderline personality" may have been a more informative label. This raises the question of labeling in psychiatry. While it does not have the precision of some of the other nosologies in medicine, it can be helpful as long as it is not required to say more about the patient than is implied in such labeling.

In addition to the obvious brief psychotic regressive episodes, other narcissistic aspects of the personality were certainly prominent. The primitive ego-ideal and superego aspects have been previously described. This patient also showed rather strong exhibitionistic trends, grandiosity, denial, projection, the quality of being special as described in John Murray's paper on entitlement, together with a magical sense of invulnerability.

> If the narcissistic world of omnipotence, with its unlimited power of magical thinking and unlimited entitlement to the lusts and destructions of pregenital excitements, is not given up in favor of the more ideal-oriented relationships with mature libidinal fulfillments, individual and social aims and relations, the resultant therapeutic achievements will be critically limited, circumscribed, indefinite, and perhaps only passing. On the other hand, a willingness to forego the narcissistic prerogatives in order effectively to analyze this aspect of the core of the problem greatly enhances the possibilities for victory in the struggle against the patient's neurosis. The potential, the desire, and the ability to do so are essential in the analytic unfolding of the specific libidinal components of the symptoms and the anxieties associated with their origin. Upon these factors depend analytic progress and therapeutic response. I believe these difficulties are the ones Freud had in mind when he expressed his trepidation regarding the treatment of the narcissistic neuroses.[7]

Such patients have an unrealistic, narcissistic belief that they are magically protected and can therefore be involved in various daredevil pursuits and activities which set them apart from reality. One patient described this as "lady luck" riding on his shoulder. People who have this part of their personality rather prominently developed will disregard the ordinary hazards in life, such as on the highway or on the water, and will sometimes appear to be courageous in situations of danger, such as on a battlefield. Actually, they are oblivious to the reality aspects of their situation at the moment. With this sense of invulnerability, the person is apt to rely on "lady luck" rather than on people who are considered to be untrustworthy. In his formative years this patient's life seemed to be populated with persons who were so unpredictable that he would have to come to rely on something magical to ease his anxiety. This type of person also tends to tempt fate, live dangerously, and bring about actively what is feared might happen to him passively. Rather than feel threatened by the potentially dangerous world around them, such people will purposely put themselves into dangerous situations and have the experience of mastering a fearful situation. If such people commit crimes and are caught, they obtain gratification of the exhibitionism, even though the narcissistic feeling of invulnerability may be crushed at that moment. This can subsequently be denied and the person can start over again to repeat the antisocial behavior. This is part of the mechanism whereby these patients appear not to profit from experience.

POSTSCRIPT

The patient remained in treatment for only one month with his new psychiatrist. Termination occurred after he was hospitalized because of an overdose of sedation. After recovery from the acute intoxication, he ran away and signed out of treatment.

Subsequently, he married a former patient. This marriage soon failed. He made repeated attempts to work, attend school, and participate in private outpatient psychotherapy. During one period he succeeded in school while living with a former professor who fulfilled the role of a benign father-figure.

Several years following discharge he was working as a valued employee in a medical field, but with episodic excessive use of alcohol.

NOTES

1. Sigmund Freud, "Formulations Regarding the Two Principles in Mental Functioning" (1911), *Collected Papers* (London: Hogarth Press, 1950), IV, 16.
2. Joseph J. Michaels, "Character Disorder and Acting Upon Impulse," in

Morton Levitt (ed.), *Readings in Psychoanalytic Psychology* (New York: Appleton-Century-Crofts, 1959), pp. 183f.

3. Sigmund Freud, "Mourning and Melancholia" (1917), *Collected Papers* (London: Hogarth Press, 1950), IV, 153f.

4. Jacob A. Arlow, "Conflict, Regression, and Symptom Formation," *International Journal of Psychoanalysis*, XLIV (1963), 12–22.

5. Anna Freud, *The Ego and the Mechanisms of Defense* (New York: International Universities Press, 1946), pp. 117–131.

6. Edith Jacobson, "Contribution to the Metapsychology of Cyclothymic Depression," in Phyllis Greenacre (ed.), *Affective Disorders* (New York: International Universities Press, 1952), pp. 79f.

7. John M. Murray, "Narcissism and the Ego Ideal," *Journal of the American Psychoanalytic Association*, XII, No. 3 (1964), 500.

CHAPTER IX

Some Implications

In this final chapter we shall highlight some important implications that our clinical findings point up as issues in the treatment of schizophrenia. Specifically, we shall look at: (1) the psychological-developmental aspect of the origin of schizophrenia; (2) the "disease within" the patient versus the concept of the social field; (3) the problem of intrapsychic change versus outer adaptation; (4) the peculiar intensity of staff reaction—or lack of it; and (5) the reasons for the great discouragement about the treatment of schizophrenia.

THE PSYCHOLOGICAL-DEVELOPMENTAL ORIGIN OF SCHIZOPHRENIA

Emerging from the case material about these severely disordered personalities are evidences of certain basic requirements in the development of any normally functioning person. The infant must become attached to and differentiated from its mother. This takes place in the climate of maternal love, with appropriate experiences of gratification and frustration on both sides. The mother, even as she identifies with the needs of her child must have some sense of her own identity as a mother for the child to develop a sense of his identity. Similarly, the professional, in his function of caring for the patient, must have a firm sense of his own role identity and personal identity while, at the same time, having the ability to empathize with the needs of the patient. We have seen how love through relatedness is essential to such processes. By contrast, hate and a negativistic relatedness are also important modes of insuring a sense of separateness while continuing the relationship.

During severe regressive experiences of patients—and presumably of normal infants—many primitive psychological events run rampant. Rapid fluctuations in a precarious image of self, surges of feelings, a not yet developed sense of reality, vulnerability to needs in the absence of any durable confidence about obtaining satisfaction from the mothering one, and sensitivity to anxiety in others are all thought to be part of the experience. Development toward maturity takes place in a trusting relationship of tender, mothering care which promotes stable object representations and identifications within the ego as forerunners to an evolving sense of ego identity.

Disruptions in the process through child-mother configurations overloaded with anxiety, lack of differentiation, deficiency of love, prolonged absence of the mother, or some other personality warp leave the person vulnerable to experiences and reactions which might be labeled mental illness in future years. If severe enough to be called schizophrenia, the vulnerabilities are in the form of loneliness with dependency conflicts; severe anxiety in relation to both aggression and attachment; fluctuations between omnipotence and helplessness; problems around experiencing grief, loss, or separation; a punitive, threatening conscience in place of normal guilt; idealistic goals of attainment contributing to a sense that any achievement is worthless; and a defect in integrating past experience or foresight of future planning. Such anxieties and conflicts culminate in clinically manifest inabilities to ascertain reality, regressive ego disorganization with the emergence of primitive defense mechanisms, fragmentation, intense feelings of hatred, paranoid delusions, withdrawal, and the variety of psychotic processes described in the previous chapters. The etiology or etiologies of the schizophrenias are uncertain. We may be dealing with a collection of syndromes representing various combinations of experiential factors interacting with organic ones. Even so, whatever part biochemical or organic factors may play, these cases demonstrate that a psychological approach can be corrective. This cannot be ignored.

DISEASE WITHIN THE PATIENT
VERSUS A SOCIAL FIELD CONCEPT

A generation ago, making rounds in a mental hospital, an "old-time" psychiatrist pointed to various patients saying, "There is an old 'deteriorated praecox.' This one is a paretic. That one is another 'praecox.'" Thus we made our way through the building. A few years later, the situation was not a great deal different though the "praecox" was now called a "schizophrenic" and long hours of staff time were devoted to arguing about subclassifications of "catatonic," "paranoid," "hebephrenic," or "mixed" types. Even after the patient was finally placed in a diagnostic category, we had few tools with which to work out a treatment plan for him.

The thrill of encountering Sullivan's concepts of the patient and doctor in an "interpersonal" field that included "illusory others" was persuasive enough to spark a major concern about treating such patients. Sullivan, following the teaching of Adolph Meyer, viewed the patient's "illness" as unsuccessful reactions to severe anxiety—as ways of interacting with others that were not entirely different from the interpersonal processes of normal people. Accordingly, the patient was neither organically deteriorating nor so narcissistically self-contained as to be unreachable. On the contrary, the patient was seen as over-sensitive and acutely tuned in to the disjunctive anxiety processes of others—reminiscent of his responsiveness to the anxiety encountered in his early experiences of living. Consequently, extreme skill on the part of those caring for the patient was essential. Sullivan coined the concept of the psychiatrist as a "participant observer." Evolving naturally from this at The Sheppard and Enoch Pratt Hospital came his emphasis on the training of staff and, later on at Chestnut Lodge, Stanton and Schwartz's sociological frame of reference as a way of viewing a mental hospital ward.

Surely the clinical examples in the case chapters have pointed up the consequences of patients' interactions with staff whether these were therapeutic or antitherapeutic. If taken seriously the implications are truly staggering. Those who spend the most time with the patients are the least well paid and least well trained. This has been a valid concern of the psychiatric profession for a long time. It has been thoroughly investigated in the works of Belknap[1] and Greenblatt[2] among others. However, but for a few exceptions, it remains true today. The selection and training of the personnel who deal with schizophrenic patients should be made with the same care that an agency exercises in selecting adoptive parents for children.

INTRAPSYCHIC CHANGE
VERSUS BEHAVIORAL ADAPTATION

Our clinical reports gave examples of our attempts to integrate a coordinated treatment attack on both intrapsychic conflicts and behavioral malfunctioning. To separate the two is an artificial abstraction which is useful only for purposes of discussion. From a practical, clinical treatment standpoint, prolongation of treatment results from a one-sided approach which counts on the resolution of "deep problems" before expecting any disdainfully-labeled "superficial" adjustment. To our way of thinking, it is equally one sided to press for social adaptation to the exclusion of internal psychological reconstruction. Patients are being short changed if they receive tranquilizing medications in large doses merely to change their behavior in order to discharge them from the hospital as soon as possible to after-care clinics that then do nothing more than adjust drug dosage. These drugs have been valuable in increasing the participation in treatment of scores of patients, but they have increased rather than eliminated the need for staff skilled in all the areas of treatment—psychotherapy, group experiences, occupational therapy, vocational training, and other facets—detailed in previous chapters.

We believe that even the most severely disturbed and suicidal patient needs an environment which expects him to change. No matter how helpless the patient, it is important that we not assume absolute, total responsibility for him and his life. We found that not putting all disturbed patients together on a "disturbed" hall decreased the duration of disturbed behavior for all these patients. A living situation requiring self-control and performance close to maximum functioning capability will facilitate useful channeling of aggression in a way that is different from but equal in importance to the patient's mastery of his aggression after he understands the anxiety and defensive dimensions of his anger. We reemphasize the total approach.

A person's mental health cannot be viewed as something apart from real life participation. Patients sometimes resist efforts to involve them in constructive activity with the claim that they are in the hospital to "solve" their "problems." A similar viewpoint was illustrated by the father of one of our patients who was expressing his wish to leave the hospital to resume work on his Ph.D. The father replied, "Your mother and I don't care if you never get your Ph.D. It's your mental health we're interested in"—as though there were no connection between the two. A return to our healing fracture analogy makes the point. To be concerned only with the union of the bone fragments without attention to the surrounding circulation, muscular tissues, tendons, and skin will lead to only partial healing. The solving of problems, mental or physical, involves the entire organism and its activities. The emotional problems are not really solved until the individual can translate his understanding of himself into adaptive behavior.

We list the following to summarize in outline form what a treatment program should provide:

1. Physical care: diet, personal hygiene, prevention of self-harm.
2. Opportunities for socialization with other patients of a variety of ages and interests.
3. Personal-professional relationship with the staff. The staff must be "involved." Such relationships serve as sources of healthy identification for patients.
4. Stimulation of the patient as appropriate to his level of behavior on a scale ranging from "overactive" to "withdrawn."
5. Opportunities for accomplishments, whether connected with educational, job, or environmental therapy pursuits.
6. Self-understanding (insight) via group experience or a one-to-one staff relationship. Focus on here-and-now transactions as well as personal historical patterns. The patient needs feed-back to assist in self-awareness.
7. Ego support via receptive listening, clarification, regular schedule, and expectations of capable functioning.
8. Impulse control via limit setting, group pressure, and a structured environment. The patient should feel the "tug" of exceeding the limits.
9. Improved self-esteem via suitable appearance, actual accomplishments, and reflected appraisal by the staff.
10. Exercise of personal autonomy via the provision of choices and options within definitive outer limits.
11. Dependency gratification with a view to an ultimate shift from "infantile" to "mature" dependence.
12. A continuity of relationships with the staff during the patient's hospital stay.
13. Opportunity for leadership within the peer group plus chances for competition, cooperation, compromise, and collaboration.
14. Development of the patient's awareness of magical self-expectations by frustration of unrealistic, wishful needs.
15. Opportunity for the patient to engage in a negativistic relationship.
16. Flexible response to provide appropriate participation along the patient's axis of regression-progression.
17. Confirmation of the patient's identity as he is, whether that be angry, rebellious, compliant, obnoxious, or whatever.

18. A working through of the symbiotic relationship with the staff toward differentiation and separation.
19. Opportunity for the integration of various dissociated aspects of the patient's personality, i.e., synthetic function of the ego. There must be opportunities for affective verbal expressions of anger, grief, and love for integration to take place.
20. Opportunity for failure without severe consequences.
21. Encouragement of drive delay and thought in place of action (or acting out).
22. Translation of insights into action or behavior change.
23. Ways in which personnel can be aware of their own feeling reactions and use these as indices to what is going on with the patient.
24. Resolution of disagreements within the staff.

INTENSITY OF STAFF REACTION

A review of these case presentations points up a general understatement of the staff's reactions to the treatment interaction. Until the more recent emphasis, primarily by Harold Searles, the importance of this dimension of the treatment process has long been neglected. Perhaps the delay in reporting the "participant observer's" observations about himself is multiply determined. We think such tardiness is connected with strong traditions of training as to what are "acceptable professional attitudes" and psychoanalytic taboos about countertransference. But most of all it is related to the nature of the patient's psychopathology itself. As personnel have become more comfortable about sharing with one another their more private reactions to these severely disordered patients, we have come to see that their feelings are often normal—indeed necessary—components to a potentially successful treatment involvement. The symbiotic union of the psychological life of the patient with that of the treating person reaches back to the earliest period of predifferentiation. The patients' intense affects of anger, loneliness, dependency and helplessness resonate on the inner emotional life of the staff and mobilize almost equally intense responses in the staff.

Experience gained from treating these patients underscores the need for a situation in which the staff have assistance with the understanding of their feelings, together with a long enough period of continuity for both patient and staff to work through these feelings.

The staff's acknowledgment and acceptance of the dissociated aspects of the patient's personality, particularly anger and lust, makes possible a beginning of the integration of these aspects. There must, however, be limits beyond which the staff cannot tolerate the physical expression of aggressive and erotic impulses. These limits are dictated by the reality of the needs and rights of others in the environment— both staff and patients. By limiting the acting out of these impulses, the staff forces the conflict into thought, discussion, and subsequent integration by the patient.

Through the acceptance of the various aspects of their own personalities, the individual psychotherapist and the other staff working with the patient can serve as models of integration. A staff member must be able to accept his own potential for murderous rage in order to permit any feeling of this type of rage on the part of the patient.

DISCOURAGEMENT IN THE TREATMENT OF SCHIZOPHRENIC PATIENTS

While patients such as we have described may appear to be hopeless in their reactions to critical distortions of vital early experience, schizophrenia is conquerable. The degree of regression and the severity of the clinical picture is not a reliable prediction of outcome. The potential of the patient to reorganize constructively and make use of the experience—and not merely to "adjust"—is sometimes remarkable. The preservation of creativity and areas of adaptability in some of those who remain clinically manifestly psychotic is equally remarkable.

The setting in which we worked with these patients was unique. The hospital philosophy rested on the premise that these profoundly ill patients could improve. All the staff shared the willingness to try for "as long as it takes" to bring about what was considered an inevitable change toward health. Such a shared philosophy of hope in the face of overwhelming odds was more useful support than any technical device or theoretical construct.

Many patients with schizophrenic disorders, both in and out of hospitals, are not receiving treatment—or only partial treatment with tranquilizing medications—because of an assumed "inaccessibility," "irreparable ego defect," or an unknown "biochemical malfunction." With present methods and results, there is ample reason for discouragement. However, we were unable to predict which patients would be reached. We cannot yet decide in any particular case what constitutes an adequate trial of treatment. When a patient shows no improvement for seven years and then moves forward in the eighth and ninth years to return to society, could this have been predicted? While such a treatment is not "practical" on a large scale, it still must be reckoned with in accounting for the recovery.

We found that severe aggression, withdrawal, confusion, negativism, and other manifestations of "untreatability" were prolonged positions of defense against severe anxiety. Such relatively fixed defenses naturally evoke discouragement, alienation, withdrawal, and cessation of caring on the part of those entrusted with their treatment.

Concentrating large numbers of chronically discouraged patients with like-minded low morale staff and setting them apart in an isolated hospital subcommunity is the worst possible approach. It promotes a downward spiral of discouragement in a tripartite trap comprised of patients, staff, and the extra-hospital community. In such a situation, the patients' defensive withdrawal and regressive behavior is experienced as nonhuman by the staff, who routinize their functions and become pessimistically preoccupied with labeling and categorizing. The staff's unresponsiveness or automatic responses contribute to the patients' discouragement, confirming both the patients' self-evaluation and their anticipated response of rejection from others. The group expectation of social performance drops. Mutual hostility leads to feelings of hopelessness. A philosophy of hopelessness generates chronicity. Meanwhile, the extra-hospital community reacts with alienation and resentment to what is perceived as a burdensome specter of insurmountability. Further isolation and abandonment result. Any partial solution to counteract the discouragement—such as a "pilot project" of total push rehabilitation or encouragement of behavioral change through a reward system—effects only temporary improvement. As one group of chronic patients confidently predicted, "We will still be here long after you have gone." It is likely that the only successful program will be one with a multiple attack of sustained thrust, enabling human beings above all to be open with one another.

NOTES

1. Ivan Belknap, *Human Problems of a State Mental Hospital* (New York: McGraw-Hill, 1956).
2. Milton Greenblatt, "Toward a Therapeutic Community," in Milton Greenblatt, Richard H. York, and Esther Lucile Brown, *From Custodial to Therapeutic Patient Care in Mental Hospitals* (New York: Russell Sage Foundation, 1955), pp. 37–245.

INDEX

abandonment, feeling of, 47, 115, 126
accident proneness, 50
accomplishment, sense of, 52, 92, 177, 237
acting out, 58, 59, 116, 236; impulsivity and, 240–243; secondary, 240; sexual, 114; treatment approach, 243–247
acute schizophrenia, treatment of, 51–53, 166–183; case presentation, 166–174; identity diffusion and, 177–179; postacute phase, 179–180; psychological report, 168–170; specific problems, 174–177
adolescents, psychotic disorganization and, 180–182
aftercare treatment, 52, 57–58
aggression, 45–46; catatonic defense against, 204–205; conflicts about, 57, 89; confusion as defense against, 76, 77; as defense against anxiety, 260
alcoholism, 57, 91
ambivalence, 39, 74, 117, 124, 152, 157–158, 173, 241
amytal interviews, 208
anger, 14–15, 33, 36, 47, 48, 56, 63, 68, 69, 71–72, 74–75, 78, 124; catatonic, 216; conflicts over, 179; denial of, 216; repression of, 172
antisocial behavior, 226–251
anxiety: castration, 34, 41; over change, 211; confusion and, 67, 68, 70, 72, 76, 79; defenses against, 260; ego regression and, 80; failure to cope with, 4; intensification of, 175; negativism and, 100, 112, 117, 260; obsessive-compulsive defense against, 56; regressive-fragmentation reaction to, 11; separation, 29, 75, 77, 87, 100, 157, 160
Arlow, Jacob, 242
assaultiveness, 14–15, 17, 46, 48, 91–92, 94, 95, 97–99, 102, 105, 108, 109, 126, 214
assertiveness: healthy, 45; sexual, 37, 38, 41
attention getting, 242
attention span, short, 78–79

auditory hallucinations, 29, 45, 54, 61, 64, 65, 70, 114, 150, 155, 163, 166
autistic child, 87
autistic thinking, 22, 31, 40
autonomy, 6, 11, 12, 44–45, 107, 118

behavioral adaptation, intrapsychic change and, 255–258
Belknap, Ivan, 255
blanking-out periods, 66–67
blocking, 31, 61
bodily needs, gratification of, 106
body image, 106
borderline schizophrenia, antisocial behavior and, 226–251
Boverman, Maxwell, 156
Bowlby, John, 87
Bruder, Ernest E., 224
Bullard, Dexter, 77, 155–156

Cameron, John, 246
castration, 18, 29, 45, 215
castration anxiety, 34, 41
catatonic excitement, 212–216
catatonic patient, treatment of, 184–216; case presentation, 184–203; problems, 203–212; psychological testing, 188–189
change, anxiety over, 211
clinical pastoral counseling, 223–224
closeness, need for, 99, 100, 103, 104, 106–107, 237
Cohen, Robert A., 221
combativeness, 91–92, 239
Compazine, 239
competence, feeling of, 40, 119
competitive feelings, 104, 111, 179
compulsions, 37, 54–55
concentration, lack of, 91
conflict(s): over anger, 179; externalization of, 116–118
confrontations, 38, 48
confusion, 11, 12, 17, 166, 220; anxiety and, 67, 68, 70, 72, 76, 79; as defense, 61–90, 260

presentation, 14–42; discouragement in, 259–260; family and, 5, 11, 44, 81–87; interruption of relationship in, 89–90; middle phase, 50–56; overtly disturbed psychotic phase, 42–50; particular problems, 216–223; patient-therapist romantic involvements, 58–59; physical care, 49–50, 257; postpsychotic phase, 50–53; psychological testing, 21–22; 30–31; 39–41; summary of provisions, 257–258; terminal phase, 56–59; transcribed interview, 23–28

trifluoperazine, 75, 76, 142–144, 146–149

trust versus mistrust crisis, 43

violence, 18, 26–28, 71, 92; dreams involving, 31, 35, 54; and fear, 53–54; paranoid, 163; repression of, 192

Waelder, Robert, 122–123

Wechsler Adult Intelligence Scale, 64–65, 136–137, 168–169, 229

Wechsler-Bellevue Intelligence Scale, 21

Wechsler Memory Scale Form I, 188–189

wet sheet pack, 17, 18, 88, 97, 98, 100, 109, 128, 194, 212–213

White, William A., 53

Whitehorn, John, 205

Will, Otto, 6–7, 218

withdrawal, 6, 22, 70, 77, 78, 92, 99, 109, 185, 189–191, 201–203; as defense against anxiety, 260; mutual, 78; *see also* catatonic patient, treatment of

work programs, 110–111, 121, 161, 232, 243

working through, 52, 124, 126

worthlessness, sense of, 122